OPERATIONAL MATHEMATICS

Operational Mathematics

RUEL V. CHURCHILL

Professor of Mathematics

University of Michigan

Second Edition

McGRAW-HILL BOOK COMPANY

NEW YORK   TORONTO   LONDON

1958

OPERATIONAL MATHEMATICS

Copyright © 1958 by McGraw-Hill, Inc. Copyright, 1944, by McGraw-Hill, Inc. Printed in the United States of America. All rights reserved. This book, or parts thereof, may not be reproduced in any form without permission of the publishers.

Library of Congress Catalog Card Number 58-6678

10 11 12 13 – M P – 9 8 7

10869

THE MAPLE PRESS COMPANY, YORK, PA.

PREFACE

This is a textbook on theory and applications of Laplace transforms and other integral transforms. The operational properties of the Laplace transformation, developed here in considerable detail, are followed in a natural manner by the operational mathematics for various Fourier transformations and their generalizations and by the theory and applications of eigenvalue problems. A procedure is described for selecting the proper operational mathematics to solve a given boundary value problem.

The book is an extensive revision of "Modern Operational Mathematics in Engineering," published in 1944. It is intended to be a sound mathematical treatment that will give the reader a clear understanding of the subject and its applications. The book is written for students of mathematics, engineering, physics, and other sciences, whose mathematical background has reached the level of advanced calculus. Some material from advanced calculus is reviewed here in order to make the exposition more nearly self-contained.

The applications are chiefly to problems in engineering and physics that involve differential equations, with emphasis on boundary value problems in partial differential equations. Problems in vibrating mechanical systems, electric circuits, and servomechanisms, involving systems of ordinary differential equations, are given considerable attention. The physical problems are kept on a fairly elementary level. Readers who have had a year of college physics should be able to understand and appreciate the applications. No previous preparation in the subject of partial differential equations is required.

The book is a companion volume to "Fourier Series and Boundary Value Problems" and "Complex Variables and Applications." The three books together cover these principal methods of solving linear boundary value problems in partial differential equations: the methods of operational mathematics, separation of variables and Fourier series, and conformal mapping. This book includes generalizations of the Fourier methods. It summarizes and uses material from complex variables.

The subject matter in the first four chapters, on real Laplace transforms and their applications, is given in a short basic course in operational mathematics at the University of Michigan. Chapter 10, on Fourier transforms, can well be included in such a course. The rest of the book is covered in a more advanced course on methods in partial differential equations.

Important results are stated as theorems. Conditions under which the results are reliable are carefully established and stated. Simple practical conditions are employed, although more sophisticated conditions would sometimes give more elegant theorems.

In the course of writing the book the author has taken advantage of various devices, improvements, and corrections proposed by students and colleagues. Professors R. C. F. Bartels, J. R. Britton, J. W. Cell, C. L. Dolph, B. Dushnik, G. E. Hay, E. D. Rainville, and E. H. Rothe deserve special thanks for their suggestions. The publications of G. Doetsch, J. C. Jaeger, N. W. McLachlan, I. N. Sneddon, and other authors have influenced the selection of material.

Ruel V. Churchill

CONTENTS

CHAPTER 1

THE LAPLACE TRANSFORMATION

1. Introduction. The operation of differentiating functions is a transformation from functions $F(t)$ to functions $F'(t)$. If the operator is represented by the letter D, the transformation can be written

$$D\{F(t)\} = F'(t).$$

The function $F'(t)$ is the image, or the transform, of $F(t)$ under this transformation; the function $3t^2$, for example, is the image of the function t^3.

Another transformation of functions that is prominent in calculus is that of integration,

$$I\{F(t)\} = \int_0^x F(t)\ dt.$$

The result of this operation is a function $f(x)$, the image of $F(t)$ under this transformation. A still simpler transformation of functions is the operation of multiplying all functions by the same constant, or by a specified function.

In each of the above examples an inverse transformation exists; that is, when the image is given, a function $F(t)$ exists which has that image.

A transformation $T\{F(t)\}$ is *linear* if for every pair of functions $F_1(t)$ and $F_2(t)$ and for each pair of constants C_1 and C_2, it satisfies the relation

$$(1) \qquad T\{C_1F_1(t) + C_2F_2(t)\} = C_1T\{F_1(t)\} + C_2T\{F_2(t)\}.$$

Thus the transform of a linear combination of two functions is the same linear combination of the transforms of those functions, if the transformation is linear. Note the special cases of equation (1) when $C_2 = 0$ and when $C_1 = C_2 = 1$. The examples cited above represent linear transformations.

The class of functions to which a given transformation applies must generally be limited to some extent. The transformation $D\{F(t)\}$ applies to all differentiable functions, and the transformation $I\{F(t)\}$ to all integrable functions.

Linear integral transformations of functions $F(t)$ defined on a finite or infinite interval $a < t < b$ are particularly useful in solving problems in differential equations. Let $K(t,s)$ denote some prescribed function of the variable t and a parameter s. A general *linear integral transformation* of functions $F(t)$ with respect to the kernel $K(t,s)$ is represented by the equation

$$(2) \qquad\qquad T\{F(t)\} \;=\; \int_a^b K(t,s)F(t)\,dt.$$

It represents a function $f(s)$, the *image,* or *transform,* of the function $F(t)$. The class of functions to which $F(t)$ may belong and the range of the parameter s are to be prescribed in each case. In particular, they must be so prescribed that the integral (2) exists.

We shall see that with certain kernels $K(t,s)$ the transformation (2), when applied to prescribed linear differential forms in $F(t)$, changes those forms into algebraic expressions in $f(s)$ that involve certain boundary values of the function $F(t)$. Consequently, classes of problems in ordinary differential equations transform into algebraic problems in the image of the unknown function. If an inverse transformation is possible, the solution of the original problem can be determined. Boundary value problems in partial differential equations can be simplified in a similar way.

The operational mathematics presented in this book is the theory as well as the application of such linear integral transformations that bears on the treatment of problems in differential equations. Later on, we shall return to the general transformation (2) and to the question of deciding upon the special cases that apply to a given problem in differential equations. First we present the special case that is of greatest general importance, the operational mathematics of the Laplace transformation. Other prominent cases include the various Fourier transformations, to be presented later.

When $a = 0$ and $b = \infty$ and $K(t,s) = e^{-st}$, the transformation (2) becomes the Laplace transformation. The direct application of this transformation replaces the symbolic procedure known as Heaviside's operational calculus.[1] The development of the transformation and the accompanying operational calculus was begun before Heaviside's time; Laplace (1749–1827) and Cauchy (1789–1857) were two of the earlier contributors to the subject.[2]

In this chapter we present the basic operational property of the Laplace transformation, the property that gives the image of differentiation of functions as an algebraic operation on the transforms of those functions. In the following chapters further properties of the transformation will be derived and applied to problems in engineering, physics, and other subjects. Applications to boundary value problems in partial differential equations will be emphasized.

Our study of the Laplace transformation leads to the theory of expanding functions in series of the characteristic functions of Sturm-Liouville systems. Such expansions form the basis of the method of solving boundary value problems by separation of variables, a classical method of great importance in partial differential equations. In addition to this, that theory enables us to present the operational mathematics based on the general linear integral transformation (2).

2. Definition of the Laplace Transformation. If a function $F(t)$, defined for all positive values of the variable t, is multiplied by e^{-st} and integrated with respect to t from zero to infinity, a new function $f(s)$ of the parameter s is obtained; that is,

$$\int_0^\infty e^{-st}F(t)\ dt = f(s).$$

As indicated in the preceding section, this operation on a function $F(t)$ is called the *Laplace transformation* of $F(t)$. It will be abbreviated here by the symbol $L\{F\}$, or by $L\{F(t)\}$; thus

$$L\{F\} = \int_0^\infty e^{-st}F(t)\ dt.$$

The new function $f(s)$ is called the *Laplace transform*, or the *image*, of $F(t)$. Wherever it is convenient to do so, we shall denote the original function by a capital letter and its transform

---

[1] Oliver Heaviside, English electrical engineer, 1850–1925.

[2] For historical accounts see J. L. B. Cooper, Heaviside and the Operational Calculus, *Math. Gazette*, vol. 36, pp. 5–19, 1952, and the references given there.

by the same letter in lower case. At other times we shall use a bar to indicate the transform, for example,

$$\bar{F}(s) = L\{F(t)\}.$$

For the present, the variable s is assumed to be real. Later on, we shall let it assume complex values. The limitations on the character of the function $F(t)$ and on the range of the variable s will be discussed soon.

Let us note the transforms of a few functions. First, let $F(t) = 1$ when $t > 0$. Then

$$L\{F\} = \int_0^\infty e^{-st}\, dt = -\frac{1}{s} e^{-st} \Big]_0^\infty ;$$

hence, when $s > 0$,

$$L\{1\} = \frac{1}{s}.$$

Let $F(t) = e^{kt}$ when $t > 0$, where k is a constant. Then

$$L\{F\} = \int_0^\infty e^{kt} e^{-st}\, dt = \frac{1}{k-s} e^{-(s-k)t} \Big]_0^\infty ;$$

hence, when $s > k$,

$$L\{e^{kt}\} = \frac{1}{s-k}.$$

With the aid of elementary methods of integration, the transforms of many other functions can be written. For instance,

$$L\{t\} = \frac{1}{s^2}, \qquad L\{t^2\} = \frac{2}{s^3},$$

and
$$L\{\sin kt\} = \frac{k}{s^2 + k^2};$$

but we shall soon have still simpler ways to obtain these transforms.

It follows from elementary properties of integrals that the Laplace transformation is linear in the sense defined by equation (1), Sec. 1. We can illustrate the use of this property by writing

$$L\{\tfrac{1}{2}e^{kt} - \tfrac{1}{2}e^{-kt}\} = \frac{1}{2}\frac{1}{s-k} - \frac{1}{2}\frac{1}{s+k};$$

that is,

$$L\{\sinh kt\} = \frac{k}{s^2 - k^2}.$$

PROBLEMS

1. Use the linearity property and known transforms to obtain these transformations, where a, b, and c are constants:

(a) $L\{a + bt\} = \dfrac{as + b}{s^2}$;

(b) $L\{a + bt + ct^2\} = \dfrac{as^2 + bs + 2c}{s^3}$;

(c) $L\{\cosh ct\} = \dfrac{s}{s^2 - c^2}$;

(d) $L\{e^{at} - e^{bt}\} = \dfrac{a - b}{(s - a)(s - b)}$.

2. Show that the linearity property (1), Sec. 1, can be extended to linear combinations of three or more functions.

3. If for all functions $F(t)$ and $G(t)$ and for every constant C a transformation satisfies the two conditions

$$T\{F(t) + G(t)\} = T\{F(t)\} + T\{G(t)\}, \qquad T\{CF(t)\} = CT\{F(t)\},$$

prove that the transformation is linear.

3. Functions of Exponential Order.

A function $F(t)$ is *sectionally continuous* on a finite interval $a \leq t \leq b$ if it is such that the interval can be subdivided into a finite number of parts, in each of which $F(t)$ is continuous and has finite limits as t approaches either end point of the subinterval from the interior. Any discontinuities of such a function on the interval (a,b) are of the type known as ordinary points of discontinuity, where the value of the function takes on a finite jump. The class of sectionally continuous functions includes continuous functions. The integral of every function of this class, over the interval (a,b), exists; it is the sum of the integrals of the continuous functions over the subintervals.

The unit step function

$$\begin{aligned} S_k(t) &= 0 && \text{when } 0 < t < k, \\ &= 1 && \text{when } t > k, \end{aligned}$$

is an example of a function that is sectionally continuous in the interval $0 \leqq t \leqq T$ for every positive number T (Fig. 1). The Laplace transform of this function is

$$\int_0^\infty S_k(t)e^{-st}\,dt = \int_k^\infty e^{-st}\,dt = \left. -\frac{1}{s}\,e^{-st} \right]_k^\infty ;$$

thus, assuming $s > 0$,

$$L\{S_k(t)\} = \frac{e^{-ks}}{s}.$$

A function $F(t)$ is of *exponential order* as t tends to infinity provided some constant α exists such that the product

$$e^{-\alpha t}|F(t)|$$

is bounded for all t greater than some finite number T. Thus $|F(t)|$ does not grow more rapidly than $Me^{\alpha t}$ as $t \to \infty$, where M is some constant. This is also expressed by saying that $F(t)$ is of the order of $e^{\alpha t}$, or that $F(t)$ is $O(e^{\alpha t})$.

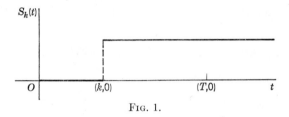

FIG. 1.

The function $S_k(t)$ above, as well as the function t^n, is of the order of $e^{\alpha t}$ as $t \to \infty$ for any positive α; in fact for the first function and, when $n = 0$, for the second, we may write $\alpha = 0$. The function e^{2t} is of exponential order $(\alpha \geqq 2)$; but the function e^{t^2} is not of exponential order.

The Laplace transform of a function $F(t)$ exists if $F(t)$ is sectionally continuous in every finite interval in the range $t \geqq 0$ and if the function is of exponential order as $t \to \infty$. This follows from a well-known comparison test for the convergence of improper integrals. For under the conditions stated, the integrand of the Laplace integral is integrable over the finite interval $0 \leqq t \leqq T$ for every positive number T, and

$$|e^{-st}F(t)| < Me^{-(s-\alpha)t},$$

where M is some constant. But the integral from 0 to ∞ of the function on the right exists provided $s > \alpha$. These facts estab-lish[1] not only the convergence, but also the absolute convergence, of the Laplace integral when $s > \alpha$.

The above conditions for the existence of the transform of a function are elementary and practical for most of our applica-tions; but they are sufficient rather than necessary conditions. The function $F(t)$ may have an infinite discontinuity at $t = 0$, for instance, provided $|t^n F(t)|$ remains bounded there for some positive n, where $n < 1$; then if $F(t)$ satisfies the above con-ditions when $t > 0$, its transform still exists. Let $F(t) = t^{-\frac{1}{2}}$, for example. Then its transform is

$$(1) \qquad \int_0^\infty t^{-\frac{1}{2}} e^{-st}\, dt = \frac{2}{\sqrt{s}} \int_0^\infty e^{-x^2}\, dx \qquad (s > 0),$$

and hence (see Prob. 5, Sec. 5)

$$L\{t^{-\frac{1}{2}}\} = \left(\frac{\pi}{s}\right)^{\frac{1}{2}} \qquad (s > 0).$$

4. Transforms of Derivatives. By a formal integration by parts we have

$$L\{F'(t)\} = \int_0^\infty e^{-st} F'(t)\, dt$$
$$= e^{-st} F(t) \Big]_0^\infty + s \int_0^\infty e^{-st} F(t)\, dt.$$

Let $F(t)$ be of order of $e^{\alpha t}$ as t approaches infinity. Then when-ever $s > \alpha$ the first term on the right becomes $-F(0)$ and it follows that

$$(1) \qquad L\{F'(t)\} = sf(s) - F(0),$$

where $f(s) = L\{F(t)\}$.

Therefore in our correspondence between functions, *differenti-ation* of the object function corresponds to the *multiplication* of the result function by its variable s and the addition of the con-stant $-F(0)$. Formula (1) thus gives the fundamental oper-ational property of the Laplace transformation, the property that makes it possible to replace the operation of differentiation by a simple algebraic operation on the transform.

[1] See, for instance, Philip Franklin, "Treatise on Advanced Calculus," p. 271, 1940.

As noted above, formula (1) was obtained only in a formal, or manipulative, manner.   It is not even correct when $F(t)$ has discontinuities.   The following theorem will show to what extent we can rely on our formula.

Theorem 1.   *Let the function $F(t)$ be continuous with a sectionally continuous derivative $F'(t)$, in every finite interval $0 \leqq t \leqq T$.   Also let $F(t)$ be of order of $e^{\alpha t}$ as $t \rightarrow \infty$.   Then when $s > \alpha$, the transform of $F'(t)$ exists and*

(2) $$L\{F'(t)\} = sL\{F(t)\} - F(0).$$

Since $F(t)$ is continuous at $t = 0$, the number $F(0)$ here is the same as $F(+0)$, the limit of $F(t)$ as t approaches zero through positive values.

To prove this theorem we note first that

$$L\{F'(t)\} = \lim_{T \rightarrow \infty} \int_0^T e^{-st}F'(t)\, dt,$$

if this limit exists.   We write the integral here as the sum of integrals in each of which the integrand is continuous.   For any

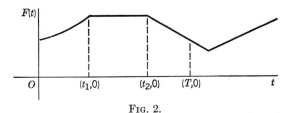

Fig. 2.

given T, let $t_1, t_2, \ldots, t_n$ denote those values of t between $t = 0$ and $t = T$ for which $F'(t)$ is discontinuous (Fig. 2).   Then

$$\int_0^T e^{-st}F'(t)\, dt = \int_0^{t_1} e^{-st}F'(t)\, dt + \int_{t_1}^{t_2} e^{-st}F'(t)\, dt + \cdots$$
$$+ \int_{t_n}^T e^{-st}F'(t)\, dt.$$

After integrating each of these integrals by parts, we can write their sum as

$$e^{-st}F(t)\Big]_0^{t_1} + e^{-st}F(t)\Big]_{t_1}^{t_2} + \cdots + e^{-st}F(t)\Big]_{t_n}^T + s \int_0^T e^{-st}F(t)\, dt.$$

Now $F(t)$ is continuous so that $F(t_1 - 0) = F(t_1 + 0)$, etc., and hence

$$(3) \quad \int_0^T e^{-st}F'(t)\,dt = -F(0) + e^{-sT}F(T) + s\int_0^T e^{-st}F(t)\,dt.$$

Since $|F(t)| < Me^{\alpha t}$ for large t for some constants α and M, it follows that

$$|e^{-sT}F(T)| < Me^{-(s-\alpha)T}$$

and since $s > \alpha$ this product vanishes as $T \to \infty$. Also the last integral in equation (3) approaches $L\{F\}$ as T tends to infinity. Hence the left-hand member of (3) has a limit and Theorem 1 is established.

If $F(t)$ is continuous except for an ordinary discontinuity at $t = t_0$, the other conditions remaining as stated in the theorem, we can see from the above proof that our formula (2) must be replaced by the formula

$$(4) \quad L\{F'(t)\} = sf(s) - F(0) - [F(t_0 + 0) - F(t_0 - 0)]e^{-t_0 s}.$$

The quantity in brackets is the jump of $F(t)$ at $t = t_0$.

The reader should note that we use the symbol $F'(t)$ here and in the sequel to denote the derivative of $F(t)$ wherever the derivative exists, even though $F(t)$ fails to have a derivative for certain values of t. In the case of our step function $S_k(t)$, for instance, $S_k'(t) = 0$ when $0 < t < k$ and when $t > k$, but $S_k'(k)$ has no value.

To obtain the transformation of the derivative of the second order $F''(t)$, we apply Theorem 1 to the function $F'(t)$. Let $F'(t)$ be continuous and $F''(t)$ sectionally continuous in each finite interval, and let $F(t)$ and $F'(t)$ be of exponential order. Since $F'(t)$ is continuous, it follows that $F(t)$ is continuous. Then

$$L\{F''(t)\} = sL\{F'(t)\} - F'(0)$$
$$= s[sL\{F(t)\} - F(0)] - F'(0).$$

Hence we have the transformation

$$(5) \quad L\{F''(t)\} = s^2 f(s) - sF(0) - F'(0).$$

By applying Theorem 1 in the same manner to the derivative of order n and using mathematical induction, we obtain the following theorem.

Theorem 2. *Let the function $F(t)$ have a continuous derivative $F^{(n-1)}(t)$ of order $n-1$ and a sectionally continuous derivative $F^{(n)}(t)$, in every finite interval $0 \leq t \leq T$. Also let $F(t)$, $F'(t)$,*

$\ldots,$ $F^{(n-1)}(t)$ *be of order of* $e^{\alpha t}$ *as* t *tends to infinity. Then the transform of* $F^{(n)}(t)$ *exists when* $s > \alpha$ *and it has the following algebraic expression in terms of the transform* $f(s)$ *of* $F(t)$:

$$(6) \quad L\{F^{(n)}(t)\} = s^n f(s) - s^{n-1}F(0) - s^{n-2}F'(0)$$
$$- s^{n-3}F''(0) - \cdots - F^{(n-1)}(0).$$

5. Examples. The Gamma Function. In order to gain familiarity with the above fundamental operational property of the transformation, let us first use it to obtain a few transforms.

Example 1. Find $L\{t\}$.

The functions $F(t) = t$ and $F'(t) = 1$ are continuous and of exponential order for any positive α. Hence,

$$L\{F'(t)\} = sL\{F(t)\} - F(0) \qquad (s > 0),$$
or $$L\{1\} = sL\{t\}.$$

Since $L\{1\} = 1/s$, it follows that

$$L\{t\} = \frac{1}{s^2} \qquad (s > 0).$$

Example 2. Find $L\{\sin kt\}$.

The function $F(t) = \sin kt$ and its derivatives are all continuous and bounded, and therefore of exponential order, where $\alpha = 0$. Hence

$$L\{F''(t)\} = s^2 L\{F(t)\} - sF(0) - F'(0) \qquad (s > 0),$$
or $$-k^2 L\{\sin kt\} = s^2 L\{\sin kt\} - k.$$

Solving for $L\{\sin kt\}$, we see that

$$L\{\sin kt\} = \frac{k}{s^2 + k^2} \qquad (s > 0).$$

Example 3. Find $L\{t^m\}$ where m is any positive integer.

The function $F(t) = t^m$ satisfies all the conditions of Theorem 2 for any positive α. Here

$$F(0) = F'(0) = \cdots = F^{(m-1)}(0) = 0,$$
$$F^{(m)}(t) = m!, \qquad F^{(m+1)}(t) = 0.$$

Applying formula (6) when $n = m + 1$, we find that

$$L\{F^{(m+1)}(t)\} = 0 = s^{m+1} L\{t^m\} - m!,$$

and therefore

$$(1) \qquad L\{t^m\} = \frac{m!}{s^{m+1}} \qquad (s > 0).$$

This formula can be generalized to the case in which the exponent is not necessarily an integer. To obtain $L\{t^k\}$ where $k > -1$, we make the substitution $x = st$ in the Laplace integral, giving

$$\int_0^\infty t^k e^{-st} \, dt = \frac{1}{s^{k+1}} \int_0^\infty x^k e^{-x} \, dx \qquad (s > 0).$$

The integral on the right represents the gamma function, or factorial function, with the argument $k + 1$. Hence

$$(2) \qquad L\{t^k\} = \frac{\Gamma(k + 1)}{s^{k+1}} \qquad (k > -1, \, s > 0).$$

Formula (1) is a special case of (2) when k is a positive integer (see Prob. 6).

Example 4.   Find $L\left\{ \int_0^t F(\tau) \, d\tau \right\}$ when $F(\tau)$ is sectionally continuous and of exponential order.

The function

$$(3) \qquad G(t) = \int_0^t F(\tau) \, d\tau$$

is continuous (Sec. 12), and $G(0) = 0$. Also $G'(t) = F(t)$, except for those values of t for which $F(t)$ is discontinuous; thus $G'(t)$ is sectionally continuous on each finite interval. If the function $G(t)$ is also of order $O(e^{\alpha t})$, then according to Theorem 1,

$$sL\{G(t)\} = L\{F(t)\} \qquad (s > \alpha);$$

thus, if $\alpha > 0$,

$$(4) \qquad L\left\{ \int_0^t F(\tau) \, d\tau \right\} = \frac{1}{s} f(s) \qquad (s > \alpha > 0).$$

To show that the integral (3) represents a function of exponential order when $F(t)$ is sectionally continuous and of exponential order, we first note that constants α and M exist such that $|F(t)| < Me^{\alpha t}$ whenever $t \geqq 0$, and if the number α is not positive it can be replaced by a positive number. Then

$$|G(t)| \leqq \int_0^t |F(\tau)| \, d\tau < M \int_0^t e^{\alpha \tau} \, d\tau = \frac{M}{\alpha} (e^{\alpha t} - 1) \qquad (\alpha > 0),$$

and therefore

$$e^{-\alpha t}|G(t)| < \frac{M}{\alpha}(1 - e^{-\alpha t}) < \frac{M}{\alpha} \qquad (\alpha > 0).$$

This establishes the exponential order of the function (3).

The operational property (4) for integration will be derived in another way later on.

PROBLEMS

1. Find the transforms of each of the following functions:

(a) $F(t) = 0$ when $0 < t < 1$, $F(t) = 1$ when $1 < t < 2$, $F(t) = 0$ when $t > 2$. $Ans.\ \dfrac{1}{s}(e^{-s} - e^{-2s}).$

(b) $F(t) = \sin t + 2\cos t$. $Ans.\ \dfrac{2s+1}{s^2+1}.$

(c) $F(t) = \sin t \cos t$. $Ans.\ \dfrac{1}{s^2+4}.$

(d) $F(t) = \cos^2 t$.   (e) $F(t) = \cos t \cos 2t$.

(f) $F(t) = \sin t$ when $0 < t < \pi$, $F(t) = 0$ when $t > \pi$.

$$Ans.\ \frac{1 + e^{-\pi s}}{s^2 + 1}.$$

2. Obtain these transforms with the aid of Theorem 2:

(a) $L\{\cos kt\} = \dfrac{s}{s^2+k^2};$ (b) $L\{\sinh kt\} = \dfrac{k}{s^2-k^2};$

(c) $L\{\cosh kt\} = \dfrac{s}{s^2-k^2};$ (d) $L\{te^{kt}\} = \dfrac{1}{(s-k)^2}.$

3. Apply formula (4), Sec. 4, to find

(a) the transform of the step function $S_k(t)$;

(b) $L\{F(t)\}$ where $F(t) = e^t$ when $0 < t < 1$, $F(t) = 0$ when $t > 1$.

$$Ans.\ \frac{1 - e^{1-s}}{s - 1}.$$

4. Use mathematical induction and Theorem 1 to prove Theorem 2.

5. Let J denote the second integral in equation (1), Sec. 3; then

$$J^2 = \int_0^\infty e^{-x^2}\,dx \int_0^\infty e^{-y^2}\,dy = \int_0^\infty \int_0^\infty e^{-(x^2+y^2)}\,dx\,dy.$$

Evaluate the iterated integral here by using polar coordinates and show that $J = \sqrt{\pi}/2$.

6. As noted in Sec. 5, the gamma function is defined for positive values of its argument r by the formula

$$\Gamma(r) = \int_0^\infty x^{r-1}e^{-x}\,dx \qquad (r > 0).$$

(a) Integrate by parts to show that this function has the factorial property $\Gamma(r + 1) = r\Gamma(r)$.

(b) Show that $\Gamma(1) = 1$, and hence that $\Gamma(n + 1) = n!$ when $n = 1, 2, \ldots$.

(c) Use the result of Prob. 5 to show that $\Gamma(\frac{1}{2}) = \sqrt{\pi}$; then use the factorial property to find $\Gamma(\frac{3}{2})$ and $\Gamma(\frac{5}{2})$. Use formula (2) to show that $L\{t^{\frac{1}{2}}\} = \frac{1}{2}\pi^{\frac{1}{2}}s^{-\frac{3}{2}}$.

7. Show that the function $F(t) = \sin(e^{t^2})$ is of exponential order ($\alpha \geqq 0$), while its derivative $F'(t)$ is not of exponential order. Also show that Theorem 1 ensures the existence of the Laplace transform of that function $F'(t)$, if $s > 0$, even though $F'(t)$ is not of exponential order.

6. The Inverse Transform. Let the symbol $L^{-1}\{f(s)\}$ denote a function whose Laplace transform is $f(s)$. Thus <u>if</u>

$$L\{F(t)\} = f(s)$$

then

$$F(t) = L^{-1}\{f(s)\}.$$

Using two of the transforms obtained in the foregoing sections we can write, for instance,

$$L^{-1}\left\{\frac{1}{s - k}\right\} = e^{kt}, \qquad L^{-1}\left\{\frac{k}{s^2 + k^2}\right\} = \sin kt.$$

This correspondence between functions $f(s)$ and $F(t)$ is called the *inverse Laplace transformation*, $F(t)$ being the *inverse transform* of $f(s)$.

<u>In the strict sense of the concept of uniqueness of functions, the inverse Laplace transform is not unique.</u> The function $F_1(t) = e^{kt}$ is an inverse transform of $1/(s - k)$; but another, for instance, is the function (Fig. 3)

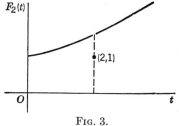

FIG. 3.

$$F_2(t) = e^{kt} \quad \text{when } 0 < t < 2, \text{ or } t > 2,$$
$$= 1 \quad \text{when } t = 2.$$

For the transform of $F_2(t)$ is

$$\int_0^\infty e^{-st}F_2(t)\, dt = \int_0^2 e^{-st}e^{kt}\, dt + \int_2^\infty e^{-st}e^{kt}\, dt,$$

and this is the same as $L\{e^{kt}\}$. The function $F_2(t)$ could have been chosen equally well as one that differs from $F_1(t)$ at any finite set of values of t, or even at such an infinite set as $t = 1$, 2, 3, ...

A theorem on the uniqueness of the inverse transform, due to Lerch, states that if two functions $F_1(t)$ and $F_2(t)$ have the same Laplace transform $f(s)$ then

$$F_2(t) = F_1(t) + N(t),$$

where $N(t)$ is a null function, that is, a function such that

$$\int_0^T N(t)\, dt = 0$$

for every positive T. In the above example, $N(t) = 0$, except when $t = 2$, and $N(2) = 1 - e^{2k}$. We shall take up the proof of Lerch's theorem later on.

In view of this theorem, we can say that the inverse transform is essentially unique, since a null function is usually of no importance in the applications. As a consequence of the theorem, a given function $f(s)$ cannot have more than one inverse transform $F(t)$ that is continuous for each positive t. But a function $f(s)$ may not have a continuous inverse transform. This is illustrated by the function $s^{-1}e^{-ks}$ whose inverse transform is the step function $S_k(t)$. It is well to note here that not every function of s is a transform. The class of functions $f(s)$ that are transforms is limited, as we shall see, by several conditions of continuity, among which are the requirements that $f(s)$ be continuous when $s > \alpha$ and that $f(s)$ vanish as s tends to infinity.

We have noted that

$$L\{AF(t) + BG(t)\} = Af(s) + Bg(s),$$

where A and B are constants. This relation can be written

$$
\begin{aligned}
L^{-1}\{Af(s) + Bg(s)\} &= AF(t) + BG(t) \\
&= AL^{-1}\{f(s)\} + BL^{-1}\{g(s)\}.
\end{aligned}
$$

Therefore the inverse transformation is a linear transformation of functions.

The most obvious way of finding the inverse transform of a given function of s consists of reading the result from a table of transforms. A fairly extensive table is given in Appendix 3. But we shall take up methods of obtaining inverse transforms of certain combinations and modifications of functions of s, as well as methods of resolving such functions into those listed in the tables.   With the aid of such procedures, we shall be able to make much use of the transformation.   In addition, there are explicit formulas for $L^{-1}\{f(s)\}$.   The most useful of these formulas involves an integral in the complex plane.   To use this integral, we must let s be a complex variable and we must be prepared to employ a few important theorems in the theory of functions of a complex variable.

7. A Theorem on Substitution.   Let the function $F(t)$ be such that its Laplace integral converges when $s > \alpha$.   Then, replacing the argument of the transform $f(s)$ by $s - a$, where a is a constant, we have

$$f(s - a) = \int_0^\infty e^{-(s-a)t}F(t)\ dt = \int_0^\infty e^{-st}e^{at}F(t)\ dt,$$

when $s - a > \alpha$.   Therefore

(1) $$f(s - a) = L\{e^{at}F(t)\} \qquad (s > \alpha + a).$$

Let us state this simple but important property as a theorem.

Theorem 3.   *The substitution of $s - a$ for the variable s in the transform corresponds to the multiplication of the object function $F(t)$ by the function e^{at}, as shown in formula (1).*

To illustrate this property, let us recall that

$$\frac{m!}{s^{m+1}} = L\{t^m\} \qquad (m = 1, 2, \ldots ; s > 0).$$

Hence $$\frac{m!}{(s - a)^{m+1}} = L\{t^m e^{at}\} \qquad (s > a).$$

As another illustration,

$$L\{\cos kt\} = \frac{s}{s^2 + k^2} \qquad (s > 0),$$

and therefore

$$L\{e^{-at} \cos kt\} = \frac{s + a}{(s + a)^2 + k^2} \qquad (s > -a).$$

8. The Use of Partial Fractions.   A few examples will show how the theory of partial fractions can be used in finding inverse transforms of quotients of polynomials in s.   In the next chapter, a more systematic use of this procedure will be introduced.

Example 1.   Find $L^{-1} \left\{ \dfrac{s+1}{s^2 + 2s} \right\}$.

The denominator of the function of s here is of higher degree than the numerator and has factors that are linear and distinct. Therefore constants A and B can be found such that

$$\frac{s+1}{s(s+2)} = \frac{A}{s} + \frac{B}{s+2}$$

for all values of s.   Clearing fractions, we have

$$s + 1 = (A + B)s + 2A,$$

and this is an identity if $A + B = 1$ and $2A = 1$.   Thus $A = B = \frac{1}{2}$ and hence

$$\frac{s+1}{s^2 + 2s} = \frac{1}{2}\frac{1}{s} + \frac{1}{2}\frac{1}{s+2}.$$

Since we know the inverse transforms of the two functions on the right, we have the result

$$L^{-1} \left\{ \frac{s+1}{s^2 + 2s} \right\} = \frac{1}{2} + \frac{1}{2} e^{-2t}.$$

The procedure can be shortened for such a simple fraction by writing

$$s + 1 = \tfrac{1}{2}(s + 2) + \tfrac{1}{2}s,$$

and hence

$$\frac{s+1}{s(s+2)} = \frac{1}{2}\frac{1}{s} + \frac{1}{2}\frac{1}{s+2}.$$

Example 2.   Find $L^{-1} \left\{ \dfrac{a^2}{s(s+a)^2} \right\}$.

In view of the repeated linear factor, we write

$$\frac{a^2}{s(s+a)^2} = \frac{A}{s} + \frac{B}{s+a} + \frac{C}{(s+a)^2}.$$

Clearing fractions and identifying coefficients of like powers of s as before, or else by noting that

$$a^2 = (s + a)^2 - s(s + a) - as,$$

we find that

$$\frac{a^2}{s(s+a)^2} = \frac{1}{s} - \frac{1}{s+a} - \frac{a}{(s+a)^2}.$$

TABLE 1. A SHORT TABLE OF TRANSFORMS

	$F(t)$	$f(s)$	α $(s > \alpha)$
1	1	$\dfrac{1}{s}$	0
2	e^{at}	$\dfrac{1}{s-a}$	a
3	t^n $(n = 1, 2, \ldots)$	$\dfrac{n!}{s^{n+1}}$	0
4	$t^n e^{at}$ $(n = 1, 2, \ldots)$	$\dfrac{n!}{(s-a)^{n+1}}$	a
5	$\sin kt$	$\dfrac{k}{s^2 + k^2}$	0
6	$\cos kt$	$\dfrac{s}{s^2 + k^2}$	0
7	$\sinh kt$	$\dfrac{k}{s^2 - k^2}$	$|k|$
8	$\cosh kt$	$\dfrac{s}{s^2 - k^2}$	$|k|$
9	$e^{-at} \sin kt$	$\dfrac{k}{(s+a)^2 + k^2}$	$-a$
10	$e^{-at} \cos kt$	$\dfrac{s+a}{(s+a)^2 + k^2}$	$-a$
11	$\sqrt{t}$	$\dfrac{\sqrt{\pi}}{2\sqrt{s^3}}$	0
12	$\dfrac{1}{\sqrt{t}}$	$\sqrt{\dfrac{\pi}{s}}$	0
13	t^k $(k > -1)$	$\dfrac{\Gamma(k+1)}{s^{k+1}}$	0
14	$t^k e^{at}$ $(k > -1)$	$\dfrac{\Gamma(k+1)}{(s-a)^{k+1}}$	a
15	$S_k(t)$ (Sec. 3)	$\dfrac{e^{-ks}}{s}$	0
16	$e^{at} - e^{bt}$ $(a > b)$	$\dfrac{a-b}{(s-a)(s-b)}$	a
17	$\dfrac{1}{a}\sin at - \dfrac{1}{b}\sin bt$	$\dfrac{b^2 - a^2}{(s^2 + a^2)(s^2 + b^2)}$	0
18	$\cos at - \cos bt$	$\dfrac{(b^2 - a^2)s}{(s^2 + a^2)(s^2 + b^2)}$	0

Referring to Table 1, we can now write the result

$$L^{-1}\left\{\frac{a^2}{s(s+a)^2}\right\} = 1 - e^{-at} - ate^{-at}.$$

Example 3.   Find $L^{-1}\left\{\dfrac{s}{(s^2+a^2)(s^2+b^2)}\right\}$ where $a^2 \neq b^2$.

Since

$$\frac{s}{(s^2+a^2)(s^2+b^2)} = \frac{s}{a^2-b^2}\frac{(s^2+a^2)-(s^2+b^2)}{(s^2+a^2)(s^2+b^2)}$$

$$= \frac{1}{b^2-a^2}\left(\frac{s}{s^2+a^2}-\frac{s}{s^2+b^2}\right),$$

when $a^2 \neq b^2$, it follows that

$$L^{-1}\left\{\frac{s}{(s^2+a^2)(s^2+b^2)}\right\} = \frac{1}{b^2-a^2}(\cos at - \cos bt).$$

Example 4.   Find $F(t)$ if $f(s) = \dfrac{5s+3}{(s-1)(s^2+2s+5)}$.

In view of the quadratic factor, we write

$$\frac{5s+3}{(s-1)(s^2+2s+5)} = \frac{A}{s-1} + \frac{Bs+C}{s^2+2s+5}.$$

Proceeding as before, we find that $A = 1$, $B = -1$, and $C = 2$, so that

$$f(s) = \frac{1}{s-1} - \frac{s-2}{(s+1)^2+4}$$

$$= \frac{1}{s-1} - \frac{s+1}{(s+1)^2+4} + \frac{3}{(s+1)^2+4}.$$

Referring to Table 1, or to Theorem 3, we see that

$$F(t) = e^t - e^{-t}(\cos 2t - \tfrac{3}{2}\sin 2t).$$

PROBLEMS

1. Obtain the following inverse transforms:

(a) $L^{-1}\left\{\dfrac{a}{s(s+a)}\right\} = 1 - e^{-at}.$

(b) $L^{-1}\left\{\dfrac{a^3}{s(s+a)^3}\right\} = 1 - (1 + at + \tfrac{1}{2}a^2t^2)e^{-at}.$

(c) $L^{-1}\left\{\dfrac{k^2}{s(s^2+k^2)}\right\} = 1 - \cos kt.$

× **2.** Derive the inverse transforms shown in entries 16 and 17 of Table 1.

3. Use Theorem 3, (*a*) to find $L^{-1}\{(s - k)^{-\frac{1}{2}}\}$ from the inverse transformation of $s^{-\frac{1}{2}}$; (*b*) to obtain entry 9 from entry 5, in Table 1.

9. The Solution of Simple Differential Equations. The application of the Laplace transformation to the solution of linear ordinary differential equations with constant coefficients, or systems of such equations, can now be made clear by means of examples. Such problems can of course be solved also by the methods studied in a first course in differential equations. Later on, when we have developed further properties of the transformation, we shall solve problems of this sort with greater efficiency. We shall also be able to solve much more difficult problems in differential equations.

Example 1. Find the general solution of the differential equation

$$Y''(t) + k^2 Y(t) = 0.$$

Let the value of the unknown function at $t = 0$ be denoted by the constant A and the value of its first derivative at $t = 0$ by the constant B; that is,

$$Y(0) = A, \qquad Y'(0) = B.$$

In view of the differential equation, we can write

$$L\{Y''(t)\} + k^2 L\{Y(t)\} = 0.$$

If the unknown function satisfies the conditions of Theorem 2, then

$$L\{Y''(t)\} = s^2 y(s) - As - B,$$

where $y(s) = L\{Y(t)\}$. Hence $y(s)$ must satisfy the equation

$$s^2 y(s) - As - B + k^2 y(s) = 0,$$

which is a simple *algebraic equation*. Its solution is clearly

$$y(s) = A \frac{s}{s^2 + k^2} + \frac{B}{k} \frac{k}{s^2 + k^2}.$$

Now $Y(t) = L^{-1}\{y(s)\}$, and the inverse transforms of the functions on the right in the last equation are known. Hence

$$Y(t) = A \cos kt + \frac{B}{k} \sin kt,$$
$$= A \cos kt + B' \sin kt,$$

where A and B' are arbitrary constants since the initial conditions were not prescribed.

It is easy to verify that the result is the solution of the differential equation, so it is not necessary to justify the use of Theorem 2. However, the function $A \cos kt + B' \sin kt$ does satisfy the conditions of that theorem, and the order of the steps taken above can be reversed to show in another way that this function does satisfy the differential equation. These remarks on the verification of the solution apply equally well to the other examples and problems to follow in this section.

Example 2. Find the solution of the differential equation

$$Y''(t) - Y'(t) - 6Y(t) = 2$$

satisfying the initial conditions

$$Y(0) = 1, \qquad Y'(0) = 0.$$

Applying the transformation to both members of the differential equation, and letting $y(s)$ denote the transform of $Y(t)$, we obtain the algebraic equation

$$s^2 y(s) - s - sy(s) + 1 - 6y(s) = \frac{2}{s},$$

where we have used the initial conditions in writing the transforms of $Y''(t)$ and $Y'(t)$. Hence

$$(s^2 - s - 6)y(s) = \frac{s^2 - s + 2}{s},$$

or $\qquad y(s) = \dfrac{s^2 - s + 2}{s(s-3)(s+2)} = \dfrac{A}{s} + \dfrac{B}{s-3} + \dfrac{C}{s+2}.$

Evaluating the coefficients A, B, and C as in the last section, we find that

$$y(s) = -\frac{1}{3}\frac{1}{s} + \frac{8}{15}\frac{1}{s-3} + \frac{4}{5}\frac{1}{s+2}.$$

Hence $\qquad Y(t) = -\frac{1}{3} + \frac{8}{15}e^{3t} + \frac{4}{5}e^{-2t}.$

This result is easily verified.

Example 3. Find the functions $Y(t)$ and $Z(t)$ that satisfy the following system of differential equations:

$$Y''(t) - Z''(t) + Z'(t) - Y(t) = e^t - 2,$$
$$2Y''(t) - Z''(t) - 2Y'(t) + Z(t) = -t,$$
$$Y(0) = Y'(0) = Z(0) = Z'(0) = 0.$$

Let $y(s)$ and $z(s)$ denote the transforms of $Y(t)$ and $Z(t)$, respectively. Then in view of the differential equations and the initial conditions, these transforms satisfy the following simultaneous algebraic equations:

$$s^2 y(s) - s^2 z(s) + s z(s) - y(s) = \frac{1}{s-1} - \frac{2}{s},$$

$$2s^2 y(s) - s^2 z(s) - 2sy(s) + z(s) = -\frac{1}{s^2}.$$

These equations can be written

$$(s+1)y(s) - sz(s) = -\frac{s-2}{s(s-1)^2},$$

$$2sy(s) - (s+1)z(s) = -\frac{1}{s^2(s-1)}.$$

Eliminating $z(s)$, we find that

$$(s^2 - 2s - 1)y(s) = \frac{s^2 - 2s - 1}{s(s-1)^2}.$$

With the aid of partial fractions, we find

$$y(s) = \frac{1}{s(s-1)^2} = \frac{A}{s} + \frac{B}{s-1} + \frac{C}{(s-1)^2}$$

$$= \frac{1}{s} - \frac{1}{s-1} + \frac{1}{(s-1)^2}.$$

Therefore $Y(t) = 1 - e^t + te^t.$

Likewise we find that

$$z(s) = \frac{2s-1}{s^2(s-1)^2} = -\frac{1}{s^2} + \frac{1}{(s-1)^2},$$

and therefore $Z(t) = -t + te^t.$

Example 4. Solve the problem

$$Y'''(t) - 2Y''(t) + 5Y'(t) = 0,$$
$$Y(0) = 0, \qquad Y'(0) = 1, \qquad Y(\pi/8) = 1.$$

Let C denote the unknown initial value $Y''(0)$. Then

$$s^3 y(s) - s - C - 2s^2 y(s) + 2 + 5sy(s) = 0,$$

so that

$$y(s) = \frac{C - 2 + s}{s(s^2 - 2s + 5)}$$

$$= \frac{C-2}{5}\left[\frac{1}{s} - \frac{s-1}{(s-1)^2 + 4}\right] + \frac{C+3}{10}\frac{2}{(s-1)^2 + 4}.$$

Thus $Y(t) = \dfrac{C-2}{5} + e^t \left(\dfrac{C+3}{10} \sin 2t - \dfrac{C-2}{5} \cos 2t \right).$

Since $Y(\pi/8) = 1$, it follows that

$$1 = \frac{C-2}{5} + \frac{e^{\pi/8}}{10\sqrt{2}}(C+3-2C+4),$$

or that $C = 7$.   Hence the solution is

$$Y(t) = 1 + e^t(\sin 2t - \cos 2t).$$

PROBLEMS

Solve the following problems and verify your solution.

1. $Y''(t) - k^2 Y(t) = 0 (k \neq 0).$ *Ans.* $Y(t) = C_1 e^{kt} + C_2 e^{-kt}$

2. $Y''(t) - (a+b)Y'(t) + abY(t) = 0 (a \neq b).$

3. $Y''(t) + k^2 Y(t) = a(k \neq 0).$

Ans. $Y(t) = C_1 \sin kt + C_2 \cos kt + \dfrac{a}{k^2}.$

4. $Y''(t) + 2kY'(t) + k^2 Y(t) = 0.$ *Ans.* $Y(t) = e^{-kt}(C_1 + C_2 t).$

5. $Y''(t) - 2aY'(t) + (a^2 + b^2)Y(t) = 0,\ Y(0) = 0,\ Y'(0) = 1.$

Ans. $Y(t) = \dfrac{1}{b} e^{at} \sin bt.$

6. $Y''(t) + 4Y(t) = \sin t,\ Y(0) = Y'(0) = 0.$

Ans. $Y(t) = \frac{1}{3} \sin t - \frac{1}{6} \sin 2t.$

7. $Y'''(t) + Y'(t) = e^{2t},\ Y(0) = Y'(0) = Y''(0) = 0.$

Ans. $Y(t) = -\frac{1}{2} + \frac{1}{10}e^{2t} - \frac{1}{5} \sin t + \frac{2}{5} \cos t.$

8. $Y''(t) + Y'(t) = t^2 + 2t,\ Y(0) = 4,\ Y'(0) = -2.$

Ans. $Y(t) = \frac{1}{3}t^3 + 2e^{-t} + 2.$

9. $Y^{(4)}(t) + Y'''(t) = \cos t,\ Y(0) = Y'(0) = Y'''(0) = 0,\ Y''(0)$ arbitrary.   *Ans.* $Y(t) = -1 + t + Ct^2 + \frac{1}{2}(e^{-t} + \cos t - \sin t).$

10. $Y'(t) - Z'(t) - 2Y(t) + 2Z(t) = 1 - 2t,\ Y''(t) + 2Z'(t) + Y(t) = 0,$ $Y(0) = Z(0) = Y'(0) = 0.$

Ans. $Y(t) = 2 - 2e^{-t} - 2te^{-t},\ Z(t) = 2 - 2e^{-t} - 2te^{-t} - t.$

11. $X'(t) + Y'(t) + X(t) + Y(t) = 1,\ Y'(t) - 2X(t) - Y(t) = 0,$ $X(0) = 0,\ Y(0) = 1.$ *Ans.* $X(t) = e^{-t} - 1,\ Y(t) = 2 - e^{-t}.$

12. $Y''(t) - Y(t) = \sin t,\ Y(0) = Y'(0) = 0.$

13. $Y''(t) - 2Y'(t) + Y(t) = 0,\ Y(0) = 0,\ Y(1) = 2.$

Ans. $Y(t) = 2te^{t-1}.$

14. $\dfrac{d^2 y}{dx^2} + y = x,\ \dfrac{dy}{dx} = 1$ when $x = 0, y = 0$ when $x = \pi.$

Ans. $y = x + \pi \cos x.$

15. $y''(x) + 2y'(x) = 0,\ y(0) = 0,\ y(-1) = 1.$

CHAPTER 2

FURTHER PROPERTIES OF THE TRANSFORMATION

10. Translation of $F(t)$. There are several further operational properties of the Laplace transformation that are important in the applications. Those properties whose derivations and applications do not necessarily involve the use of complex variables will be taken up in this chapter.

We begin with an analogue of Theorem 3 of the first chapter. According to that theorem, the multiplication of the object function by an exponential function corresponds to a linear substitution for s in the transform. Now let us note the correspondence arising from the multiplication of the transform by an exponential function.

Let $F(t)$ have a transform,

$$f(s) = \int_0^\infty e^{-st}F(t)\,dt.$$

Then
$$e^{-bs}f(s) = \int_0^\infty e^{-s(t+b)}F(t)\,dt,$$

where b is a constant, assumed to be positive. Substituting $t + b = \tau$, we can write the last integral in the form

$$\int_b^\infty e^{-s\tau}F(\tau - b)\,d\tau = \int_0^b 0 + \int_b^\infty e^{-s\tau}F(\tau - b)\,d\tau.$$

Thus if we define a function $F_b(t)$ as follows,

(1)
$$\begin{aligned} F_b(t) &= 0 &&\text{when } 0 < t < b,\\ &= F(t - b) &&\text{when } t > b, \end{aligned}$$

we see that
$$f(s)e^{-bs} = \int_0^\infty e^{-s\tau}F_b(\tau)\,d\tau.$$

The following property is therefore established.

Theorem 1. *If $f(s) = L\{F(t)\}$ then for any positive constant b,*

(2)
$$e^{-bs}f(s) = L\{F_b(t)\},$$

where $F_b(t)$ is the function defined by equation (1).

The function $F_b(t)$ is illustrated in Fig. 4. Its graph is obtained by translating the graph of $F(t)$ to the right through a distance of b units and making $F_b(t)$ identically zero between $t = 0$ and $t = b$. We can refer to $F_b(t)$ as the translated function.

Our unit step function $S_b(t)$ is the translation of the function $S_0(t) = 1 \ (t > 0)$. It serves as a familiar illustration of the above theorem, since its transform is $s^{-1}e^{-bs}$. This step function can be used to describe the translation of any function $F(t)$ by writing

$$F_b(t) = S_b(t)F(t - b) \qquad (t > 0),$$

provided that $F(t - b)$ is defined where $t > 0$; that is, provided that $F(t)$ has numerical values for those values of t in the range

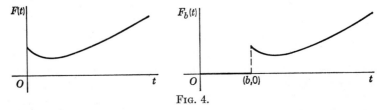

Fig. 4.

$t > -b$. Since the function $F(t) = \sin kt$ is defined for all t, for example, we can write

$$F_b(t) = S_b(t) \sin k(t - b) = L^{-1}\left\{\frac{ke^{-bs}}{s^2 + k^2}\right\} \qquad (t > 0).$$

But when the function $F(t)$ is not defined over part of the range $t > -b$, the product $S_b(t)F(t)$ has no meaning in that part.

On some occasions it is convenient to define $F(t)$ as zero for all negative values of t. When this is done the graph of $F_b(t)$ is simply the translation of the graph of $F(t)$, and

$$F_b(t) = F(t - b) \qquad \text{for all } t.$$

2) In Theorem 1 the substitution of $t - b$ for the variable t was involved. Consider the simpler linear substitution of replacing t by at where a is a positive constant. Since

$$L\{F(at)\} = \int_0^\infty e^{-st}F(at)\ dt$$
$$= \frac{1}{a}\int_0^\infty e^{-(s/a)\tau}F(\tau)\ d\tau = \frac{1}{a}f\left(\frac{s}{a}\right),$$

we have established the following theorem.

Theorem 2.   *If $L\{F(t)\} = f(s)$ when $s > \alpha$, then*

$$(3) \qquad L\{F(at)\} = \frac{1}{a} f\left(\frac{s}{a}\right) \qquad (s > a\alpha,\ a > 0).$$

This correspondence can of course be written in the form

$$(4) \qquad L^{-1}\{f(cs)\} = \frac{1}{c} F\left(\frac{t}{c}\right) \qquad (c > 0).$$

Given, for example, that

$$\frac{s}{s^2 + 1} = L\{\cos t\},$$

it follows from formula (3) that

$$\frac{s}{s^2 + k^2} = \frac{1}{k} \frac{s/k}{(s/k)^2 + 1} = L\{\cos kt\}.$$

The effect of a general linear substitution for s can be seen from formula (4) and Theorem 3, Chap. 1, since

$$(5) \quad f(as - b) = f\left[a\left(s - \frac{b}{a}\right)\right] = L\left[\frac{1}{a} e^{(b/a)t} F\left(\frac{t}{a}\right)\right] \quad (a > 0).$$

11. Step Functions.   When t is a positive number, the bracket symbol $[t]$ is used in mathematics to denote the greatest integer, 0, 1, 2, . . . , that does not exceed the number t.   Thus $[\pi] = 3 = [3]$.   The function $[t]$ is therefore a step function of the type that is sometimes called a staircase function with unit rise and run:

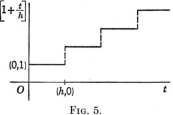

$$[t] = 0 \quad (0 \leqq t < 1),$$
$$= 1 \quad (1 \leqq t < 2),$$
$$= 2 \quad (2 \leqq t < 3), \ . \ . \ . \ .$$

Fig. 5.

The staircase function with an arbitrary positive run h, and with a unit rise beginning at the origin $t = 0$ (Fig. 5), is then represented by the symbol $[1 + t/h]$ or $1 + [t/h]$.   The function $c[1 + t/h]$ has the rise c and the run h.

To obtain the transform of the function

$$(1) \qquad Y(t) = \left[1 + \frac{t}{h}\right],$$

we may describe the function by means of a difference equation of the first order together with an initial condition, as follows.

$$Y(t) = Y(t - h) + 1 \qquad\qquad (t \geqq 0),$$
$$= 0 \qquad\qquad (t < 0).$$

The function $Y(t - h)$ is then the same as the translated function $Y_h(t)$ and, in view of Theorem 1, the transform $y(s)$ of the function $Y(t)$ satisfies the equation

$$y(s) = e^{-hs}y(s) + \frac{1}{s} \qquad\qquad (s > 0).$$

Therefore the transform of the staircase function (1) is

$$(2) \qquad y(s) = L\left\{\left[1 + \frac{t}{h}\right]\right\} = \frac{1}{s}\frac{1}{1 - e^{-hs}} \qquad (s > 0).$$

Another useful step function is the unit finite impulse function

$$(3) \qquad I(h, t - t_0) = \frac{1}{h} \text{ when } t_0 < t < t_0 + h,$$
$$I_{t_0}(h, t) = 0 \text{ when } t < t_0 \text{ and when } t > t_0 + h,$$

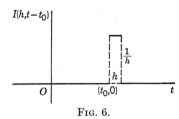

$I(h,t-t_0)$

$\frac{1}{h}$

h

O $(t_0,0)$ t

FIG. 6.

illustrated in Fig. 6. Let us introduce a variation of our unit step function $S_k(t)$, one that is defined to be zero when t is negative; namely,

$$(4) \quad S_0(t - t_0) = 0 \quad \text{when } t < t_0,$$
$$= 1 \quad \text{when } t > t_0.$$

Then our function I can be written

$$(5) \qquad I(h, t - t_0) = \frac{S_0(t - t_0) - S_0(t - t_0 - h)}{h}.$$

It follows at once from the transform of $S_0(t - t_0)$ that

$$(6) \qquad L\{I(h, t - t_0)\} = e^{-st_0}\frac{1 - e^{-hs}}{hs} \qquad (t_0 \geqq 0, s > 0).$$

It is clear from the definition (3) that

$$(7) \qquad \lim_{h \to 0} I(h, t - t_0) = 0 \qquad\qquad \text{when } t \neq t_0.$$

Also, the area under the graph of the function I is unity for every positive h; hence

$$(8) \qquad \lim_{h \to 0} \int_{-\infty}^{\infty} I(h, t - t_0)\, dt = 1.$$

The order of the positions of the limit and the integral here is important, for in view of equation (7)

$$\int_{-\infty}^{\infty} \lim_{h \to 0} I(h, t - t_0)\, dt = 0.$$

It is interesting to note the behavior of the transform of the finite unit impulse function as h tends to zero. By evaluating the limit of the right-hand member of equation (6) we find that

$$(9) \qquad \lim_{h \to 0} L\{I(h, t - t_0)\} = e^{-st_0} \qquad (t_0 \geq 0, s > 0).$$

But note that

$$L\{\lim_{h \to 0} I(h, t - t_0)\} = L\{0\} = 0.$$

Equation (9) presents the *exponential function* e^{-st_0}, or $\exp(-st_0)$, not as the transform of a function, but as a limit of transforms of functions of the set $I(h, t - t_0)$ consisting of one function for each positive value of the parameter h.

For the purpose of reducing the number of steps in certain types of problems the proper order of the limit processes noted in the preceding paragraphs is sometimes disregarded. The limit of the function $I(h, t - t_0)$, as h tends to zero, is referred to as the unit impulse symbol $\delta(t - t_0)$ or the Dirac delta function in such formal procedures. These formal properties are assigned to the symbol $\delta(t - t_0)$:

$$(10) \qquad \begin{aligned} \delta(t - t_0) &= 0 & (t \neq t_0), \\ \int_{-\infty}^{\infty} \delta(t - t_0)\, dt &= 1, & \\ L\{\delta(t - t_0)\} &= e^{-st_0} & (t_0 \geq 0); \end{aligned}$$

also (see Probs. 10 and 11)

$$(11) \quad \delta(t - t_0) = S_0'(t - t_0), \qquad \int_{-\infty}^{\infty} \delta(t - t_0)F(t)\, dt = F(t_0).$$

Note that no *function* can satisfy all these properties.

Formal procedures of using the impulse symbol $\delta(t - t_0)$ will be illustrated later on. Results obtained by such methods should be verified if those results are to be relied upon.

Generalizations of functions, usually called distributions, have been developed which include the symbol $\delta(t - t_0)$ and generalized derivatives of that symbol. The theory of distributions contains rigorous treatments of properties and transforms of the impulse symbol. The theoretical developments in these treatments, however, are lengthy and involved.

The Stieltjes integral, a generalization of the common Riemann integral used in this book, also furnishes a sound procedure that takes the place of some formal manipulations with the impulse symbol.

PROBLEMS

1. Use Theorem 1 and established transformations to find the inverse transform $F(t)$ of each of the following transforms, and draw a graph of $F(t)$ in each case.

(a) $f(s) = \dfrac{e^{-bs}}{s^2}$ $(b > 0)$.

$\qquad$ Ans. $F(t) = 0$ $(0 < t < b)$, $F(t) = t - b$ $(t > b)$.

(b) $f(s) = \dfrac{e^{-\pi s}}{s^2 + 1}$.

$\qquad$ Ans. $F(t) = 0$ $(0 < t < \pi)$, $F(t) = -\sin t$ $(t > \pi)$.

(c) $f(s) = \dfrac{se^{-s/2}}{s^2 + \pi^2}$.

$\qquad$ Ans. $F(t) = 0$ $(0 < t < \frac{1}{2})$, $F(t) = \sin \pi t$ $(t > \frac{1}{2})$.

(d) $f(s) = s^{-\frac{3}{2}}e^{-2s}$.

2. From the Maclaurin series that represents $(1 - x)^{-1}$ when $|x| < 1$, or from the sum of an infinite geometric series, show that

$$\frac{1}{s} \frac{1}{1 - e^{-hs}} = \frac{1}{s} + \frac{e^{-hs}}{s} + \frac{e^{-2hs}}{s} + \cdots = \sum_{n=0}^{\infty} \frac{e^{-nhs}}{s} \quad (h > 0, \, s > 0).$$

Apply the inverse transformation term by term to this infinite series, formally, to obtain the result shown in equation (2); namely,

$$L^{-1} \left\{ \frac{1}{s} \frac{1}{1 - e^{-hs}} \right\} = \left[1 + \frac{t}{h} \right] \qquad (h > 0).$$

3. Show that equation (2) can be written in the form

$$L \left\{ \left[1 + \frac{t}{h} \right] \right\} = \frac{1}{2s} \left(1 + \coth \frac{hs}{2} \right).$$

4. Use the formal method indicated in Prob. 2 to find $F(t)$ when

$$f(s) = \frac{1}{s} \frac{1}{1 + e^{-s}} \qquad (s > 0).$$

Draw the graph of $F(t)$.   Note that $F(t)$ can be written in terms of the bracket symbol $[t]$ as follows:

$$F(t) = \tfrac{1}{2} + \tfrac{1}{2}(-1)^{[t]}.$$

5. Given that the transformation indicated in Prob. 4 is correct, apply Theorem 2 to show that

$$L\{\tfrac{1}{2} + \tfrac{1}{2}(-1)^{[t/h]}\} = \frac{1}{s} \frac{1}{1 + e^{-hs}} \qquad (h > 0, s > 0).$$

6. Find the function $Y(t)$ that satisfies the following difference equation of the first order and the accompanying initial condition.

$$Y(t) - cY(t - h) = F(t)$$
$$Y(t) = 0 \qquad \text{when } t < 0,$$

where c and h are constants and $h > 0$, and where $F(t) = 0$ when $t < 0$. The expansion of $(1 - ce^{-hs})^{-1}$ in powers of ce^{-hs} is helpful here (compare Prob. 2).   Show that the solution can be written

$$Y(t) = \sum_{n=0}^{\infty} c^n F(t - nh);$$

but for each fixed value of t this series is a finite series because $F(t - nh) = 0$ when $t - nh < 0$.   Thus an alternate form of the solution is

$$Y(t) = F(t) + cF(t - h) + c^2F(t - 2h) + \cdots + c^m F(t - mh),$$

where $m = 0, 1, 2, \ldots$, when $mh < t < (m + 1)h$.   Verify the solution.

7. Find the function $Y(t)$ that satisfies the following difference equation of the second order and the accompanying initial condition.

$$Y(t) - (a + b)Y(t - h) + abY(t - 2h) = F(t)$$
$$Y(t) = 0 \qquad \text{when } t < 0,$$

where $F(t) = 0$ when $t < 0$.   The constants a and b are such that $a \neq b$, and the constant h is positive.   Note that the solution of the transformed problem can be simplified, with the aid of partial fractions in the variable e^{-hs}, to

$$y(s) = \frac{f(s)}{a - b} \left(\frac{a}{1 - ae^{-hs}} - \frac{b}{1 - be^{-hs}} \right).$$

$$Ans. \ Y(t) = \frac{1}{a - b} \sum_{n=0}^{\infty} (a^{n+1} - b^{n+1})F(t - nh).$$

8. Solve Prob. 7 when $b = a$. *Ans.* $Y(t) = \displaystyle\sum_{n=0}^{\infty} (n + 1)a^n F(t - nh)$.

9. Solve the difference-differential equation

$$Y'(t) - aY(t - 1) = F(t),$$

where $F(t) = b$ when $t > 0$ and $F(t) = 0$ when $t < 0$, under the condition that $Y(t) = 0$ when $t \leqq 0$.

Ans. $Y(t) = b \left[t + \dfrac{a}{2!} (t - 1)^2 + \cdots + \dfrac{a^n}{(n + 1)!} (t - n)^{n+1} \right]$,

where $n < t < n + 1$ and $n = 0, 1, 2, \ldots$.

10. Show that the first of equations (11) is true when $t \neq t_0$.

11. According to the law of the mean for integrals,

$$\int_{t_0}^{t_0+h} F(t) \, dt = hF(t_0 + \theta h)$$

for some number $\theta (0 < \theta < 1)$, when $F(t)$ is a continuous function. When $F(t)$ is defined for all t and continuous over an interval with t_0 as an interior point, prove that

$$\lim_{h \to 0} \int_{-\infty}^{\infty} I(h, t - t_0) F(t) \, dt = F(t_0).$$

This is the sound form of the second of equations (11).

12. Draw the graph of the difference quotient

$$\frac{\Delta I(h, t - t_0)}{h} = \frac{I(h, t - t_0) - I(h, t - h - t_0)}{h} \qquad (h > 0, t_0 \geqq 0),$$

as a function of t. Show that

$$\lim_{h \to 0} L \left\{ \frac{\Delta I(h, t - t_0)}{h} \right\} = se^{-st_0}$$

and note that this result suggests the formal property

$$L\{\delta'(t - t_0)\} = se^{-st_0}.$$

12. Integrals Containing a Parameter. We shall now summarize some properties of integrals that will be useful in the sequel.

Let x denote a parameter and let $f(x,t)$ be a continuous function of the two variables (x,t) in a region $\alpha(x) \leqq t \leqq \beta(x)$, $c \leqq x \leqq d$, where $\alpha(x)$ and $\beta(x)$ are continuous functions. Then *the integral*

$$(1) \qquad \int_{\alpha(x)}^{\beta(x)} f(x,t) \, dt = g(x) \qquad (c \leqq x \leqq d)$$

represents a continuous function of x. If the derivatives $\alpha'(x)$ and $\beta'(x)$ exist, and if $\partial f / \partial x$ as well as f is continuous, then the derivative of the integral (1) is given by the *generalized Leibnitz formula,*

$$(2) \quad g'(x) = \int_{\alpha(x)}^{\beta(x)} \frac{\partial}{\partial x} f(x,t) \, dt + f[x,\beta(x)]\beta'(x) - f[x,\alpha(x)]\alpha'(x).$$

The foregoing two properties of the integral (1) are established in advanced calculus from fairly elementary considerations. Let us indicate here how the continuity requirement on the integrand can be relaxed in establishing certain properties.

Let a, b, and c denote constants, and let the integrand of the integral

$$(3) \qquad\qquad \int_0^{ax+b} f(x,t) \, dt = h(x) \qquad\qquad (0 \leq x \leq c)$$

be such that the region $0 \leq t \leq ax + b$, $0 \leq x \leq c$ can be divided into polygonal subregions by a finite number of straight lines $t = a_0 x + b_i$ $(i = 1, 2, \ldots, m)$ and

$$x = x_j \; (j = 1, 2, \ldots, n),$$

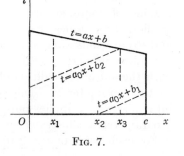

where $f(x,t)$ is continuous in each subregion up to its boundary (Fig. 7). Thus the values of $f(x,t)$ may make finite jumps when the point (x,t) moves across the boundary of a subdivision. The function $f(x,t)$ is then continuous by subregions.

Fig. 7.

When $x_1 \leq x \leq x_2$ in Fig. 7 for instance, the integral can be written as a finite sum of integrals of the type (1), such as

$$(4) \qquad\qquad \int_{a_0 x + b_2}^{ax+b} f(x,t) \, dt \qquad\qquad (x_1 \leq x \leq x_2),$$

in which the integrand is continuous so that the integral represents a continuous function of $x(x_1 \leq x \leq x_2)$. Similarly, when x is between any two adjacent x_j's, $h(x)$ is continuous. Consequently *the function $h(x)$ in equation (3) is sectionally continuous on the interval $0 \leq x \leq c$.*

As a special case, when the integrand is a sectionally continuous function $f(t)$, the integral (3) represents a continuous function of x.

The integral of the sectionally continuous function (3)

$$(5) \qquad \int_0^c h(x)\, dx = \int_0^c \int_0^{ax+b} f(x,t)\, dt\, dx$$

exists. It can be written as the sum of iterated integrals over each of the subregions in which $f(x,t)$ is continuous. When the order of integration is interchanged in each subregion, the sum of the integrals represents the iterated integral, with order interchanged, over the entire region.

Thus our condition of continuity by subregions permits *the interchange of order of integration with respect to t and x.* In particular, when $a = 0$ so that the limits are constants,

$$(6) \qquad \int_0^c \int_0^b f(x,t)\, dt\, dx = \int_0^b \int_0^c f(x,t)\, dx\, dt.$$

These conclusions can be reached by the same procedure for regions of more general shapes. The argument used above applies, for instance, when the lower limits of the integrals (5) and (6) are constants other than zero.

Similar properties of improper integrals can be established with the aid of a condition of uniform convergence with respect to the parameter x. The concept of uniform convergence of integrals, which applies only to improper integrals that involve a parameter, is illustrated in the following example.

For each value of $x(x \geqq 0)$ the integral

$$(7) \qquad p(x) = \int_0^\infty x e^{-xt}\, dt$$

exists; it has the values

$$(8) \qquad \begin{aligned} p(0) &= 0 \\ p(x) &= 1 \end{aligned} \qquad \text{when } x > 0.$$

It can be written as a definite integral plus a remainder,

$$p(x) = \int_0^T x e^{-xt}\, dt + \int_T^\infty x e^{-xt}\, dt = 1 - e^{-xT} + R(x,T),$$

where

$$(9) \qquad \begin{aligned} R(0,T) &= 0 \\ R(x,T) &= e^{-xT} \end{aligned} \qquad \text{when } x > 0.$$

Uniform convergence of the integral for all x in a prescribed interval means that the remainder can be made arbitrarily small in absolute value by taking T sufficiently large, uniformly for all x in the interval. Thus when $x \geqq 1$ and ϵ is any small positive number, we see that

$$|R(x,t)| = e^{-xT} \leqq e^{-T} < \epsilon$$

when $T > \log (1/\epsilon)$, a value that is independent of x, so that the integral converges uniformly with respect to x when $x \geqq 1$. In the same way we can see that it converges uniformly when $x \geqq x_1$ whenever $x_1 > 0$.

But the convergence is not uniform in the range $x \geqq 0$ or $x > 0$, because the remainder (9) when $x > 0$ is small only if xT is large. Since x can be arbitrarily small, the value of T that makes $R(x,T)$ small must depend on x. A consequence of this lack of uniform convergence in the range $x \geqq 0$ is the discontinuity of the function $p(x)$ at $x = 0$ that is pointed out in equations (8).

The *Weierstrass test for uniform convergence* of the integral

$$(10) \qquad \int_0^\infty f(x,t)\, dt = q(x) \qquad (0 \leqq x \leqq c)$$

can be stated as follows. Let $f(x,t)$ be continuous by subregions, in the sense described above, in the region $0 \leqq x \leqq c, 0 \leqq t \leqq T$, for each positive constant T. If a function $M(t)$, independent of x, exists such that

$$|f(x,t)| \leqq M(t) \qquad (0 \leqq x \leqq c, t > 0)$$

and such that the integral $\int_0^\infty M(t)\, dt$ exists, then the integral (10) is uniformly convergent with respect to $x(0 \leqq x \leqq c)$. This test is established by showing that the absolute value of the remainder for the integral (10), for all x in the interval $(0,c)$, does not exceed the value of the remainder in the integral of $M(t)$. The latter remainder is independent of x.

If the integral (10) is uniformly convergent with respect to x and if $f(x,t)$ is continuous by subregions in the rectangle $0 \leqq x \leqq c$, $0 \leqq t \leqq T$ for each positive T, then $q(x)$ *is sectionally continuous* and

$$(11) \quad \int_0^c q(x)\, dx = \int_0^c \int_0^\infty f(x,t)\, dt\, dx = \int_0^\infty \int_0^c f(x,t)\, dx\, dt;$$

that is, the order of integration can be interchanged.

In particular, let $f(x,t)$ be continuous in each rectangle $0 \le x \le c$, $0 \le t \le T$, except possibly for finite jumps across a set of lines $t = t_i$ $(i = 1, 2, \ldots , n)$. Then $q(x)$ *is continuous* if the integral (10) is uniformly convergent. Suppose that $\partial f/\partial x$ as well as f satisfies those continuity requirements and that the integral $\int_0^\infty \partial f/\partial x \, dt$ converges uniformly and the integral (10) exists. Then the derivative of the latter integral exists and

$$(12) \qquad \frac{d}{dx} \int_0^\infty f(x,t) \, dt = \int_0^\infty \frac{\partial}{\partial x} f(x,t) \, dt \qquad (0 < x < c).$$

The continuity of $q(x)$ can be seen by writing

$$q(x) = \int_0^T f(x,t) \, dt + R(x,T) \qquad (0 \le x \le c).$$

For each fixed T the integral on the right is a sum of integrals of the type

$$\int_{t_{i-1}}^{t_i} f(x,t) \, dt$$

with continuous integrands; hence it is a continuous function of x so that the change in its value is small when the change Δx in x is small. But $|R(x,T)|$ and $|R(x + \Delta x, T)|$ are small for all x and $x + \Delta x$ in the interval $(0,c)$ as long as T is taken sufficiently large, because of the uniform convergence of the integral (10). Thus by taking T large first, then Δx small, the continuity of $q(x)$ follows; that is, $|q(x + \Delta x) - q(x)|$ is arbitrarily small when $|\Delta x|$ is sufficiently small.

The proof of property (11) follows the plan commonly used in advanced calculus, where $f(x,t)$ is generally assumed to be continuous. The details are left to Prob. 10 at the end of Sec. 14.

Property (12) can be established in the following manner. Because of the uniform convergence of the integral on the right in equation (12) and the continuity by subregions of $\partial f/\partial x$, for each $r(0 < r < c)$ we can write

$$(13) \qquad \int_0^r \int_0^\infty \frac{\partial f}{\partial x} \, dt \, dx = \int_0^\infty \int_0^r \frac{\partial f}{\partial x} \, dx \, dt$$
$$= \int_0^\infty f(r,t) \, dt - \int_0^\infty f(0,t) \, dt,$$

where we have used property (11) to invert the order of integration. Since $\int_0^\infty \partial f/\partial x\ dt$ is a continuous function of x, differentiation of the first and last members of equations (13) with respect to r leads to the equation

$$\int_0^\infty \frac{\partial}{\partial x} f(x,t) \Big]_{x=r} dt = \frac{d}{dr} \int_0^\infty f(r,t)\ dt \quad (0 < r < c),$$

which is the same as equation (12) with x replaced by r.

13. Convolution. We now determine the operation on two functions of t that corresponds to multiplying their transforms together. This convolution operation, which gives the inverse transform of the product of two transforms directly in terms of the original functions, is one of primary importance in operational mathematics.

Let $F(t)$ and $G(t)$ denote any two functions that are sectionally continuous in each finite interval $0 \leq t \leq T$ and of the order of $e^{\alpha t}$, and let

$$f(s) = L\{F(t)\}, \qquad g(s) = L\{G(t)\} \qquad (s > \alpha).$$

It will be convenient to define $G(t)$ to be zero when $t < 0$; but our final result depends only on the values of $F(t)$ and $G(t)$ when $t > 0$. According to Theorem 1, for each fixed $\tau (\tau \geq 0)$,

$$e^{-s\tau}g(s) = L\{G(t - \tau)\} = \int_0^\infty e^{-st}G(t - \tau)\ dt,$$

where $s > \alpha$. Hence

$$f(s)g(s) = \int_0^\infty F(\tau)e^{-s\tau}g(s)\ d\tau = \int_0^\infty F(\tau) \int_0^\infty e^{-st}G(t - \tau)\ dt\ d\tau;$$

that is,

$$(1) \qquad f(s)g(s) = \lim_{T\to\infty} \int_0^T \int_0^\infty F(\tau)e^{-st}G(t - \tau)\ dt\ d\tau.$$

Since $f(s)$ and $g(s)$ exist when $s > \alpha$, the limit here exists.

The integrand of the inner integral in equation (1) is continuous by subregions, in the sense of Sec. 12, over the rectangular region $0 \leq \tau \leq T$, $0 \leq t \leq R$, for each pair of positive constants T and R. For if the jumps of $F(\tau)$ and $G(t)$ occur at $\tau = \tau_i$ ($i = 1, 2, \ldots, m$) and $t = t_j$ ($j = 1, 2, \ldots, n$), then the jumps of the integrand occur at the lines $\tau = \tau_i$ and $t = \tau + t_j$. In view of equation (11), Sec. 12, the order of integration in equation (1) can be interchanged, provided that the improper integral there is uniformly convergent with respect to its parameter $\tau(0 \leqq \tau \leqq T)$.

The uniform convergence is seen by noting that, owing to the exponential order of F and G, a constant N exists such that

$$(2) \qquad |F(\tau)e^{-st}G(t-\tau)| < Ne^{\alpha\tau}e^{-st}e^{\alpha(t-\tau)} = M(t),$$

where $M(t) = N \exp[-(s-\alpha)t]$. The function $M(t)$ satisfies the conditions of the Weierstrass test (Sec. 12); that is, $M(t)$ is independent of τ and integrable from zero to infinity.

Equation (1) can now be written in the form

$$(3) \qquad f(s)g(s) = \lim_{T \to \infty} \int_0^\infty e^{-st} \int_0^T F(\tau)G(t-\tau)\, d\tau\, dt$$

$$= \lim_{T \to \infty} [I_1(T) + I_2(T)],$$

where
$$I_1(T) = \int_0^T e^{-st} \int_0^T F(\tau)G(t-\tau)\, d\tau\, dt,$$

$$I_2(T) = \int_T^\infty e^{-st} \int_0^T F(\tau)G(t-\tau)\, d\tau\, dt.$$

In view of condition (2)

$$|I_2(T)| < N \int_T^\infty e^{-(s-\alpha)t} \int_0^T d\tau\, dt = \frac{NT}{s-\alpha} e^{-(s-\alpha)T};$$

therefore
$$\lim_{T \to \infty} I_2(T) = 0.$$

The region of integration for the integral $I_1(T)$ is the square $0 \leqq \tau \leqq T, 0 \leqq t \leqq T$. But $G(t-\tau) = 0$ when $\tau > t$. Therefore

$$I_1(T) = \int_0^T e^{-st} \int_0^t F(\tau)G(t-\tau)\, d\tau\, dt$$

and equation (3) reduces to

$$(4) \quad f(s)g(s) = \lim_{T \to \infty} I_1(T) = \int_0^\infty e^{-st} \int_0^t F(\tau)G(t-\tau)\, d\tau\, dt.$$

The *convolution* $F * G$ of the functions $F(t)$ and $G(t)$ is defined as the function

$$(5) \qquad F(t) * G(t) = \int_0^t F(\tau)G(t-\tau)\, d\tau,$$

so that equation (4) can be written

$$(6) \qquad f(s)g(s) = L\{F(t) * G(t)\}.$$

We summarize our result as follows.

Theorem 3.   *If* $f(s)$ *and* $g(s)$ *are the transforms of two functions* $F(t)$ *and* $G(t)$ *that are sectionally continuous on each interval* $0 \leq t \leq T$ *and of the order of* $e^{\alpha t}$ *as t tends to infinity, then the transform of the convolution* $F(t) * G(t)$ *exists when* $s > \alpha$; *it is* $f(s)g(s)$. *Thus the inverse transform of the product* $f(s)g(s)$ *is given by the formula*

$$(7) \qquad L^{-1}\{f(s)g(s)\} = F(t) * G(t).$$

The functions $F(t) = t$ and $G(t) = e^{\alpha t}$, for example, satisfy the conditions of Theorem 3.   Consequently

$$L^{-1}\left\{\frac{1}{s^2}\frac{1}{s-a}\right\} = t * e^{at} = \int_0^t \tau e^{a(t-\tau)}\, d\tau$$

$$= e^{at} \int_0^t \tau e^{-a\tau}\, d\tau = \frac{1}{a^2}(e^{at} - at - 1).$$

Partial fractions can also be used to obtain this result.

When $G(t) = F(t)$, we have the formula

$$(8) \qquad [f(s)]^2 = L\{F * F\}.$$

As an example that is useful in finding inverse transforms with the aid of partial fractions, we note that

$$(9) \quad L^{-1}\left\{\frac{1}{(s^2+k^2)^2}\right\} = \frac{1}{k^2}\sin kt * \sin kt$$

$$= \frac{1}{k^2}\int_0^t \sin k\tau \sin k(t-\tau)\, d\tau$$

$$= \frac{1}{2k^3}(\sin kt - kt \cos kt).$$

The conditions stated in Theorem 3 are narrower than necessary for the validity of formula (7).   If $F(t) = t^{-\frac{1}{2}}$ for example, $F(t)$ is not sectionally continuous on an interval $0 \leq t \leq T$, but the Laplace integral of $F(t)$ is absolutely convergent and formula (7) is still valid if $G(t)$ satisfies the conditions in the theorem. Thus

$$L^{-1}\left\{\frac{1}{\sqrt{s}\,(s-1)}\right\} = \frac{1}{\sqrt{\pi t}} * e^t = \frac{2e^t}{\sqrt{\pi}}\int_0^t e^{-\tau}\frac{d\tau}{2\sqrt{\tau}}.$$

If we make the substitution $r = \sqrt{\tau}$ here we find that

$$(10) \qquad L^{-1}\left\{\frac{1}{\sqrt{s}\,(s-1)}\right\} = e^t \operatorname{erf}(\sqrt{t}),$$

where the *error function* erf (x), also called the probability integral, is a tabulated function defined by the equation

$$(11) \qquad \text{erf } (x) = \frac{2}{\sqrt{\pi}} \int_0^x e^{-r^2} dr.$$

It was shown in Prob. 5 at the end of Sec. 5 that erf $(\infty) = 1$.

Since the substitution of $s + 1$ for s in a transform corresponds to multiplication of the object function by e^{-t}, it follows from equation (10) that

$$(12) \qquad L^{-1} \left\{ \frac{1}{s \sqrt{s+1}} \right\} = \text{erf } (\sqrt{t}).$$

14. Properties of Convolution. By substituting the new variable of integration $\lambda = t - \tau$ in the convolution integral (5), Sec. 13, we find that *the convolution operation is commutative;* that is,

$$(1) \qquad F(t) * G(t) = G(t) * F(t) = \int_0^t F(t - \lambda)G(\lambda) \, d\lambda.$$

The operation is clearly *distributive* with respect to addition:

$$(2) \qquad F(t) * [G(t) + H(t)] = F(t) * G(t) + F(t) * H(t).$$

Also, $F * (kG) = k(F * G)$ if k is a constant.

Properties (1) and (2) are valid whenever the functions are sectionally continuous in an interval $(0,T)$ that contains the point t. For such functions *the operation is also associative:*

$$(3) \qquad F(t) * [G(t) * H(t)] = [F(t) * G(t)] * H(t).$$

To prove this we first write, in view of equation (1),

$$F * (G * H) = \int_0^t F(\tau) \int_0^{t-\tau} G(t - \tau - \lambda)H(\lambda) \, d\lambda \, d\tau$$

and observe that the iterated integral here represents an integration over the triangular region shown in Fig. 8. When the order of integration is reversed, the integral becomes

$$\int_0^t H(\lambda) \int_0^{t-\lambda} F(\tau)G(t - \lambda - \tau) \, d\tau \, d\lambda,$$

which represents $H * (F * G)$ or $(F * G) * H$. Note that for each fixed value of t the integrand of the first iterated integral is a function of τ and λ that is continuous by subregions, in the sense used in Sec. 12, over the region $0 \leqq \lambda \leqq t - \tau, 0 \leqq \tau \leqq t$, because of the sectional continuity of the functions F, G, and H.   The interchange of order of integration is therefore justified (Sec. 12).

The convolution of a sectionally continuous function $F(t)$ and our unit step function $S_k(t)$ can be written

$$(4) \quad F(t) * S_k(t) = \int_0^t S_k(\tau)F(t - \tau) \, d\tau = 0 \qquad \text{when } 0 \leqq t \leqq k,$$

$$= \int_k^t F(t - \tau) \, d\tau = \int_0^{t-k} F(\lambda) \, d\lambda$$

$$\text{when } t \geqq k.$$

Since the integral of a sectionally continuous function $F(\lambda)$ is a continuous function of its upper limit when the lower limit is a constant (Sec. 12) and since the function (4) is continuous at $t = k$, it follows that $F * S_k$ is continuous on the interval $0 \leqq t \leqq T$ if $F(t)$ is sectionally continuous there.   A proof, based on the continuity of $F * S_k$, that *the convolution of any pair of sectionally continuous functions is a continuous function*, will be left to the problems.

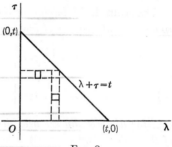

Fig. 8.

If two functions $F(t)$ and $G(t)$ are sectionally continuous on each finite interval and of the order of $e^{\alpha t}$ as t tends to infinity, then for some constant M_1

$$|F * G| < M_1 \int_0^t e^{\alpha\tau}e^{\alpha(t-\tau)} \, d\tau = M_1 t e^{\alpha t} \qquad (t > 0).$$

But if ϵ is any positive number and if M_2 represents the maximum value of the function $te^{-\epsilon t}$ when $t \geqq 0$, then

$$M_1 t e^{\alpha t} = M_1 t e^{-\epsilon t} e^{(\alpha+\epsilon)t} \leqq M e^{(\alpha+\epsilon)t},$$

where $M = M_1 M_2$.   Consequently $F * G$ is of *exponential order*:

$$(5) \qquad\qquad |F(t) * G(t)| < M e^{(\alpha+\epsilon)t} \qquad (\epsilon > 0, t > 0).$$

Now, if three functions $F(t)$, $G(t)$, and $H(t)$ satisfy the conditions of Theorem 3, then the function $G * H$ satisfies those conditions and its transform is $g(s)h(s)$.   Therefore

$$f(s)g(s)h(s) = L\{F(t) * [G(t) * H(t)]\};$$

but since the convolution operation is associative, this equation can be written in the form

$$(6) \qquad f(s)g(s)h(s) = L\{F(t) * G(t) * H(t)\}.$$

A similar formula can be written for the product of n transforms.

When $G(t) = 1$ in Theorem 3, we have a result noted earlier (Sec. 5):

$$\frac{1}{s} f(s) = L\{F(t) * 1\} = L\left\{\int_0^t F(\tau)\, d\tau\right\}.$$

When $G(t) = H(t) = 1$ in formula (6), we obtain a formula for the inverse transform of $f(s)/s^2$. These results can be stated as follows.

Theorem 4. *Division of the transform of a function by s corresponds to integration of the function between the limits 0 and t:*

$$(7) \qquad L^{-1}\left\{\frac{1}{s} f(s)\right\} = \int_0^t F(\tau)\, d\tau,$$

$$(8) \qquad L^{-1}\left\{\frac{1}{s^2} f(s)\right\} = \int_0^t \int_0^\tau F(\lambda)\, d\lambda\, d\tau,$$

etc., for division by s^n, provided $F(t)$ is sectionally continuous and of the order of $e^{\alpha t}$ ($\alpha > 0$), where $s > \alpha$.

As examples, we note that

$$L^{-1}\left\{\frac{k}{s(s^2 + k^2)}\right\} = \int_0^t \sin k\tau\, d\tau = \frac{1}{k}(1 - \cos kt),$$

$$L^{-1}\left\{\frac{k}{s^2(s^2 + k^2)}\right\} = \int_0^t \int_0^\tau \sin k\lambda\, d\lambda\, d\tau = \frac{1}{k^2}(kt - \sin kt).$$

PROBLEMS

1. Show that another form of the inverse transformation (8) is

$$L^{-1}\left\{\frac{1}{s^2} f(s)\right\} = t\int_0^t F(\tau)\, d\tau - \int_0^t \tau F(\tau)\, d\tau.$$

2. With the aid of equation (9), Sec. 13, show that

$$L^{-1}\left\{\frac{8}{(s^2 + 1)^3}\right\} = 3(\sin t - t\cos t) - t^2 \sin t.$$

3. Show that

$$\frac{1}{\sqrt{s} - 1} = \frac{1}{s - 1} + \frac{1}{\sqrt{s}}\left(1 + \frac{1}{s - 1}\right)$$

and, in view of formula (10), Sec. 13, that

$$L^{-1}\left\{\frac{1}{\sqrt{s}-1}\right\} = e^t + \frac{1}{\sqrt{\pi t}} + e^t \operatorname{erf}(\sqrt{t}).$$

4. Generalize formula (10), Sec. 13, by replacing s by s/a^2 to obtain transform 40, Appendix 3.

5. Generalize formula (12), Sec. 13, to obtain transform 44, Appendix 3.

6. Find $L^{-1}\{(s+1)^{-1}s^{-\frac{1}{2}}\}$ and generalize to obtain transform 41, Appendix 3.

7. Obtain the inverse transformation

$$L^{-1}\left\{\frac{s^{-\frac{3}{2}}}{s-1}\right\} = e^t \operatorname{erf}(\sqrt{t}) - 2\sqrt{\frac{t}{\pi}}.$$

8. Let $t = h$ and $t = k$ be the points of discontinuity of a sectionally continuous function $G(t)$ on an interval $0 \leq t \leq T$, and let j_h and j_k denote the jumps in the value of $G(t)$ at those points. With the aid of a graph of $G(t)$, note that the function

$$G_c(t) = G(t) - j_h S_h(t) - j_k S_k(t) \qquad (0 \leq t \leq T)$$

is continuous if its values at $t = h$ and $t = k$ are properly defined. Write $F * G$ in terms of $F * G_c$ and of convolutions like the one in equation (4) to show that if $F(t)$ is sectionally continuous, then $F * G$ is continuous. Also note how the result can be generalized to permit $G(t)$ to have n jumps in the interval.

9. From formula (8), Sec. 12, note that the equation

$$\lim_{x \to 0} \int_0^\infty x e^{-xt}\, dt = 1 \qquad (x > 0)$$

is true. Show that this equation is not true if the limit as $x \to 0$ is taken inside, rather than outside, the integral.

10. Prove property (11), Sec. 12, under the conditions stated there. This can be done by first showing that for each positive number T

$$\int_0^c q\, dx = \int_0^c \int_0^T f\, dt\, dx + \int_0^c R(x,T)\, dx$$

and hence that, corresponding to each positive number ϵ, a number T_ϵ exists such that when $T > T_\epsilon$

$$\left| \int_0^c q\, dx - \int_0^T \int_0^c f\, dx\, dt \right| < c\epsilon.$$

11. Show that the integral

$$u(x) = \int_0^\infty \frac{x}{1 + x^2 t^2}\, dt$$

has the values $u(x) = -\pi/2$ when $x < 0$, $u(x) = \pi/2$ when $x > 0$ and $u(0) = 0$. Examine the remainder $R(x,T)$ for this improper integral and show that the integral is not uniformly convergent with respect to x over any interval that contains the point $x = 0$ in its interior or as an end point.

15. Differential and Integral Equations. General nonhomogeneous differential equations with constant coefficients can be solved with the aid of the convolution property.

Example 1. Find the general solution of the differential equation

$$(1) \qquad Y''(t) + k^2 Y(t) = F(t)$$

in terms of the constant k and the function $F(t)$.

We assume for the present that $F(t)$ is sectionally continuous and of exponential order, that the derivative $Y''(t)$ of the unknown function satisfies those conditions, and that $Y'(t)$ is continuous and of exponential order. Then the equation in the transforms of $Y(t)$ and $F(t)$ can be written

$$s^2 y(s) - sY(0) - Y'(0) + k^2 y(s) = f(s),$$

where $Y(0)$ and $Y'(0)$ are arbitrary constants. Hence

$$y(s) = \frac{1}{k} \frac{k}{s^2 + k^2} f(s) + Y(0) \frac{s}{s^2 + k^2} + \frac{Y'(0)}{k} \frac{k}{s^2 + k^2},$$

and therefore

$$Y(t) = \frac{1}{k} (\sin kt) * F(t) + Y(0) \cos kt + \frac{Y'(0)}{k} \sin kt.$$

This general solution of equation (1) can be written

$$(2) \quad Y(t) = \frac{1}{k} \int_0^t \sin k(t - \tau) F(\tau)\, d\tau + C_1 \cos kt + C_2 \sin kt,$$

where C_1 and C_2 are arbitrary constants.

The function $C_1 \cos kt + C_2 \sin kt$ is the general solution of the homogeneous equation that arises when $F(t) = 0$ in equation (1). To verify the solution (2) it is therefore sufficient to show that the first term on the right is a solution of equation (1). If $F(\tau)$ has jumps at $\tau = t_1, t_2, \ldots, t_n$ when $0 < \tau < t$, that term can be written

$$Z(t) = \frac{1}{k} \int_0^{t_1} \sin k(t - \tau)F(\tau)\, d\tau + \cdots$$

$$+ \frac{1}{k} \int_{t_n}^{t} \sin k(t - \tau)F(\tau)\, d\tau.$$

The Leibnitz formula (2), Sec. 12, applies to each of the integrals in this equation; thus

$$Z'(t) = \int_0^{t_1} \cos k(t - \tau)F(\tau)\, d\tau + \cdots$$

$$+ \int_{t_n}^{t} \cos k(t - \tau)F(\tau)\, d\tau + 0.$$

By applying that formula again to the integrals here and collecting the resulting integrals, we find that

$$Z''(t) = -k \int_0^t \sin k(t - \tau)F(\tau)\, d\tau + F(t)$$

or $Z'' = -k^2 Z + F$. Therefore $Z(t)$ satisfies equation (1), and the function (2) is verified as the general solution of that equation for all values of t.

The function $Y(t)$ given by equation (2) is continuous, together with $Y'(t)$, when $F(t)$ is sectionally continuous, in view of the above expressions for $Z(t)$ and $Z'(t)$. The condition of exponential order on $F(t)$ was not used in verifying the solution (2); the condition that $F(t)$ be sectionally continuous, on an interval containing all values of t to be considered, was sufficient.

An equation in which the unknown function occurs inside an integral is called an *integral equation*. In certain applied problems, to be illustrated in the following chapter, the integral in the equation is a convolution integral. Such integral equations of the convolution type transform into algebraic equations.

Example 2. Solve the integral equation

$$Y(t) = at + \int_0^t Y(\tau) \sin (t - \tau)\, d\tau.$$

We can write this equation in the form

$$Y(t) = at + Y(t) * \sin t$$

and transform both members to get the algebraic equation

$$y(s) = \frac{a}{s^2} + y(s)\, \frac{1}{s^2 + 1},$$

whose solution is

$$y(s) = a\left(\frac{1}{s^2} + \frac{1}{s^4}\right).$$

Therefore $$Y(t) = a(t + \tfrac{1}{6}t^3),$$

which can be verified directly as the solution of the above integral equation.

The general integral equation of the convolution type has the form

$$(3) \qquad Y(t) = F(t) + \int_0^t G(t - \tau)Y(\tau)\, d\tau,$$

where the functions $F(t)$ and $G(t)$ are given and $Y(t)$ is to be found. Since the transformed equation is

$$y(s) = f(s) + g(s)y(s),$$

the transform of the unknown function is

$$(4) \qquad y(s) = \frac{f(s)}{1 - g(s)}.$$

Even if equation (3) is modified by replacing $Y(t)$ by linear combinations of $Y(t)$ and its derivatives, where the coefficients in these combinations are constants, the transform of the modified equation is an algebraic equation in $y(s)$. For instance, the integrodifferential equation

$$(5) \qquad aY(t) + bY'(t) = F(t) + \int_0^t G(t - \tau)Y(\tau)\, d\tau,$$

where a and b are constants, gives rise to the transformed equation

$$(a + bs)y(s) - bY(0) = f(s) + g(s)y(s),$$

which is easily solved for $y(s)$.

The equation

$$(6) \qquad F(t) = \int_0^t (t - \tau)^{-b}Y'(\tau)\, d\tau \qquad (0 < b < 1),$$

is known as Abel's integral equation. The unknown function could of course be considered here as $Y'(t)$ instead of $Y(t)$; but no advantage is gained in this way. The solution of this equation is

$$(7) \qquad Y(t) = Y(0) + \frac{1}{\Gamma(b)\Gamma(1 - b)}\, t^{b-1} * F(t),$$

valid when $F(t)$ satisfies certain conditions of continuity. The formal derivation of this solution is left to the problems.

PROBLEMS

Solve the following differential equations.

1. $Y''(t) - k^2 Y(t) = F(t)$, if $Y(0) = Y'(0) = 0 (k \neq 0)$.

$$\text{Ans. } 2kY(t) = e^{kt} \int_0^t e^{-k\tau} F(\tau) \, d\tau - e^{-kt} \int_0^t e^{k\tau} F(\tau) \, d\tau.$$

2. $Y''(t) - 2kY'(t) + k^2 Y(t) = F(t)$.

$$\text{Ans. } e^{-kt} Y(t) = C_1 + C_2 t + \int_0^t (t - \tau) e^{-k\tau} F(\tau) \, d\tau.$$

3. $2Y''(t) - 3Y'(t) - 2Y(t) = F(t)$, if $Y(0) = Y'(0) = 0$. Verify that your function satisfies the differential equation and the initial conditions.

4. $Y''(t) + 4Y'(t) + 5Y(t) = F(t)$, if $Y(0) = Y(\pi/2) = 0$.

$$\text{Ans. } e^{2t} Y(t) = \sin t \int_{\pi/2}^t F(\tau) e^{2\tau} \cos \tau \, d\tau - \cos t \int_0^t F(\tau) e^{2\tau} \sin \tau \, d\tau.$$

5. $Y'''(t) - Y'(t) = F(t)$.   Verify your result.

6. $Y'''(t) - Y''(t) + Y'(t) - Y(t) = F(t)$, if $Y(0) = Y'(0) = Y''(0)$

$= 0$. $$\text{Ans. } 2Y(t) = \int_0^t F(t - \tau)(e^\tau - \cos \tau - \sin \tau) \, d\tau.$$

7. Show that the solution of the system of differential equations

$$X'(t) - 2Y'(t) = F(t), \qquad X''(t) - Y''(t) + Y(t) = 0,$$

under the conditions $X(0) = X'(0) = Y(0) = Y'(0) = 0$, so that $F(0) = 0$, is

$$X(t) = \int_0^t F(\tau) \, d\tau - 2 \int_0^t F(\tau) \cos (t - \tau) \, d\tau,$$

$$Y(t) = - \int_0^t F(\tau) \cos (t - \tau) \, d\tau.$$

8. Solve the following system and verify your result:

$$X'(t) + Y(t) = F(t), \qquad Y'(t) + X(t) = 1, \qquad X(0) = 1, \qquad Y(0) = 0.$$

9. Solve for $Y(t)$ and verify your solution:

$$\int_0^t Y(\tau) \, d\tau - Y'(t) = t, \qquad Y(0) = 2.$$

10. Derive the solution (7) of Abel's integral equation (6).

11. Solve the integral equation

$$Y(t) = a \sin t - 2 \int_0^t Y(\tau) \cos (t - \tau) \, d\tau.$$

$$\text{Ans. } Y(t) = ate^{-t}.$$

12. When $b > c > 0$, find the solution of the integral equation

$$Y(t) = a \sin bt + c \int_0^t Y(\tau) \sin b(t - \tau) \, d\tau.$$

$$\text{Ans. } Y(t) = ab(b^2 - bc)^{-\frac{1}{2}} \sin (t \sqrt{b^2 - bc}).$$

13. Solve the integral equation

$$Y(t) = a \sin t + \int_0^t Y(\tau) \sin (t - \tau) \, d\tau.$$

14. Give a formal solution of the integrodifferential equation

$$Y(t) = \frac{2}{\sqrt{\pi}} \left[\sqrt{t} + \int_0^t \sqrt{t - \tau} \, Y'(\tau) \, d\tau \right] \quad \text{if } Y(0) = 0.$$

Ans. $Y(t) = e^t(1 + \operatorname{erf} \sqrt{t}) - 1$.

16. Derivatives of Transforms. When the Laplace integral

$$(1) \qquad f(s) = \int_0^\infty e^{-st} F(t) \, dt$$

is formally differentiated with respect to the parameter s by carrying out the differentiation inside the integral sign, the formula

$$f'(s) = \int_0^\infty e^{-st}(-t)F(t) \, dt = L\{-tF(t)\}$$

is obtained. Another formal manipulation with the integral (1) indicates that $f(s) \to 0$ as $s \to \infty$. We shall establish conditions under which those formulas are valid.

First, we note that if $F(t)$ is of the order of $e^{\alpha t}$ as $t \to \infty$, then the function $t^n F(t)$, where $n = 0, 1, 2, \ldots$, is of exponential order. Let ϵ be a positive number. Then constants N_1 and N_2 exist such that

$$|t^n F(t)| < t^n N_1 e^{\alpha t} = N_1 t^n e^{-\epsilon t} e^{(\alpha + \epsilon)t} \leqq N_1 N_2 e^{(\alpha + \epsilon)t} \quad (t > 0),$$

where N_2 represents the maximum value of the function $t^n e^{-\epsilon t}$ when $t > 0$. Thus the function $t^n F(t)$ is of the order of $e^{\alpha_0 t}$, where $\alpha_0 = \alpha + \epsilon$.

Also let $F(t)$ be sectionally continuous on each interval $0 \leqq t \leqq T$. Then $t^n F(t)$ has that property. The absolute value of the integrand of the Laplace integral of $t^n F(t)$ satisfies the condition

$$(2) \qquad |t^n F(t)e^{-st}| < Ne^{-(s-\alpha_0)t} \quad (n = 0, 1, 2, \ldots),$$

where N denotes a constant. Consequently when $s > \alpha_0$,

$$(3) \qquad \left| \int_0^\infty t^n F(t)e^{-st} \, dt \right| < N \int_0^\infty e^{-(s-\alpha_0)t} \, dt = \frac{N}{s - \alpha_0};$$

therefore $L\{t^n F(t)\} \to 0$ as $s \to \infty$. Moreover, if $s \geqq \alpha_1$ where

$\alpha_1 > \alpha_0$, then according to condition (2),

$$\left| t^n F(t) e^{-st} \right| < N e^{-(\alpha_1 - \alpha_0)t} = M(t),$$

where this exponential function $M(t)$ is independent of s and integrable from zero to infinity.   It follows from the Weierstrass test (Sec. 12) that the Laplace integral

$$\int_0^\infty t^n F(t) e^{-st} \, dt \qquad (n = 0, 1, 2, \ldots)$$

converges uniformly with respect to s when $s \geqq \alpha_1 > \alpha_0$.

Theorem 5. *If $F(t)$ is sectionally continuous and of the order of $e^{\alpha t}$, then each of the Laplace integrals $L\{F(t)\}$, $L\{tF(t)\}$, $L\{t^2 F(t)\}, \ldots$, is uniformly convergent when $s \geqq \alpha_1$ where $\alpha_1 > \alpha$; moreover*

$$(4) \qquad \lim_{s \to \infty} f(s) = 0 \qquad and \qquad \lim_{s \to \infty} L\{t^n F(t)\} = 0$$

$$(n = 1, 2, \ldots).$$

The function $F(t)e^{-st}$ and its partial derivative of each order, with respect to s, satisfy our conditions for the validity of formula (12), Sec. 12.   Hence differentiation with respect to s can be performed in equation (1) inside the integral sign, and the following theorem is established.

Theorem 6. *Differentiation of the transform of a function corresponds to the multiplication of the function by $-t$:*

$$(5) \qquad f^{(n)}(s) = L\{(-t)^n F(t)\} \qquad (n = 1, 2, \ldots);$$

moreover, $f^{(n)}(s) \to 0$ as $s \to \infty$.   These properties hold true whenever $F(t)$ is sectionally continuous and of the order of $e^{\alpha t}$, if $s > \alpha$ in formula (5).

Since a function is continuous wherever its derivative exists, it is true that $f(s)$ and each of its derivatives are continuous when $s > \alpha$.

To illustrate the last theorem, we can note that since

$$\frac{k}{s^2 + k^2} = L\{\sin kt\} \qquad\qquad (s > 0),$$

it follows that

$$\frac{-2ks}{(s^2 + k^2)^2} = L\{-t \sin kt\}.$$

Thus we have a formula that is useful in finding inverse transforms with the aid of partial fractions:

$$(6) \qquad L\{t \sin kt\} = \frac{2ks}{(s^2 + k^2)^2} \qquad (s > 0).$$

17. Differential Equations with Variable Coefficients. We have seen that

$$L\{t^n Y(t)\} = (-1)^n \frac{d^n}{ds^n} L\{Y(t)\} = (-1)^n y^{(n)}(s),$$

and therefore we can write the transform of the product of t^n by any derivative of $Y(t)$ in terms of $y(s)$; for instance,

$$L\{t^2 Y'(t)\} = \frac{d^2}{ds^2} [sy(s) - Y(0)] = sy''(s) + 2y'(s),$$

$$L\{tY''(t)\} = -\frac{d}{ds} [s^2 y(s) - sY(0) - Y'(0)]$$
$$= -s^2 y'(s) - 2sy(s) + Y(0).$$

A linear differential equation in $Y(t)$ whose coefficients are polynomials in t transforms into a linear differential equation in $y(s)$ whose coefficients are polynomials in s. In case the transformed equation is simpler than the original, the transformation may enable us to find the solution of the original equation.

If the coefficients are polynomials of the first degree, the transformed equation is a linear equation of the first order, whose solution can be written in terms of an integral. To find the solution of the original equation, however, the inverse transform of the solution of the new equation must be obtained.

Example 1. Find the solution of the problem

$$Y''(t) + tY'(t) - Y(t) = 0, \qquad Y(0) = 0, \qquad Y'(0) = 1.$$

The transformed equation is

$$s^2 y(s) - 1 - \frac{d}{ds} [sy(s)] - y(s) = 0,$$

or
$$y'(s) + \left(\frac{2}{s} - s\right) y(s) = -\frac{1}{s},$$

which is a linear equation of the first order. An integrating factor is

$$e^{\int \left(\frac{2}{s} - s\right) ds} = s^2 e^{-\frac{1}{2}s^2},$$

so the equation can be written

$$\frac{d}{ds}\,[s^2e^{-\frac{1}{2}s^2}y(s)] = -se^{-\frac{1}{2}s^2}.$$

Integrating, we have

$$y(s) = \frac{1}{s^2} + \frac{C}{s^2}\,e^{\frac{1}{2}s^2},$$

where C is a constant of integration.   But C must vanish if $y(s)$ is a transform since $y(s)$ must vanish as s tends to infinity.   It follows that

$$Y(t) = t,$$

and this is readily verified as the solution.

Example 2.   Solve Bessel's equation with index zero,

$$tY''(t) + Y'(t) + tY(t) = 0$$

under the conditions that $Y(0) = 1$ and $Y(t)$ and its derivatives have transforms.

The point $t = 0$ is a singular point[1] of this differential equation such that one of the two fundamental solutions is a function that behaves like log t near that singular point, and the Laplace transform of the derivative of the function does not exist.

The transformed equation is

$$-\frac{d}{ds}\,[s^2y(s) - s - Y'(0)] + sy(s) - 1 - \frac{d}{ds}\,y(s) = 0,$$

or

$$(s^2 + 1)y'(s) + sy(s) = 0.$$

Separating variables, we have

$$\frac{dy}{y} = -\frac{s\,ds}{s^2 + 1},$$

and upon integrating and simplifying, we find that

$$y(s) = \frac{C}{\sqrt{s^2 + 1}},$$

where C is a constant of integration.

Expanding the function for $y(s)$ by the binomial series we have,

[1] See E. D. Rainville, "Intermediate Differential Equations," 1943.

when $s > 1$,

$$y(s) = \frac{C}{s}\left(1 + \frac{1}{s^2}\right)^{-\frac{1}{2}} = \frac{C}{s}\left[1 - \frac{1}{2}\frac{1}{s^2} + \frac{1 \times 3}{2^2 2!}\frac{1}{s^4} - \cdots\right]$$

$$= C\sum_0^\infty \frac{(-1)^n}{(2^n n!)^2}\frac{(2n)!}{s^{2n+1}},$$

where $0! = 1$. Applying the inverse transformation formally to the terms of this series, we find that

$$Y(t) = C\sum_0^\infty \frac{(-1)^n}{(2^n n!)^2} t^{2n}.$$

If this function is to satisfy the condition $Y(0) = 1$, it is necessary that $C = 1$, and our formal solution becomes

$$Y(t) = \sum_0^\infty \frac{(-1)^n}{(2^n n!)^2} t^{2n}.$$

This power series is easily seen to be convergent for all t, and it is not difficult to show that it satisfies the differential equation. The function defined by the series is Bessel's function $J_0(t)$; that is

$$J_0(t) = 1 - \frac{t^2}{2^2} + \frac{t^4}{2^2 \times 4^2} - \frac{t^6}{2^2 \times 4^2 \times 6^2} + \cdots.$$

Our first formula for $y(s)$ above indicates that

$$(1) \qquad L\{J_0(t)\} = \frac{1}{\sqrt{s^2 + 1}},$$

a transformation that can be established rigorously when $s > 0$.

The differential equation

$$(2) \qquad t^2 Y''(t) + t Y'(t) + (t^2 - n^2) Y(t) = 0$$

is *Bessel's equation of index n.* It will be left to the problems to derive the solution $Y(t) = CJ_n(t)$ when $n = 2, 3, \ldots,$ where $J_n(t)$ is Bessel's function of the first kind, defined by the equation

$$(3) \qquad J_n(t) = \sum_{k=0}^\infty \frac{(-1)^k}{k!(n+k)!}\left(\frac{t}{2}\right)^{n+2k} \qquad (n = 0, 1, 2, \ldots).$$

The special case $n = 1$ will be considered now.

Example 3.   Solve Bessel's equation (2) when $n = 1$, under the condition that $Y(t)$ and its derivatives have transforms.

Regardless of the values of the constants $Y(0)$ and $Y'(0)$ the transformed equation becomes

$$(s^2 + 1)y''(s) + 3sy'(s) = 0,$$

an equation of the first order in $y'(s)$.   The general solution

$$y(s) = \frac{C_1 s}{\sqrt{s^2 + 1}} + C_2$$

has the property that $y(s) \to C_1 + C_2$ as $s \to \infty$.   Hence $C_1 + C_2 = 0$ if $y(s)$ is a transform.   Then

(4)
$$y(s) = C_1 \left(\frac{s}{\sqrt{s^2 + 1}} - 1 \right);$$

but the function inside the parentheses is the transform of $J_0'(t)$, in view of equation (1) and the fact that $J_0(0) = 1$.   Therefore

$$Y(t) = C_1 J_0'(t) = -C_1 J_1(t),$$

since $J_1(t)$ as defined by equation (3) is the same as $-J_0'(t)$.

According to equation (4)

(5) $$L\{J_1(t)\} = 1 - \frac{s}{\sqrt{s^2 + 1}} = \frac{1}{\sqrt{s^2 + 1} \, (s + \sqrt{s^2 + 1})}.$$

PROBLEMS

1. Find $L\{J_0(at)\}$ and $L\{J_1(at)\}$ with the aid of Theorem 2 and equations (1) and (5) above, and compare the results with transforms 55 and 56, Appendix 3.

Solve the following equations for $Y(t)$ if $Y(t)$ and its derivatives are to have transforms.

2. $Y''(t) + atY'(t) - 2aY(t) = 1$, $Y(0) = Y'(0) = 0$, $a > 0$.
Ans. $Y(t) = t^2/2$.

3. $tY''(t) + (2t + 3)Y'(t) + (t + 3)Y(t) = ae^{-t}$.
Ans. $Y(t) = (C + at/3)e^{-t}$.

4. $tY''(t) + (1 - a - t)Y'(t) + aY(t) = t - 1$, $Y(0) = 0$, $a > 0$ and $a \neq 1$.
Ans. $Y(t) = \dfrac{t}{a - 1} + Ct^a$.

5. $tY''(t) - (2t + 1)Y'(t) + (t + 1)Y(t) = 0$, $Y(0) = 0$.   Verify your result.

6. Under the substitution $Y(t) = t^{-n}Z(t)$ in Bessel's equation (2), show that

$$tZ''(t) + (1 - 2n)Z'(t) + tZ(t) = 0.$$

Solve this equation and thus derive the solution $Y(t) = CJ_n(t)$ of Bessel's equation. Assume $Y(t)$ continuous $(t \geqq 0)$ and $n = 1, 2, \ldots$; then $Z(0) = 0$.

7. Show that if $y(s) = s^{-\frac{3}{2}} \exp(-k \sqrt{s})$, then

$$4sy''(s) + 6y'(s) - k^2 y(s) = 0,$$

and if $y(s) = L\{Y(t)\}$, then

$$4t^2 Y'(t) + (2t - k^2)Y(t) = 0.$$

Find $Y(t)$ here, noting that $Y(t) = (\pi t)^{-\frac{1}{2}}$ when $k = 0$. These manipulations suggest the transformation

$$Y(t) = \frac{1}{\sqrt{\pi t}} e^{-k^2/(4t)} \qquad \text{when } y(s) = \frac{1}{\sqrt{s}} e^{-k\sqrt{s}} \qquad (k \geqq 0),$$

which will be established later (Sec. 23).

18. Integration of Transforms. When a function $F(t)$ is sectionally continuous and of the order of $e^{\alpha t}$, then its Laplace integral

$$f(x) = \int_0^\infty e^{-xt}F(t)\, dt$$

is uniformly convergent with respect to x in every interval $x \geqq \alpha_1$, where $\alpha_1 > \alpha$, according to Theorem 5. It follows from formula (11), Sec. 12, that when $r > s > \alpha$, then

$$\int_s^r f(x)\, dx = \int_s^r \int_0^\infty e^{-xt}F(t)\, dt\, dx = \int_0^\infty F(t) \int_s^r e^{-xt}\, dx\, dt.$$

If the function $F(t)$ is such that $F(t)/t$ has a limit as t tends to zero, then the latter function is also sectionally continuous and of exponential order. Under these conditions the last equation can be written as

$$\int_s^r f(x)\, dx = \int_0^\infty \frac{F(t)}{t} e^{-st}\, dt - \int_0^\infty \frac{F(t)}{t} e^{-rt}\, dt = g(s) - g(r),$$

where $g(s) = L\{F(t)/t\}$. But $g(r) \to 0$ as $r \to \infty$ (Theorem 5); hence

$$(1) \qquad \int_s^\infty f(x)\, dx = \int_0^\infty \frac{F(t)}{t} e^{-st}\, dt \qquad (s > \alpha)$$

and we have established the following theorem.

Theorem 7. *Division of the function $F(t)$ by t corresponds to integration of the transform $f(s)$, in this manner:*

$$(2) \qquad L\left\{\frac{F(t)}{t}\right\} = \int_s^\infty f(x)\, dx.$$

Sufficient conditions for the validity of formula (2) are that $F(t)$ be sectionally continuous and of the order of $e^{\alpha t}$, that $s > \alpha$ in formula (2), and further that the limit of $F(t)/t$ exists as $t \to +0$.

The function $F(t) = \sin kt$, for example, satisfies the above conditions when $\alpha = 0$; in particular, $t^{-1} \sin kt \to k$ as $t \to 0$. Hence when $s > 0$,

$$(3) \quad L\left\{\frac{\sin kt}{t}\right\} = \int_s^\infty \frac{k\, dx}{x^2 + k^2} = \frac{\pi}{2} - \arctan\frac{s}{k} = \text{arccot}\,\frac{s}{k}.$$

Recalling how integration with respect to t corresponds to division by s, we can now write the transform of the *sine-integral function*

$$(4) \qquad \text{Si } t = \int_0^t \frac{\sin \tau}{\tau}\, d\tau.$$

This function is of some importance in applied mathematics. Its values are tabulated in the more extensive mathematical tables. If $k = 1$ in equation (3), it follows from equation (4) that

$$(5) \qquad L\{\text{Si } t\} = \frac{1}{s}\,\text{arccot } s \qquad\qquad (s > 0).$$

As another illustration of Theorem 7 we note that

$$L\left\{\frac{e^{-at} - e^{-bt}}{t}\right\} = \int_s^\infty \left(\frac{1}{x+a} - \frac{1}{x+b}\right) dx = \log\frac{x+a}{x+b}\Big]_s^\infty,$$

when $s > -a$ and $s > -b$.   Hence

$$(6) \qquad L\left\{\frac{e^{-at} - e^{-bt}}{t}\right\} = \log\frac{s+b}{s+a}.$$

When $a = 0$ and $b = 1$, we have the special case

$$(7) \qquad L\left\{\frac{1 - e^{-t}}{t}\right\} = \log\left(1 + \frac{1}{s}\right) \qquad (s > 0).$$

19. Periodic Functions.   Let $F(t)$ be a periodic function with period a; that is,

$$F(t + a) = F(t) \qquad (t > 0).$$

If it is sectionally continuous over a period $0 \leqq t \leqq a$, then its transform exists and we can write it as the sum of integrals over successive periods:

$$f(s) = \int_0^\infty e^{-st}F(t)\,dt = \sum_{n=0}^\infty \int_{na}^{(n+1)a} e^{-st}F(t)\,dt \qquad (s > 0).$$

If we substitute $\tau = t - na$ and note that $F(\tau + na) = F(\tau)$ because of the periodicity of the function, we find that

$$f(s) = \sum_0^\infty e^{-nas} \int_0^a e^{-s\tau}F(\tau)\,d\tau.$$

The integral on the right is a factor of the series, and the sum of the geometric series with terms e^{-nas} is $(1 - e^{-as})^{-1}$.   The following result is therefore derived.

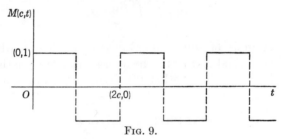

Fig. 9.

Theorem 8.   *If $F(t)$ is periodic with the period a, then*

(1)
$$f(s) = \frac{\int_0^a e^{-st}F(t)\,dt}{1 - e^{-as}} \qquad (s > 0).$$

Let us apply this formula to the function

$$\begin{aligned} M(c,t) &= 1 &&\text{when } 0 < t < c, \\ &= -1 &&\text{when } c < t < 2c, \\ M(c,\, t + 2c) &= M(c,t). \end{aligned}$$

This is sometimes called the *square-wave function* (Fig. 9).   In terms of the bracket symbol (Sec. 11) the function can be written

$$M(c,t) = (-1)^{[t/c]}.$$

Since

$$\int_0^{2c} e^{-st} M(c,t)\, dt = \int_0^c e^{-st}\, dt - \int_c^{2c} e^{-st}\, dt = \frac{1}{s}(1 - e^{-cs})^2,$$

the transform of $M(c,t)$ is

$$\frac{(1 - e^{-cs})^2}{s(1 - e^{-2cs})} = \frac{1 - e^{-cs}}{s(1 + e^{-cs})}.$$

Hence

(2) $$L\{M(c,t)\} = \frac{1}{s} \tanh \frac{cs}{2} \qquad (s > 0).$$

The integral of the function $M(c,t)$ from 0 to t is the function $H(c,t)$ defined as follows:

$$H(c,t) = t \qquad\qquad \text{when } 0 < t < c,$$
$$= 2c - t \qquad \text{when } c < t < 2c,$$
$$H(c,\, t + 2c) = H(c,t).$$

This function, whose graph is the triangular wave shown in

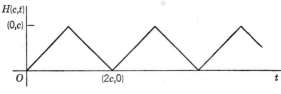

FIG. 10.

Fig. 10, has the transform

(3) $$L\{H(c,t)\} = \frac{1}{s^2} \tanh \frac{cs}{2}.$$

Since $$\frac{1}{s}\left(1 + \tanh \frac{cs}{2}\right) = \frac{2}{s(1 + e^{-cs})},$$

it follows from the transformation (2) that

(4) $$L\{\tfrac{1}{2} + \tfrac{1}{2}M(c,t)\} = \frac{1}{s(1 + e^{-cs})}.$$

Note that the function $\frac{1}{2} + \frac{1}{2}M(c,t)$ has the value 1 when $0 < t < c$ and 0 when $c < t < 2c$ and that it is periodic with the period $2c$; thus in the terminology of electrical engineering this function represents the half-wave rectification of the function $M(c,t)$.

Consider the half-wave rectification $F(t)$ of the function $\sin t$,

(5) $$\begin{aligned} F(t) &= \sin t &&\text{when } 0 < t < \pi, \\ &= 0 &&\text{when } \pi < t < 2\pi, \end{aligned}$$

where $F(t + 2\pi) = F(t)$ (Fig. 11). By applying formula (1), the reader can verify that

(6) $$f(s) = \frac{1}{(s^2 + 1)(1 - e^{-\pi s})}.$$

By translating the graph of $F(t)$ through a distance π along the t axis, which corresponds to multiplying the transform (6) by

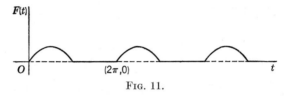

FIG. 11.

$e^{-\pi s}$, and then adding the ordinates from this graph to those in Fig. 11, we obtain at once the transform of the full-wave rectification $|\sin t|$ of the sine function:

(7) $$L\{|\sin t|\} = \frac{1}{s^2 + 1} \frac{1 + e^{-\pi s}}{1 - e^{-\pi s}} = \frac{1}{s^2 + 1} \coth \frac{\pi s}{2}.$$

The above observations are easily generalized. If $F(t)$ is any antiperiodic function, that is, if

(8) $$F(t + c) = -F(t) \qquad\qquad (t > 0),$$

then $F(t + 2c) = F(t)$, and it can be seen from formula (1) that

(9) $$\begin{aligned} f(s) &= \frac{1 - e^{-cs}}{1 - e^{-2cs}} \int_0^c e^{-st} F(t)\, dt \\ &= \frac{1}{1 + e^{-cs}} \int_0^c e^{-st} F(t)\, dt. \end{aligned}$$

If $F_1(t)$ is the half-wave rectification of the function $F(t)$, then

(10) $$f_1(s) = \frac{f(s)}{1 - e^{-cs}}.$$

The proof of this formula is left to the problems.

The method used above to derive equation (7) can be used

here to show that the transform of the full-wave rectification $F_2(t)$ of the antiperiodic function $F(t)$ is

$$(11) \qquad L\{F_2(t)\} = f(s) \coth \frac{cs}{2}.$$

PROBLEMS

In Probs. 1 to 3 show that $tG(t)$ satisfies all conditions in Theorem 7, give a value of α, and find $g(s)$.

1. $G(t) = \dfrac{1 - \cos at}{t}$.   *Ans.* See transform 105, Appendix 3.

2. $G(t) = \dfrac{1 - \cosh at}{t}$.   *Ans.* See transform 106, Appendix 3.

3. $G(t) = \dfrac{e^t - \cos t}{t}$.   *Ans.* $g(s) = \dfrac{1}{2} \log \dfrac{s^2 + 1}{(s - 1)^2}$.

4. Derive equation (10) above.

5. Derive equation (11) above.

6. Show that the transform of the half-wave rectification of the function $\sin kt$ is $k(s^2 + k^2)^{-1}(1 - e^{-\pi s/k})^{-1}$.

20. Partial Fractions. We shall now systematize the procedure of finding inverse transforms of quotients of polynomials in s. Let $p(s)$ and $q(s)$ denote polynomials in the variable s with no factor in common, and let the degree of $p(s)$ be lower than that of $q(s)$. We shall see that the inverse transform of the function $f(s) = p(s)/q(s)$ exists and that it can be found when the elementary factors of $q(s)$ can be determined.

Consider first the case in which $q(s)$ has a linear factor $s - a$, not repeated. Let $\phi(s)$ denote the function that is left after removing that factor from the denominator of $f(s)$; that is,

$$(1) \qquad f(s) = \frac{p(s)}{q(s)} = \frac{\phi(s)}{s - a}.$$

Note that $\phi(s)$ may be a quotient of polynomials. According to the theory of partial fractions a constant C exists such that

$$(2) \qquad \frac{\phi(s)}{s - a} = \frac{C}{s - a} + h(s),$$

where $h(s)$ represents the sum of the partial fractions that correspond to the other linear and quadratic factors of $q(s)$, any of which may be repeated.

In order to determine the value of C we multiply both members of equation (2) by $s - a$, when $s \neq a$, to obtain the equation

$$\phi(s) = C + (s - a)h(s),$$

which is satisfied identically for all values of s in a neighborhood of the point $s = a$, except possibly at that point. But both members of the equation are continuous functions of s at that point; thus their limits as $s \to a$ are the same as their values when $s = a$. Therefore $C = \phi(a)$. The inverse transform of the partial fraction corresponding to the factor $s - a$, or the term in $F(t)$ corresponding to that factor, is $\phi(a)e^{at}$.

In view of equation (1), we can also write

$$\lim_{s \to a} \phi(s) = \lim_{s \to a} \left[p(s) \frac{s - a}{q(s)} \right] = p(a) \frac{1}{q'(a)},$$

where we have evaluated the limit of $(s - a)/q(s)$ as the limit of the quotient of the derivatives of $s - a$ and $q(s)$, since $q(a) = 0$. Consequently $\phi(a) = p(a)/q'(a)$.

When all the factors of $q(s)$ are linear and not repeated and when $q(s)$ is written in the form

$$(3) \qquad q(s) = (s - a_1)(s - a_2) \cdots (s - a_m),$$

where all the constants a_n are distinct, we can write the inverse transform of $f(s)$ in full. Let $q_n(s)$ denote the product of all the factors on the right of equation (3) except the factor $s - a_n$, so that the function $\phi(s)$ corresponding to that factor is $p(s)/q_n(s)$. Then

$$(4) \qquad L^{-1} \left\{ \frac{p(s)}{q(s)} \right\} = \sum_{n=1}^{m} \frac{p(a_n)}{q_n(a_n)} e^{a_n t} = \sum_{n=1}^{m} \frac{p(a_n)}{q'(a_n)} e^{a_n t}.$$

The second sum here is sometimes called Heaviside's expansion.

The principal results are stated in the following theorem.

Theorem 9. *If $f(s)$ is the quotient $p(s)/q(s)$ of two polynomials such that $q(s)$ has the higher degree and contains the factor $s - a$ which is not repeated, then the term in $F(t)$ corresponding to that factor can be written in either of these two forms:*

$$(5) \qquad \phi(a)e^{at} \qquad or \qquad \frac{p(a)}{q'(a)} e^{at},$$

where $\phi(s)$ is the quotient of $p(s)$ divided by the product of all factors of $q(s)$ except $s - a$.

Example: Find $F(t)$ when

$$f(s) = \frac{2s^2 - 4s}{(2s + 1)(s^2 + 1)}.$$

We display the factors of the type $s - a$ by writing

$$f(s) = \frac{s^2 - 2s}{(s + \frac{1}{2})(s - i)(s + i)}.$$

Using the first of the two forms (5), or the first of the expansions (4), we find that

$$F(t) = \frac{\frac{5}{4}}{\frac{5}{4}} e^{-t/2} - \frac{1 + 2i}{(i + \frac{1}{2})2i} e^{it} + \frac{-1 + 2i}{(-i + \frac{1}{2})(-2i)} e^{-it}$$

$$= e^{-t/2} - 2 \frac{e^{it} - e^{-it}}{2i} = e^{-t/2} - 2 \sin t.$$

PROBLEMS

1. Find the inverse transforms tabulated below, where a, b, and c are distinct constants.

$f(s)$	$F(t)$
(a) $\dfrac{1}{(s - a)(s - b)}$	$\dfrac{e^{at} - e^{bt}}{a - b}$
(b) $\dfrac{s}{(s - a)(s - b)}$	$\dfrac{ae^{at} - be^{bt}}{a - b}$
(c) $\dfrac{-1}{(s - a)(s - b)(s - c)}$	$\dfrac{(b - c)e^{at} + (c - a)e^{bt} + (a - b)e^{ct}}{(a - b)(b - c)(c - a)}$

2. Use Theorem 9 to find the inverse transforms of the following functions.

(a) $f(s) = \dfrac{4s + 1}{(s^2 + s)(4s^2 - 1)}.$ *Ans.* $F(t) = e^{t/2} - e^{-t/2} + e^{-t} - 1.$

(b) $f(s) = \dfrac{s}{s^2 - k^2}.$ (c) $f(s) = \dfrac{s}{s^2 + k^2}.$

Use Theorem 9 in solving the following differential equations.

3. $Y''(t) - Y(t) = 1 + e^{3t}.$ *Ans.* $Y(t) = C_1 e^t + C_2 e^{-t} - 1 + \frac{1}{8}e^{3t}.$

4. $Y'''(t) + Y''(t) - 4Y'(t) - 4Y(t) = F(t),$ if $Y(0) = Y''(0) = 0$ and $Y'(0) = 2.$ *Ans.* $Y(t) = \sinh 2t + \frac{1}{12}F(t) * (e^{2t} + 3e^{-2t} - 4e^{-t}).$

5. $Y^{(4)}(t) - 2Y'''(t) - Y''(t) + 2Y'(t) = 6F(t),$ if $Y(t)$ and its first three derivatives are zero when $t = 0.$

21. Repeated Linear Factors. We now consider the case in which the polynomial $q(s)$ contains a repeated linear factor $(s - a)^{n+1}$. We write

$$(1) \qquad f(s) = \frac{p(s)}{q(s)} = \frac{\phi(s)}{(s - a)^{n+1}},$$

where $\phi(s)$ is the quotient of polynomials obtained by removing the factor $(s - a)^{n+1}$ from the denominator of the fraction $p(s)/q(s)$. As before, the degree of the polynomial $p(s)$ is assumed to be lower than the degree of $q(s)$. Note that $\phi(s)$ and its derivatives are continuous functions at the point $s = a$.

The representation of $f(s)$ in partial fractions now has the form

$$(2) \qquad \frac{\phi(s)}{(s - a)^{n+1}} = \frac{A_0}{s - a} + \frac{A_1}{(s - a)^2} + \cdots$$
$$+ \frac{A_r}{(s - a)^{r+1}} + \cdots + \frac{A_n}{(s - a)^{n+1}} + h(s),$$

where the numbers A_r are independent of s, and $h(s)$ is the sum of the partial fractions corresponding to the remaining factors of $q(s)$. It follows from equation (2) that

$$(3) \quad \phi(s) = A_0(s - a)^n + \cdots$$
$$+ A_r(s - a)^{n-r} + \cdots + A_n + (s - a)^{n+1}h(s)$$

in a neighborhood of the point $s = a$. When $s \to a$ we see that $A_n = \phi(a)$.

To find the remaining coefficients A_r we differentiate both members of equation (3) with respect to s, $n - r$ times, in order to isolate the number A_r. When $s \to a$ in the resulting equation, we find that

$$\phi^{(n-r)}(a) = (n - r)!A_r.$$

Equation (2) can now be written in the form

$$(4) \qquad f(s) = \sum_{r=0}^{n} \frac{\phi^{(n-r)}(a)}{(n - r)!} \frac{1}{(s - a)^{r+1}} + h(s),$$

where $0! = 1$ and $\phi^{(0)}(a) = \phi(a)$.

If $H(t) = L^{-1}\{h(s)\}$, it follows that the inverse transform of $f(s)$ is

$$(5) \qquad F(t) = \sum_{r=0}^{n} \frac{\phi^{(n-r)}(a)}{(n - r)!r!} t^r e^{at} + H(t).$$

This equation can be simplified by recalling the formula for the derivative of order n of the product of two functions $u(s)$ and $v(s)$, namely,

$$\frac{d^n}{ds^n}(uv) = \sum_{r=0}^{n} \frac{n!}{(n-r)!r!}\, u^{(n-r)}(s)v^{(r)}(s).$$

When $u = \phi(s)$ and $v = e^{st}$, then $\partial^r v/\partial s^r = t^r e^{st}$ and equation (5) reduces to the form

(6) $$F(t) = \frac{1}{n!}\left\{\frac{\partial^n}{\partial s^n}[\phi(s)e^{st}]\right\}_{s=a} + H(t).$$

This result can be stated as follows.

Theorem 10.   *If $f(s)$ is the quotient $p(s)/q(s)$ of two polynomials such that $q(s)$ has the higher degree and contains the factor $(s-a)^{n+1}$, then the term in $F(t)$ corresponding to that factor is $\Phi_n(a,t)$, where*

(7) $$\Phi_n(s,t) = \frac{1}{n!}\frac{\partial^n}{\partial s^n}[\phi(s)e^{st}]$$

and $\phi(s)$ is the function indicated by equation (1).

The term in $F(t)$ corresponding to a factor $(s-a)^2$ in $q(s)$, for instance, is

(8) $$\Phi_1(a,t) = [\phi'(a) + \phi(a)t]e^{at},$$

and the term corresponding to a factor $(s-a)^3$ is

(9) $$\Phi_2(a,t) = \tfrac{1}{2}[\phi''(a) + 2\phi'(a)t + \phi(a)t^2]e^{at}.$$

As an example, if

$$f(s) = \frac{1}{(s-1)(s-2)^2},$$

then the term in $F(t)$ corresponding to the factor $s-1$ is e^t. Corresponding to the factor $(s-2)^2$ we have $\phi(s) = (s-1)^{-1}$ and $\phi'(s) = -(s-1)^{-2}$ so that $\phi(2) = 1$ and $\phi'(2) = -1$. In view of formula (8) the term in $F(t)$ is $(-1+t)e^{2t}$. Hence

$$F(t) = e^t + (t-1)e^{2t}.$$

Since the number a may be imaginary and since a factorization of every polynomial into linear factors, real or imaginary, exists, Theorems 9 and 10 provide a systematic way of finding inverse transforms of quotients of polynomials in all cases where the factors of the denominator can be determined. If, however, imaginary factors are present the results are given in terms of imaginary functions. The reduction of the results to real forms is sometimes tedious. To obtain the real form of the inverse transform directly, and to observe the character of that function in general, we may proceed as follows.

22. Quadratic Factors. In this section we assume that the polynomials $p(s)$ and $q(s)$ have real coefficients. Then the imaginary linear factors of $q(s)$ arise from real quadratic factors $s^2 + \alpha s + \beta$, where $\alpha^2 - 4\beta < 0$. By completing the square here we can write such factors in the form

$$(1) \qquad\qquad (s - a)^2 + b^2 \qquad\qquad (b > 0),$$

where a and b are real numbers. Note that $s = a \pm ib$ are roots of the equation $q(s) = 0$.

Let $q(s)$ have the factor (1), not repeated. Then

$$(2) \quad f(s) = \frac{p(s)}{q(s)} = \frac{\phi(s)}{(s - a)^2 + b^2} = \frac{As + B}{(s - a)^2 + b^2} + h(s),$$

where A and B are real constants and $h(s)$ represents the sum of partial fractions corresponding to the remaining factors of $q(s)$. Upon multiplying the members of equation (2) by the factor (1) and letting s approach $a + ib$, we find that

$$\phi(a + ib) = (a + ib)A + B.$$

If ϕ_1 and ϕ_2 are the real and imaginary components of the complex number $\phi(a + ib)$,

$$(3) \qquad\qquad \phi(a + ib) = \phi_1 + i\phi_2,$$

it follows that

$$aA + B = \phi_1, \qquad bA = \phi_2.$$

Hence $bB = b\phi_1 - a\phi_2$ and formula (2) can be written

$$f(s) = \frac{1}{b} \frac{(s - a)\phi_2 + b\phi_1}{(s - a)^2 + b^2} + h(s);$$

thus

$$(4) \qquad F(t) = \frac{1}{b} e^{at}(\phi_2 \cos bt + \phi_1 \sin bt) + H(t).$$

Let θ represent the polar coordinate angle of the point (ϕ_1, ϕ_2), the argument of the complex number (3), then

(5) $$\sin \theta = \frac{\phi_2}{|\phi(a + ib)|}, \qquad \cos \theta = \frac{\phi_1}{|\phi(a + ib)|},$$
$$|\phi(a + ib)| = \sqrt{\phi_1^2 + \phi_2^2},$$

and the term in equation (4) corresponding to the factor (1) can be written

(6) $$\frac{1}{b} |\phi(a + ib)| e^{at} \sin (bt + \theta).$$

Note that if $a = 0$ the term (6) is a sine function of t and if $a < 0$ it is a damped sine function. These types of terms, corresponding to the values $a \leqq 0$, represent *stable oscillations* in the theory of control of mechanical and electrical systems where t denotes time. Stable oscillations are bounded as $t \to \infty$. When $a > 0$ the oscillation is unstable.

Let us find $F(t)$ when

$$f(s) = \frac{4s}{(s - 2)(s^2 + 4)}.$$

Corresponding to the quadratic factor here, $\phi(s) = 4s/(s - 2)$ and

$$\phi(2i) = \frac{8i}{2i - 2} = 2(1 - i).$$

Hence $\theta = -\pi/4$ and $|\phi(2i)| = 2\sqrt{2}$. Accounting for the linear factor $s - 2$ in the usual way and including the term (6) we find that

$$F(t) = \sqrt{2} \sin \left(2t - \frac{\pi}{4} \right) + e^{2t}.$$

When $q(s)$ contains a repeated quadratic factor, a similar procedure can be followed to obtain $F(t)$ directly in terms of real functions. We confine our attention here to the important case in which the square of the factor appears; then $p(s)/q(s)$ can be written in the forms

(7) $$\frac{\phi(s)}{[(s - a)^2 + b^2]^2} = \frac{As + B}{(s - a)^2 + b^2} + \frac{Cs + D}{[(s - a)^2 + b^2]^2} + h(s).$$

By multiplying both members of equation (7) by the square of the quadratic factor and differentiating once with respect to s, then substituting $a + ib$ for s in the two resulting equations and equating real parts and imaginary parts, we can solve for A, B, C, and D. Let the angle θ' be the argument of the complex number $\phi'(a + ib)$,

(8) $$\theta' = \arg[\phi'(a + ib)].$$

With the aid of the transformations (9), Sec. 13, and (6), Sec. 16, the term in $F(t)$ corresponding to the repeated quadratic factor can be written in the form

(9) $$\frac{1}{2b^3} e^{at}\{|\phi(a + ib)|[\sin(bt + \theta) - bt\cos(bt + \theta)]$$
$$- b|\phi'(a + ib)|\cos(bt + \theta')\},$$

where θ is defined by equations (5). Details of the derivation are left to the problems.

The presence of the quadratic factor to the power $n + 1$ will introduce terms in $F(t)$ of types $t^r e^{at}\sin bt$ and $t^r e^{at}\cos bt$ ($r = 0, 1, 2, \ldots, n$). This fact follows from Theorem 10 when the factor $(s - a)^{n+1}$ considered in that theorem is replaced by either of the factors $(s - a \pm ib)^{n+1}$.

Theorem 11. *When $f(s) = p(s)/q(s)$, where $p(s)$ and $q(s)$ are polynomials with real coefficients, the component of $F(t)$ that corresponds to a distinct quadratic factor $(s - a)^2 + b^2$ in $q(s)$ is the term* (6). *The component that corresponds to the square of that factor in $q(s)$ is the term* (9).

Note that the component (9) of $F(t)$ represents a stable oscillation if and only if the real part of the zero of the quadratic factor is negative: $a < 0$. If $a = 0$, the component contains a term proportional to $t\cos(bt + \theta)$, representing an unstable oscillation.

PROBLEMS

1. Find the inverse transforms tabulated below:

$f(s)$	$F(t)$
(a) $\dfrac{s + a}{(s + b)(s + c)^2}$	$\dfrac{a - b}{(b - c)^2} e^{-bt} + \left[\dfrac{a - c}{b - c}t - \dfrac{a - b}{(b - c)^2}\right] e^{-ct}$
(b) $\dfrac{s + 3}{(2s + 1)(s^2 + 2s + 2)}$	$e^{-\frac{1}{2}t} - e^{-t}\cos t$
(c) $\dfrac{2b^4}{(s^2 + b^2)s^3}$	$2\cos bt + b^2 t^2 - 2$

(d) $\dfrac{s^2 - b^2}{(s^2 + b^2)^2}$ $t \cos bt$

(e) $\dfrac{25s^2}{(s + 1)^2(s^2 + 4)}$ $(5t - 8)e^{-t} + 10 \sin (2t + \theta),$

$\theta = \arg (3 + 4i)$

2. Without finding $F(t)$, determine whether the oscillations of that function are stable or unstable when its transform is

(a) $f(s) = \dfrac{2s^2 + 1}{2s^3 + 2s^2 + s}.$ *Ans.* Stable.

(b) $f(s) = \dfrac{s}{(2s^2 + 4s + 3)(s^2 + 2)^2}.$ *Ans.* Unstable.

3. Solve the following differential equations:

(a) $Y''(t) - 2Y'(t) + Y(t) = 1.$ *Ans.* $Y(t) = (C_1 + C_2 t)e^t + 1.$

(b) $Y''(t) + Y(t) = 2 \sin t$, if $Y(0) = 0$ and $Y'(0) = -1.$

Ans. $Y(t) = -t \cos t.$

(c) $4Y'''(t) + 4Y''(t) + Y'(t) = F(t).$

(d) $Y^{(4)}(t) + 2Y''(t) + Y(t) = 0$, if $Y(0) = 0, Y'(0) = 1, Y''(0) = 2,$ and $Y'''(0) = -3.$ *Ans.* $Y(t) = t(\sin t + \cos t).$

4. Derive the expression (9).

23. Tables of Operations and Transforms.

A list of operations on the function $F(t)$ and the corresponding operations on the transform $f(s)$ will be found in the Table of Operations in Appendix 2.   The list serves as a summary of our results on the theory of the Laplace transformation.

The Table of Laplace Transforms in Appendix 3 contains a fairly extensive list of transforms of particular functions.   Derivations of a number of them have been presented above.   References to more extensive tables of transforms and operations will be found in the Bibliography, Appendix 1, under the names of Erdélyi and Doetsch.   Some additional derivations of transforms are given below.

The function

(1) $F(t) = t^{-\frac{3}{2}} \exp \left(-\dfrac{k^2}{4t}\right)$ $(k > 0)$

is of considerable importance especially in the theory of heat conduction and diffusion.   Its transform can be written as

$$f(s) = \int_0^\infty \exp \left(-\dfrac{k^2}{4t}\right) e^{-st} t^{-\frac{3}{2}} \, dt$$

$$= \frac{4}{k} \int_0^\infty \exp (-\tau^2) \exp \left(-\dfrac{k^2 s}{4\tau^2}\right) d\tau,$$

where we have made the substitution $\tau = k/(2 \sqrt{t})$. Combining the exponents in the last integral and completing the square in the exponent, we have

$$(2) \qquad f(s) = \frac{4}{k} e^{-k\sqrt{s}} \int_0^\infty \exp\left[-\left(\tau - \frac{k \sqrt{s}}{2\tau}\right)^2\right] d\tau.$$

We now write $k \sqrt{s}/2 = b$ and $b/\tau = \lambda$. Then

$$\int_0^\infty \exp\left[-\left(\tau - \frac{b}{\tau}\right)^2\right] d\tau = \int_0^\infty \frac{b}{\lambda^2} \exp\left[-\left(\lambda - \frac{b}{\lambda}\right)^2\right] d\lambda,$$

and upon adding the integral on the left to each member of this equation, we have the equation

$$2\int_0^\infty \exp\left[-\left(\tau - \frac{b}{\tau}\right)^2\right] d\tau = \int_0^\infty \left(1 + \frac{b}{\lambda^2}\right) \exp\left[-\left(\lambda - \frac{b}{\lambda}\right)^2\right] d\lambda.$$

Finally we substitute $x = \lambda - b/\lambda$ in the last integral to get the formula

$$\int_0^\infty \exp\left[-\left(\tau - \frac{b}{\tau}\right)^2\right] d\tau = \frac{1}{2} \int_{-\infty}^\infty e^{-x^2} dx = \frac{1}{2} \sqrt{\pi}.$$

Therefore, in view of equation (2), our result becomes

$$(3) \qquad\qquad f(s) = \frac{2 \sqrt{\pi}}{k} e^{-k\sqrt{s}};$$

that is,

$$(4) \qquad L\left\{\frac{k}{2 \sqrt{\pi t^3}} \exp\left(-\frac{k^2}{4t}\right)\right\} = e^{-k\sqrt{s}} \quad (k > 0, s > 0).$$

Since multiplying by t corresponds to differentiating with respect to s and changing sign, it follows from Theorem 6 and formula (4) that

$$(5) \qquad L\left\{\frac{1}{\sqrt{\pi t}} \exp\left(-\frac{k^2}{4t}\right)\right\} = \frac{1}{\sqrt{s}} e^{-k\sqrt{s}} \quad (k \geqq 0, s > 0).$$

Finally, in view of the transformation (4), we note that

$$L^{-1}\left\{\frac{1}{s} e^{-k\sqrt{s}}\right\} = \frac{k}{2 \sqrt{\pi}} \int_0^t \exp\left(-\frac{k^2}{4\tau}\right) \tau^{-\frac{3}{2}} d\tau = \frac{2}{\sqrt{\pi}} \int_{\frac{k}{2\sqrt{t}}}^\infty e^{-\lambda^2} d\lambda$$

$$= \frac{2}{\sqrt{\pi}} \int_0^\infty e^{-\lambda^2} d\lambda - \frac{2}{\sqrt{\pi}} \int_0^{\frac{k}{2\sqrt{t}}} e^{-\lambda^2} d\lambda.$$

Therefore

(6) $\qquad L^{-1}\left\{\dfrac{1}{s}\,e^{-k\sqrt{s}}\right\} = 1 - \text{erf}\left(\dfrac{k}{2\sqrt{t}}\right) \qquad (k \geqq 0,\ s > 0),$

where erf (x) is the error function defined in Sec. 13.   This formula can be written

(7) $\qquad L\left\{\text{erfc}\left(\dfrac{k}{2\sqrt{t}}\right)\right\} = \dfrac{1}{s}\,e^{-k\sqrt{s}} \qquad (k \geqq 0,\ s > 0),$

where the *complementary error function* erfc (x) is defined as

$$\text{erfc}\,(x) = 1 - \text{erf}\,(x) = \frac{2}{\sqrt{\pi}}\int_x^\infty e^{-\lambda^2}\,d\lambda.$$

PROBLEMS

1. Solve for $Y(t)$ and verify your solution:

$tY''(t) + 2Y'(t) - (t - 2)Y(t) = 2e^t, \qquad Y(0) = 0. \quad Ans.\ Y = \sinh t.$

2. Solve for $Y(t)$ and verify your result fully:

$\qquad (t - t^2)Y''(t) + 2Y'(t) + 2Y(t) = 6t, \qquad Y(0) = Y(2) = 0.$

Also, show that $Y''(t)$ is continuous for all t.

$\qquad Ans.\ Y = t^2$ when $t \leqq 1$, $Y = t^2 - 8t^{-1}(t - 1)^3$ when $t \geqq 1$.

3. Solve for $F(t)$:

(a) $F'(t) + k^2 \displaystyle\int_0^t F(x)\cosh k(t - x)\,dx = 0.$

$\qquad Ans.\ F = C(1 - k^2t^2/2).$

(b) $F(t) + 2 \displaystyle\int_0^t F(x)\cos(t - x)\,dx = 9e^{2t}.$

$\qquad Ans.\ F = 5e^{2t} + 4e^{-t} - 6te^{-t}.$

4. Find $F(t)$ and show it graphically when

(a) $f(s) = \dfrac{1}{s^2(1 + e^{-s})}.$ $\qquad Ans.\ F = \displaystyle\sum_{n=0}^\infty (-1)^n(t - n)S_n(t).$

(b) $f(s) = \dfrac{1}{s} - \dfrac{1}{s\cosh s}.$ $\qquad Ans.\ F = (-1)^{n(t)},\ n(t) = \left[\dfrac{t + 1}{2}\right].$

5. If $F(t) \geqq G(t)$ for every positive value of t, show that $f(s) \geqq g(s)$ for every real s for which the transforms $f(s)$ and $g(s)$ exist.   Also illustrate this property by using some particular functions.   Such properties that give the behavior of transforms in terms of the behavior of the object functions are called properties of *Abelian* type.   Note that the case $F(t) = 2\sin t$, $G(t) = \sin 2t$ shows that the converse of the above property is not always valid.

6. Let $F(t)$ be continuous and have a sectionally continuous derivative $F'(t)$, on every interval $0 \leq t \leq T$; also let both functions be of exponential order. From the formula for $L\{F'(t)\}$ and Theorem 5, if A is any constant, prove that the condition

$$\lim_{s \to \infty} sf(s) = A \text{ implies that } F(0) = A.$$

This is a property of *Tauberian* type: one that gives the behavior of object functions in terms of the behavior of transforms.

7. Illustrate the Tauberian property given in Prob. 6 with these particular functions: (a) $F(t) = A$; (b) $F(t) = t$; (c) $F(t) = \sin kt$; (d) $F(t) = \cos kt$; (e) $F(t) = e^t$.

8. If the term of highest degree in a polynomial $p(s)$ is $a_n s^n$ and the term of highest degree in a polynomial $q(s)$ is $b_{n+1} s^{n+1}$ and if $f(s) = p(s)/q(s)$, use the property stated in Prob. 6 to prove that $F(0) = a_n/b_{n+1}$.

9. Let $F(t)$ and $F'(t)$ be continuous and let $F''(t)$ be sectionally continuous on every interval $0 \leq t \leq T$; also let all three functions be of exponential order. Prove that the condition

$$\lim_{s \to \infty} s^2 f(s) = A \text{ implies that } F(0) = 0 \text{ and } F'(0) = A.$$

Also, use particular functions to illustrate this Tauberian property.

10. When $F(t)$ is sectionally continuous in an interval $0 \leq t \leq T$ while $G(t)$ and $G'(t)$ are continuous there, show that, at each point $t(0 < t < T)$ where $F(t)$ is continuous,

$$\frac{d}{dt} [F(t) * G(t)] = F(t) * G'(t) + G(0)F(t).$$

11. Show that the integral

$$\int_0^\infty \frac{x}{t^2 + x^2} \, dt$$

is not uniformly convergent with respect to x in the semi-infinite range $x > 1$. Also note that the limit, as $x \to \infty$, of the integral is $\pi/2$ while the integral of the limit of the integrand, as $x \to \infty$, is zero.

12. Under the following conditions the limit of the integral

$$q(x) = \int_0^\infty f(x,t) \, dt \qquad\qquad (x > c),$$

as $x \to \infty$, is the same as the integral of the limit. Let $f(x,t)$ be continuous in each rectangle $c \leq x \leq C$, $0 \leq t \leq T$, except possibly for finite jumps across any of a finite number of lines $t = t_i$ in each rectangle. Let the above integral converge uniformly with respect to x when $x > c$. Also let $F(t)$ exist, where

$$\lim_{x \to \infty} f(x,t) = F(t)$$

uniformly with respect to t in each interval $0 \leq t \leq T$; that is, to each positive ϵ there corresponds a number N independent of t such that

$$|F(t) - f(x,t)| < \epsilon \quad \text{whenever } x > N \quad (0 \leq t \leq T),$$

and let $\int_0^\infty F(t)\, dt$ exist.   Prove that

$$\lim_{x \to \infty} q(x) = \int_0^\infty F(t)\, dt.$$

Suggestion: Note that the difference between the last integral and $q(x)$ can be written

$$\int_0^T [F(t) - f(x,t)]\, dt + \int_T^\infty F(t)\, dt - \int_T^\infty f(x,t)\, dt = \Delta q.$$

Take T large first, independent of x, then x large, to show that $|\Delta q|$ is small.

13. Let $f(s)$ and $f_2(s)$ denote the transforms of $F(t)$ and $F(t^2)$ respectively.   With the aid of formula (5), Sec. 23, note that

$$f_2(p) = \int_0^\infty \frac{1}{2\sqrt{r}} e^{-p\sqrt{r}} F(r)\, dr = \int_0^\infty F(r) \int_0^\infty e^{-rt} \psi(p,t)\, dt\, dr,$$

where $2\psi(p,t) = (\pi t)^{-\frac{1}{2}} \exp\, [-p^2/(4t)]$.   Show formally that

$$f_2(p) = \int_0^\infty f(t)\psi(p,t)\, dt = \frac{1}{2\sqrt{\pi}} \int_0^\infty f\left(\frac{1}{y}\right) y^{-\frac{3}{2}} \exp\left(-\frac{p^2 y}{4}\right) dy;$$

hence that

$$2\sqrt{\pi} f_2(2\sqrt{s}) = L\left\{ t^{-\frac{3}{2}} f\left(\frac{1}{t}\right)\right\}.$$

Remark: If $F(t)$ is bounded, $|F(t)| < M$ for all positive t, and sectionally continuous in each interval $0 \leq t \leq T$, then the above steps can be justified for each positive s and p, by careful application of the results of Prob. 12 and Sec. 12.

14. Use the final formula in Prob. 13 to find $f(s)$ when (a) $F(t) = \sin \sqrt{t}$; (b) $F(t) = J_0(\sqrt{t})$.   Compare your results with transforms 78 and 75, Appendix 3.

15. Let $f(s,t')$ denote the transform of a function $F(t,t')$ with respect to t and let $\bar{f}(s,s')$ denote this iterated transform:

$$\bar{f}(s,s') = \int_0^\infty e^{-s't'} f(s,t')\, dt'.$$

It is convenient to write $F(t,t') = 0$ when either $t < 0$ or $t' < 0$.   Show formally that

$$\bar{f}(s,s) = L\{F * (t)\}, \quad \text{where } F * (t) = \int_0^t F(t - t',t')\, dt'.$$

This is a *generalized convolution property* of the transformation.   Show that it reduces to property (5), Sec. 13, when $F(t,t') = F(t)G(t')$.

16. If $|F(t,t')| < M \exp [\alpha(t + t')]$ for all positive t and t' and if $F(t,t')$ is continuous in each rectangle $0 \leqq t \leqq T$, $0 \leqq t' \leqq T'$, except possibly for finite jumps across each of a finite number of lines $t = t_i$ or $t' = t_i'$ in each rectangle, prove that the generalized convolution property written in Prob. 15 is valid whenever $s > \alpha$ (cf. Sec. 13).

17. When $L\{F(t)\} = f(s)$ and $F(c/s)/s = L\{G(t,c)\}$ for each positive c, where $s > 0$, use the generalized convolution property (Prob. 15) to show formally that

$$f(s^2) = L \left\{ \int_0^t G(t - x, x) \, dx \right\}.$$

In case $F(t) = e^{-t}$, show that this integration formula follows:

$$\int_0^t J_0[2 \sqrt{x(t - x)}] \, dx = \sin t.$$

18. Write $F(t,t') = t^{t'}/\Gamma(t' + 1)$ in Prob. 15 to show that

$$\frac{1}{s(s + \log s)} = L \left\{ \int_0^t \frac{(t - x)^x}{\Gamma(x + 1)} \, dx \right\}.$$

CHAPTER 3

ELEMENTARY APPLICATIONS

The properties of the Laplace transformation that we have derived up to this point enable us to solve many problems in engineering and physics involving ordinary and partial differential equations. In this chapter we shall solve a number of problems in elastic vibrations involving ordinary differential equations. These are problems in which our method is very convenient, although not at all essential. We shall also treat one or two simple applications of integral equations.

The next chapter contains applications that involve partial differential equations. The solution of problems of this type is the primary objective of this book. In later chapters we shall extend our treatment of such problems.

24. Free Vibrations of a Mass on a Spring. Let a body of mass m attached to the end of a coil spring (Fig. 12) be given an initial displacement and an initial velocity and allowed to vibrate. The other end of the spring is assumed to be kept fixed, and the spring is assumed to obey Hooke's law, so that the force exerted by the free end is proportional to the displacement of that end. The factor k of proportionality is called the spring constant. We also assume that the mass of the spring can be neglected in comparison with the mass m and that no frictional forces or other external forces act on m.

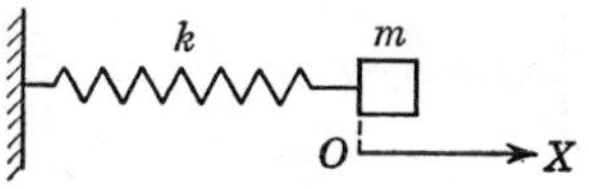

Fig. 12.

Let X denote the displacement of m from the position of equilibrium; that is, let the origin O denote the position of m when the spring is not deformed. Then according to Newton's second law of motion,

$$(1) \qquad m\frac{d^2X}{dt^2} = -kX.$$

Let x_0 denote the initial displacement and v_0 the initial velocity, so that the function $X(t)$ satisfies the conditions

$$(2) \qquad X(0) = x_0, \qquad X'(0) = v_0.$$

We can determine the function $X(t)$ by applying the Laplace transformation to both members of equation (1) and using the conditions (2). Thus if $x(s)$ denotes the transform of $X(t)$, it follows that

$$m[s^2x(s) - sx_0 - v_0] = -kx(s),$$

and therefore

$$x(s) = x_0 \frac{s}{s^2 + (k/m)} + v_0 \frac{1}{s^2 + (k/m)}.$$

Hence

$$(3) \qquad X(t) = x_0 \cos \omega_0 t + \frac{v_0}{\omega_0} \sin \omega_0 t$$

$$= \sqrt{x_0{}^2 + \left(\frac{v_0}{\omega_0}\right)^2} \sin (\omega_0 t + \alpha),$$

where
$$\omega_0 = \sqrt{\frac{k}{m}}, \qquad \tan \alpha = \frac{x_0\omega_0}{v_0}.$$

The motion described by formula (3) is a simple vibration with angular frequency ω_0, called the natural frequency of this system, and phase angle α, and with the amplitude $[x_0{}^2 + (v_0/\omega_0)^2]^{\frac{1}{2}}$.

If a viscous damping force proportional to the velocity also acts upon the mass m, as indicated by the presence of a dashpot c in Fig. 13, the equation of motion becomes

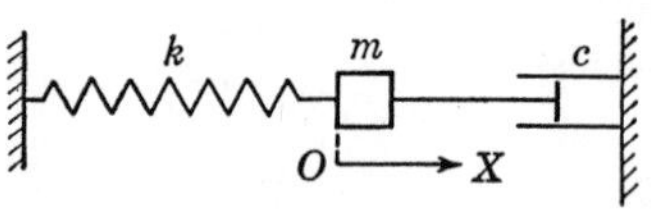

$$(4) \quad mX''(t) = -kX(t) - cX'(t).$$

In this case let the mass start from O with the initial velocity v_0,

FIG. 13.

$$X(0) = 0, \qquad X'(0) = v_0.$$

The equation in the transform $x(s)$ becomes

$$ms^2x(s) - mv_0 = -kx(s) - csx(s)$$

or, if we let $2b = c/m$, and again write $\omega_0{}^2 = k/m$,

$$(5) \qquad x(s) = \frac{v_0}{s^2 + 2bs + \omega_0{}^2} = \frac{v_0}{(s + b)^2 + \omega_0{}^2 - b^2}.$$

If $b^2 < \omega_0{}^2$, that is, if the coefficient of damping is small enough

that
$$c^2 < 4km,$$

then the formula for the displacement is

(6) $X(t) = v_0(\omega_0^2 - b^2)^{-\frac{1}{2}}e^{-bt}\sin(t\sqrt{\omega_0^2 - b^2}).$

In the case of critical damping, that is, when $\omega_0 = b$ **or**

$$c^2 = 4km,$$

it follows from equation (5) that

(7) $X(t) = v_0te^{-bt}.$

It can be seen from this formula that the mass m moves in the direction of v_0 until the time $t = 1/b$, then reverses its direction and approaches O as t tends to infinity.

When $c^2 > 4km$, a similar motion of the mass takes place. The discussion of this case and the case of other initial conditions can be left to the problems.

The mathematical problem treated in this section can be interpreted also as a problem in electric circuits. This well-known analogy between problems in vibrations of mechanical systems and electric-circuit theory will be observed for other problems in this chapter. Naturally, the notation and terminology differ in the two types of problems.

In the electric circuit shown in Fig. 14, let Q be the charge accumulated in the capacitor C at time t, and I the current in the circuit, so that

(8) $I(t) = Q'(t).$

This equation requires that $I(t)$ be positive when $Q(t)$ is increasing. If the positive sense of flow $I(t)$ of positive charges is taken in the

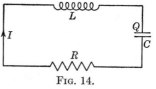

FIG. 14.

clockwise direction in Fig. 14, then $Q(t)$ measures the charge on the upper plate of the capacitor.

The circuit has a resistance R and a coil of inductance L. Since the sum of the three voltage drops in the circuit is zero in this case of no impressed voltage, then

(9) $LI'(t) + \dfrac{1}{C}Q(t) + RI(t) = 0.$

The system of first-order differential equations (8) and (9) can be used directly to determine $I(t)$ and $Q(t)$ in terms of initial values of those functions. By eliminating $I(t)$ from the two equations, however, we see that

$$(10) \qquad LQ''(t) + RQ'(t) + \frac{1}{C} Q(t) = 0.$$

Except for the notation used, this equation is the same as equation (4). When the resistance is negligible, $R = 0$, the equation reduces to our equation (1).

The initial conditions in the electrical problem can be made the same as those in the mechanical problem. For example, if the capacitor has an initial charge Q_0 and if the initial current is I_0, then

$$Q(0) = Q_0, \qquad Q'(0) = I_0,$$

which are the same as the initial conditions (2) in our first mechanical problem·

PROBLEMS

1. When $c^2 > 4km$ in the above problem of damped vibrations, show that the mass m moves in the direction of v_0 until the time

$$t = \frac{1}{2a} \log \frac{b + a}{b - a},$$

where $a = (b^2 - \omega_0^2)^{\frac{1}{2}}$, when it turns and approaches the origin.

2. When the mass m in the problem of damped vibrations is initially displaced to $X = x_0$ and released from that position with initial velocity zero, show that

$$X(t) = x_0 \frac{\omega_0}{\omega_1} e^{-bt} \sin (\omega_1 t + \alpha)$$

when $c^2 < 4km$, where $\omega_1 = \sqrt{\omega_0^2 - b^2}$ and $\tan \alpha = \omega_1/b$.

3. When $c^2 = 4km$ in Prob. 2, show that

$$X(t) = x_0 e^{-bt}(1 + bt),$$

and hence that the mass m never moves across the origin if $b > 0$.

4. At the instant $t = 0$ the current in the circuit shown in Fig. 14 is zero and the capacitor has a positive charge Q_0. If $R > 2\sqrt{L/C}$, derive the formula

$$I(t) = -\frac{2Q_0}{\alpha C} \exp\left(-\frac{Rt}{2L}\right) \sinh \frac{\alpha t}{2L} \quad \left(\alpha = \sqrt{R^2 - \frac{4L}{C}}\right)$$

for the current. Note that $I(t) \leqq 0$ and $I(\infty) = 0$. At what instant does the current have its greatest absolute value?

25. Forced Vibrations without Damping. Let an external force $F(t)$ act upon the mass in the mechanical system of the last section, assuming there is no damping (Fig. 15). The displacement $X(t)$ of the mass m then satisfies the differential equation

(1) $mX''(t) = -kX(t) + F(t).$

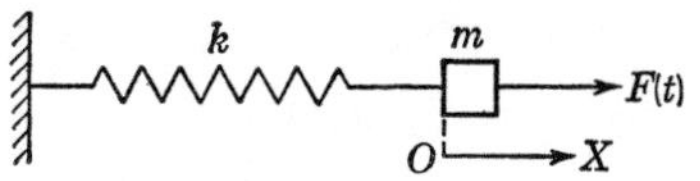

If the initial conditions are

(2) $X(0) = x_0, \qquad X'(0) = v_0,$

FIG. 15.

the equation in the transform $x(s)$ becomes

$$m[s^2 x(s) - sx_0 - v_0] = -kx(s) + f(s),$$

where $f(s)$ is the transform of the force function $F(t)$. Let ω_0 again denote the natural frequency of the system,

$$\omega_0 = \sqrt{\frac{k}{m}}.$$

Then we can write

(3) $$x(s) = \frac{x_0 s + v_0}{s^2 + \omega_0^2} + \frac{1}{m} f(s) \frac{1}{s^2 + \omega_0^2}.$$

Hence the displacement for any $F(t)$ can be written, with the aid of the convolution, as

(4) $$X(t) = x_0 \cos \omega_0 t + \frac{v_0}{\omega_0} \sin \omega_0 t + \frac{1}{m\omega_0} \int_0^t \sin \omega_0(t - \tau)F(\tau)\, d\tau,$$

a result that satisfies conditions (1) and (2) above.

But the motion of the mass under particular external forces $F(t)$ is more interesting than this general formula (4). In these special cases it is often easier to refer to the transform (3) than to (4). When $F(t)$ is a constant F_0, as in the case when the X axis is vertical and the force of gravity acts on m, equation (1) can be written

$$mX''(t) = -k\left[X(t) - \frac{F_0}{k} \right].$$

If $Y = X - F_0/k$, this becomes $mY'' = -kY$; so the motion is the same as free vibrations if displacements are measured from an origin F_0/k units from O.

In case

(5) $F(t) = F_0$ when $0 < t < t_0$,
                                  $= 0$ when $t > t_0$,

then $f(s) = F_0 \left(\dfrac{1}{s} - \dfrac{e^{-t_0 s}}{s} \right).$

If $x_0 = v_0 = 0$, it follows from equation (3) that

(6) $x(s) = \dfrac{F_0}{m} \left[\dfrac{1}{s(s^2 + \omega_0{}^2)} - \dfrac{e^{-t_0 s}}{s(s^2 + \omega_0{}^2)} \right].$

Now

$$L^{-1} \left\{ \frac{1}{s(s^2 + \omega_0{}^2)} \right\} = \frac{1}{\omega_0{}^2} (1 - \cos \omega_0 t) = \frac{2}{\omega_0{}^2} \sin^2 \frac{1}{2} \omega_0 t,$$

and if we write $\psi(t) = \sin^2 \tfrac{1}{2}\omega_0 t$ when $t > 0$,
                                  $= 0$ when $t < 0$,

it follows from equation (6) that

(7) $X(t) = \dfrac{2F_0}{k} [\psi(t) - \psi(t - t_0)].$

The graph of this function can be drawn easily by composition of ordinates.   When t_0 is approximately $\tfrac{1}{2}\pi/\omega_0$, the graph is the full-drawn curve in Fig. 16.

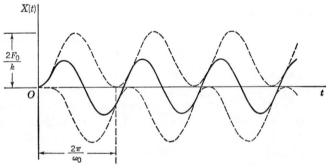

FIG. 16.

When $t_0 = 2\pi/\omega_0$, it follows from Fig. 16 that the mass m performs one oscillation and then remains at the origin (Fig. 17).

The step function (5) is proportional to the unit finite impulse function (3), Sec. 11, with impulse starting at $t = 0$.   The area under the graph of our function is $F_0 t_0$.   If this is kept fixed,

$F_0 t_0 = M_0$, while $t_0 \to 0$ and $F_0 \to \infty$, the force $F(t)$ becomes the impulse represented formally by the equation

(8) $$F(t) = M_0 \, \delta(t), \quad \text{or} \quad M_0 \, \delta(t-o) = F(t)$$

where $\delta(t)$ is the unit impulse symbol (Sec. 11). The constant M_0 represents the increase in momentum of the mass m at the instant $t = 0$.

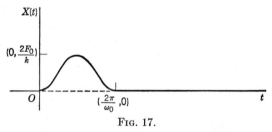

FIG. 17.

The formal transform of $M_0 \, \delta(t)$ was found to be M_0. This suggests that, in view of equation (3), when $x_0 = v_0 = 0$,

$$x(s) = \frac{M_0}{m} \frac{1}{s^2 + \omega_0^2},$$

and hence that

(9) $$X(t) = \frac{M_0}{m\omega_0} \sin \omega_0 t.$$

It will be left as an exercise to show that formula (9) follows rigorously as a limiting case of formula (7). But the formal solution can be verified as well by noting that, according to formula (9), the momentum of the mass m,

$$M(t) = mX'(t) = M_0 \cos \omega_0 t,$$

satisfies the condition $M(+0) = M_0$. If the mass started from rest, then its momentum jumped to the value M_0 at the instant $t = 0$.

26. Resonance. Let the external force in the problem of the last section be

$$F(t) = F_0 \sin \omega t,$$

where F_0 and ω are positive constants. Then according to equation (3) of Sec. 25,

(1) $$x(s) = \frac{x_0 s + v_0}{s^2 + \omega_0^2} + \frac{F_0}{m} \frac{\omega}{(s^2 + \omega_0^2)(s^2 + \omega^2)}$$

and, if $\omega \neq \omega_0$,

$$(2) \quad X(t) = x_0 \cos \omega_0 t + \frac{1}{\omega_0} \left[v_0 + \frac{F_0 \omega}{m(\omega^2 - \omega_0^2)} \right] \sin \omega_0 t$$
$$- \frac{F_0}{m(\omega^2 - \omega_0^2)} \sin \omega t.$$

That is, the motion is the superposition of two simple harmonic motions, one with frequency ω_0 and known as the natural component of vibration, and the other with frequency ω which is

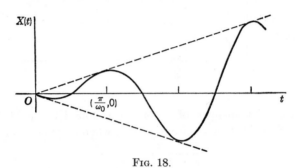

Fig. 18.

called the forced component of the vibration. Note that the natural vibrations are not present in case

$$x_0 = 0, \qquad v_0 = \frac{F_0 \omega}{m(\omega_0^2 - \omega^2)}.$$

When $\omega = \omega_0$, however, we have

$$(3) \qquad x(s) = \frac{x_0 s + v_0}{s^2 + \omega_0^2} + \frac{F_0}{m} \frac{\omega_0}{(s^2 + \omega_0^2)^2}.$$

The presence of the repeated quadratic factor in the denominator here shows that $X(t)$ will contain an unstable component (Sec. 22) having the form of the product of t by a sine or cosine function. In fact,

$$(4) \quad X(t) = x_0 \cos \omega_0 t + \frac{1}{\omega_0^2} \left(v_0 \omega_0 + \frac{F_0}{2m} \right) \sin \omega_0 t - \frac{F_0}{2m\omega_0} t \cos \omega_0 t.$$

In view of the last term here, the amplitude of the oscillations of m increases indefinitely.

In this case the force $F(t)$ is said to be in resonance with the system. We note in particular that if $x_0 = 0$ and $v_0 = -F_0/(2m\omega_0)$

in case of no damping amplitude increases without bound for resonance the resonance type of motion reduces to

$$X(t) = -\frac{F_0}{2m\omega_0} t \cos \omega_0 t,$$

shown in Fig. 18.

27. Forced Vibrations with Damping. When a force $F(t)$ acts on the mass of the damped system of Fig. 13, the equation of motion becomes

(1) $mX''(t) = -kX(t) - cX'(t) + F(t).$

If $X(0) = 0, \qquad X'(0) = 0,$

then the transformed equation has the solution

(2) $x(s) = \frac{1}{m} f(s) \dfrac{1}{(s + b)^2 + \omega_0^2 - b^2},$

where as before ω_0 is the natural frequency of the undamped system and $2b = c/m$.

Again, consider the forcing function

$$F(t) = F_0 \sin \omega t \qquad\qquad (F_0 > 0),$$

and the case $b < \omega_0$. Then equation (2) becomes

(3) $x(s) = \dfrac{\omega F_0}{m} \dfrac{1}{(s^2 + \omega^2)[(s + b)^2 + \omega_1^2]} \qquad (\omega_1^2 = \omega_0^2 - b^2),$

and it follows from Theorem 11, Sec. 22, that $X(t)$ consists of terms of the types $\sin (\omega t + \theta)$ and $e^{-bt} \sin (\omega_1 t + \theta_1)$, where θ and θ_1 are constants. Consequently the component of motion with frequency ω_1 is nearly damped out after a sufficiently long time, and the steady-state motion

(4) $X(t) = A \sin (\omega t + \theta)$

remains where, according to the term (6), Sec. 22,

(5) $A = \dfrac{F_0}{m} \dfrac{1}{|(i\omega + b)^2 + \omega_1^2|}.$

The amplitude A given by formula (5) depends on ω. The value of ω for which A takes on its maximum value is the resonance frequency in the case of damped motion. When $b \neq 0$, we can see from equation (3) that the expression for $x(s)$ contains no repeated factor of the type $(s^2 + \omega^2)^2$ in the denominator; hence no value of the frequency ω of the exciting force will induce a component of the type $t \sin (\omega t + \theta)$ in the displacement $X(t)$.

PROBLEMS

⨯ **1.** From equation (5) show that

$$\frac{F_0^2}{m^2 A^2} = (\omega^2 + 2b^2 - \omega_0^2)^2 + 4b^2\omega_1^2.$$

When $2b^2 < \omega_0^2$, show that the resonance frequency of the above system with damping has the value $(\omega_0^2 - 2b^2)^{\frac{1}{2}}$, a value that is only slightly less than the natural frequency of the undamped system if the coefficient of damping c is small.

2. When the coefficient of damping c has a value such that $\omega_0^2/2 < b^2 < \omega_0^2$, show that the amplitude A approaches its greatest value as the frequency ω approaches zero.

3. If $b = \omega_0$ in equation (3), show that

$$mX(t) = F_0 C[\omega(2bC + t)e^{-bt} + \sin(\omega t + \theta)],$$

where $C = (b^2 + \omega^2)^{-1}$ and $\theta = \arg(b^2 - \omega^2 - 2ib\omega)$.

4. When $F(t) = \delta(t)$ in the problem considered in Sec. 27, where $\delta(t)$ is the unit impulse symbol and $b < \omega_0$, show formally that

$$m\omega_1 X(t) = e^{-bt} \sin \omega_1 t.$$

Note the jump in the momentum of m at the instant $t = 0$.

⟍ **5.** If the initial conditions used in Sec. 27 are replaced by general conditions $X(0) = x_0$, $X'(0) = v_0$, show that the additional terms in $X(t)$ represent damped oscillations.

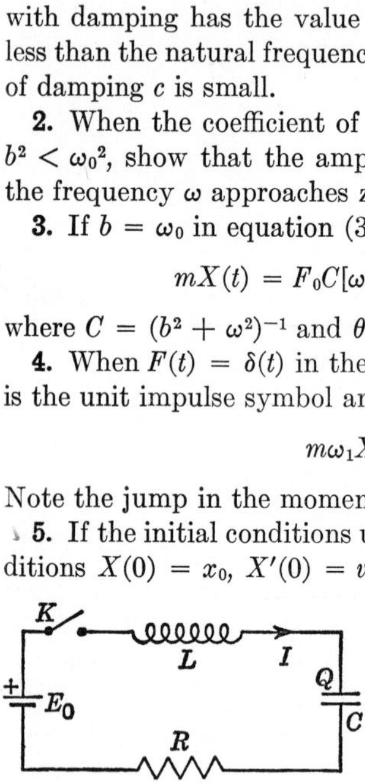

FIG. 19.

6. When the force $F(t)$ on the undamped system considered in Sec. 25 contains a component $F_0 \sin(\omega t + \theta)$, where θ is a constant, show that resonance occurs when $\omega = \omega_0$.

⨯ **7.** The electric current I and the charge Q on the capacitor in the circuit shown in Fig. 19 are functions of t that satisfy the conditions

$$L\frac{dI}{dt} + RI + \frac{Q}{C} = E_0, \qquad Q = \int_0^t I(\tau)\, d\tau, \qquad I(0) = 0,$$

where t is the time after closing the switch K, and where Q and I are initially zero. The electromotive force E_0 is constant.

(a) Derive the formula

$$I = \frac{E_0}{\omega_1 L} e^{-bt} \sin \omega_1 t,$$

where $b = \dfrac{R}{2L}$ and $\omega_1^2 = \dfrac{1}{LC} - \dfrac{R^2}{4L^2} > 0.$

(b) If $k^2 = \dfrac{R^2}{4L^2} - \dfrac{1}{LC} > 0$, show that

$$I = \frac{E_0}{kL} e^{-bt} \sinh kt.$$

28. A Vibration Absorber. We have seen that in the simple vibrating system with damping, with an exciting force $F_0 \sin \omega t$, the forced component of the vibration remains undamped. Let another spring and mass be connected in series with the original mass (Fig. 20), where the second system is undamped. Let us see whether it is possible to choose the spring constant and mass of the auxiliary system in such a way as to eliminate the forced vibrations of the first mass.

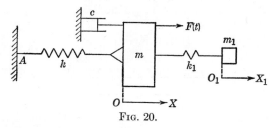

FIG. 20.

Let X and X_1 denote the displacements of the masses m and m_1, respectively, from the positions they have when neither spring is deformed. If the exciting force is

$$F(t) = F_0 \sin \omega t,$$

and if m and m_1 are initially at rest at their respective origins, then the displacements $X(t)$ and $X_1(t)$ satisfy the following system of differential equations:

$$m\frac{d^2X}{dt^2} = -kX + k_1(X_1 - X) - c\frac{dX}{dt} + F_0 \sin \omega t$$

$$m_1\frac{d^2X_1}{dt^2} = -k_1(X_1 - X),$$

$$X(0) = X'(0) = X_1(0) = X_1'(0) = 0.$$

The transforms $x(s)$ and $x_1(s)$ of $X(t)$ and $X_1(t)$ therefore satisfy the simultaneous algebraic equations

$$(ms^2 + cs + k + k_1)x(s) - k_1 x_1(s) = \frac{F_0 \omega}{s^2 + \omega^2},$$

$$k_1 x(s) - (m_1 s^2 + k_1)x_1(s) = 0.$$

Eliminating $x_1(s)$, we find that

(1) $$x(s) = F_0\omega \frac{m_1 s^2 + k_1}{(s^2 + \omega^2)p(s)},$$

where

(2) $$p(s) = (m_1 s^2 + k_1)(ms^2 + cs + k + k_1) - k_1^2.$$

In view of the presence of the quadratic factor $s^2 + \omega^2$ in the denominator of the right-hand member of equation (1), it follows that $X(t)$ will contain a term of the type

(3) $$C \sin (\omega t + \theta)$$

unless $k_1/m_1 = \omega^2$, in which case the numerator of the above fraction cancels with the factor in the denominator, leaving

(4) $$x(s) = F_0\omega m_1 \frac{1}{p(s)}.$$

The inverse transform $X(t)$ of the function (4) represents a damped oscillation of the mass m if each of the four roots, real or imaginary, of the equation $p(s) = 0$ has a negative real part (Secs. 20 to 22). Now the polynomial $p(s)$ is the determinant of this system of homogeneous equations in x and x_1:

(5) $$\begin{aligned} (ms^2 + cs + k + k_1)x - k_1 x_1 &= 0, \\ -k_1 x + (m_1 s^2 + k_1)x_1 &= 0. \end{aligned}$$

If s is any one of the four numbers for which $p(s) = 0$, then the determinant of the simultaneous equations (5) vanishes; consequently those equations have nonvanishing roots.

Let $x = z$ and $x_1 = z_1$ denote those roots, where z and z_1 are real or complex numbers. We now substitute those numbers for x and x_1 in equations (5), then multiply the members of those equations by the complex conjugates $\bar{z}$ and $\bar{z}_1$ respectively and add to obtain the equation

(6) $$(mz\bar{z} + m_1 z_1\bar{z}_1)s^2 + cz\bar{z}s + B = 0,$$

where $$\begin{aligned} B &= kz\bar{z} + k_1(z\bar{z} - z\bar{z}_1 - z_1\bar{z} + z_1\bar{z}_1) \\ &= k|z|^2 + k_1|z - z_1|^2 > 0. \end{aligned}$$

If we write $A = m|z|^2 + m_1|z_1|^2$, then equation (6) becomes

(7) $$As^2 + c|z|^2 s + B = 0,$$

where the coefficients A, $c|z|^2$ and B depend on s. However, the number s is given in terms of those positive coefficients by the quadratic formula

(8) $$s = \frac{1}{2A} \left(-c|z|^2 \pm \sqrt{c^2|z|^4 - 4AB} \right).$$

Whether the radical here is real or imaginary, it follows from formula (8) that the real part of s is negative. This completes the proof that the oscillation $X(t)$ is damped.

Thus the forced component of the vibration of the main mass m is eliminated by the system m_1, k_1, if the natural frequency of that system coincides with the frequency of the exciting force:

(9) $$\sqrt{\frac{k_1}{m_1}} = \omega.$$

Since all components of the vibration of m are then damped, that mass approaches a fixed position as t increases.

This is the principle of the Frahm vibration absorber, which has been used in such practical appliances as electric hairclippers.[1] Note that, in view of equation (9), the absorber is designed for a fixed frequency ω of the exciting force $F_0 \sin \omega t$.

By solving the above equations for $x_1(s)$, we can see that the mass m_1 has an undamped component of vibration of the type (3).

29. A Damped Absorber. The damping in the system of the foregoing section was located in the main part of the system (Fig. 20). If it is located in the absorber instead, the system is essentially as shown in Fig. 21. Although the forced vibrations of m cannot be completely absorbed by any adjustment of the latter system, the coefficient of damping of the absorber can be adjusted to give an optimum range in amplitudes of the forced vibration for a range of frequencies ω of the impressed force.

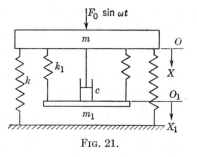

FIG. 21.

Let the displacements $X(t)$ and $X_1(t)$ of the masses m and m_1 be measured from the positions of these masses when the system is in equilibrium, and let the initial displacements and velocities

[1] Den Hartog, J. P., "Mechanical Vibrations," 4th ed., pp. 87 ff., 1956.

be zero.   Then if the impressed force is $F_0 \sin \omega t$, the equations of motion are

$$m \frac{d^2X}{dt^2} = -kX + k_1(X_1 - X) + c\left(\frac{dX_1}{dt} - \frac{dX}{dt}\right) + F_0 \sin \omega t,$$

$$m_1 \frac{d^2X_1}{dt^2} = -k_1(X_1 - X) - c\left(\frac{dX_1}{dt} - \frac{dX}{dt}\right),$$

$$X(0) = X'(0) = X_1(0) = X_1'(0) = 0.$$

The transforms $x(s)$ and $x_1(s)$ therefore satisfy the equations

$$ms^2x = -kx + k_1(x_1 - x) + cs(x_1 - x) + \frac{\omega F_0}{s^2 + \omega^2},$$

$$m_1s^2x_1 = -k_1(x_1 - x) - cs(x_1 - x).$$

Therefore $$x_1(s) = \frac{k_1 + cs}{m_1s^2 + cs + k_1} x(s)$$

and we find that

(1) $$x(s) = \frac{\omega}{s^2 + \omega^2} \psi(s),$$

where

(2) $$\psi(s) = F_0 \frac{m_1s^2 + cs + k_1}{(m_1s^2 + cs + k_1)(ms^2 + cs + k + k_1) - (cs + k_1)^2}.$$

When $c \neq 0$, it is therefore clear that the factor $s^2 + \omega^2$ will always be present in the denominator of the expression for $x(s)$ and hence that the vibration $X(t)$ of the main mass will have a forced component of the type

(3) $$A \sin (\omega t + \theta).$$

Moreover, it follows from the expression (6), Sec. 22, that the amplitude A is $|\psi(i\omega)|$.   This is easily computed from equation (2).   We find that

(4) $$\frac{A^2}{F_0^2} = \frac{(m_1\omega^2 - k_1)^2 + c^2\omega^2}{[(m\omega^2 - k)(m_1\omega^2 - k_1) - m_1k_1\omega^2]^2 + c^2\omega^2[(m + m_1)\omega^2 - k]^2}.$$

The effectiveness of the damper can be studied from this equation.[1]   The relation between A^2 and c^2 here, when ω and all other parameters are kept fixed, shows that A^2 is least either when c is zero or infinite, depending upon the magnitudes of m_1, ω, etc.   But a study of A^2 as a function of ω^2 shows that there

[1] See Den Hartog, *op. cit.*, pp. 93 ff., for a detailed discussion.

is a finite positive value of c for which the range of values of A^2 will be as small as possible for all frequencies ω. This optimum value of c is one of importance in the applications.

PROBLEMS

×**1.** Let the two masses in the system treated in Sec. 28 have arbitrary initial displacements and velocities. When condition (9) is satisfied by the elements of the absorber, show that the vibration of the main mass again contains no undamped component.

×**2.** (a) If the exciting force $F_0 \sin \omega t$ in the system of Sec. 28 is replaced by the force $F_0 \sin (\omega t + \alpha)$, where α is any constant, show that when condition (9) is satisfied the vibration of m is again entirely damped.

(b) If the exciting force is replaced by $A_1 \sin \omega_1 t + A_2 \sin \omega_2 t$, where the A's and ω's are constants and $\omega_1 \neq \omega_2$, show that the values of m_1 and k_1 cannot be adjusted so that all undamped vibrations of m are absorbed.

×**3.** Let the force $F(t)$ be removed from the mass m in Fig. 20 and let the end A of the spring k be moved horizontally so that its distance from the wall is $F(t)/k$. Show that the differential equations of motion of m and m_1 are then the same as in the original problem.

4. Prove that the polynomial in s that comprises the denominator in equation (2), Sec. 29, cannot vanish when $s = i\omega$ for any real ω; hence that it has no factor $s^2 + \omega^2$. Thus $X(t)$ has a component (3) but no component of the type $Bt \sin (\omega t + \beta)$.

×**5.** A system of two masses and two springs in series, with no damping, is shown in Fig. 22. The weights of the two masses are $m_1 g = 8$ lb and $m_2 g = 2$ lb ($g = 32$ ft/sec/sec). The spring constants have the values $k_1 = 24$ lb/ft and $k_2 = 8$ lb/ft. If a periodic force $F = F_0 \cos 2\pi ct$ acts

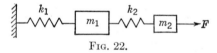

FIG. 22.

on m_2, find the frequencies c (cycles per second) of the force for which resonance occurs in the vibration of m_1. Assume zero initial displacements and velocities. Also show that resonance occurs in the vibration of m_2 for those same values of c. *Ans.* $c = 4\pi^{-1}$, $4\sqrt{3}\,\pi^{-1}$ cycles/sec.

6. For the system shown in Fig. 22, if $m_1 = m_2$ and $2k_1 = 3k_2$ and if the force $F = F_0 \sin \omega t$, where $\omega^2 = k_2/m_2$, find the formula for the displacement $X_1(t)$ of m_1 when the masses start from rest in their equilibrium positions.

Ans. $15k_2 X_1(t) = F_0[12\sqrt{2} \sin (\omega t/\sqrt{2}) + \sqrt{3} \sin (\omega t \sqrt{3})$
$$- 15 \sin \omega t].$$

7. Initially the two masses indicated in Fig. 23 are at rest and the spring has its natural length. Then a constant force $F = F_0(t > 0)$ acts on the mass m_1. Assume that the system is free from damping and friction. Find the formula for the displacement of m_2 and note that the displacement consists of a simple harmonic motion superimposed upon a uniformly accelerated motion. Also show that the spring is always compressed by an amount proportional to $1 - \cos \omega t$, where $\omega^2 = k/m_1 + k/m_2$.   *Ans.* $2\omega^2(m_1 + m_2)X_2(t) = F_0(\omega^2 t^2 - 2 + 2 \cos \omega t)$.

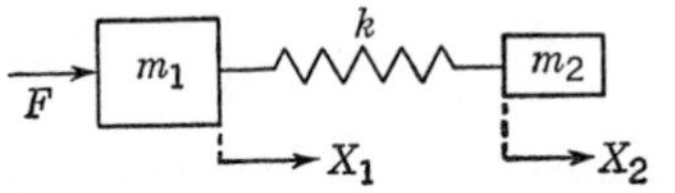

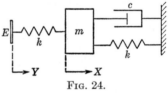

FIG. 23.

8. If the force $F = 0$ in the system shown in Fig. 23 and if the masses are initially released at rest from positions $X_1 = a_1$ and $X_2 = a_2$, show that the frequency of vibration of the masses has the value $\omega = (k/m_1 + k/m_2)^{\frac{1}{2}}$. When $a_2 = -a_1 m_1/m_2$, show that $X_1 = a_1 \cos \omega t$ and $X_2 = a_2 \cos \omega t$ and describe the vibration.

9. Let the force in the system shown in Fig. 23 be the periodic force $F = F_0 \sin \omega t$, where $\omega^2 = k/m_2$, and let a viscous damping force $-cX_1'(t)$ act on m_1. Find the steady-state vibration of m_2 and note that it does not depend on c.

Ans. $-F_0 k^{-1} \sin \omega t$.

10. In Fig. 24 the end E of the first spring has a periodic displacement $Y = A \sin \omega t$. The two springs are identical. Find the value of ω for which this damped system is in resonance, when $c^2 < 4km$.

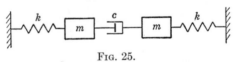

FIG. 24.

Ans. $2m^2\omega^2 = 4km - c^2$.

11. In Fig. 25 the two masses are unit masses ($m = 1$) and the two springs are identical. Initially, the springs have their natural length,

FIG. 25.

the first mass has velocity v_0 and the second mass is at rest. Find the undamped component of vibration of these masses.

Ans. $\frac{1}{2}(v_0/\sqrt{k}) \sin t \sqrt{k}$.

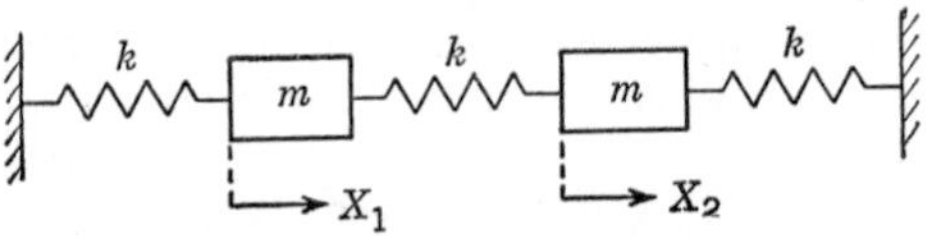

FIG. 26.

12. In the undamped system of two equal masses and three identical springs indicated in Fig. 26, the initial conditions are $X_1(0) = a_1$, $X_2(0) = a_2$, $X_1'(0) = X_2'(0) = 0$. (*a*) Show that the components of the vibration of each mass have the frequencies $\sqrt{k/m}$ and $\sqrt{3k/m}$. (*b*) Describe the vibration of the system when $a_2 = a_1$. (*c*) Describe the vibration of the system when $a_2 = -a_1$.

30. Electric Circuits. In Secs. 24 and 27 we used *Kirchhoff's voltage law:* for each closed circuit in an electrical network the impressed voltage equals the sum of the voltage drops across the elements in that circuit. His *law of currents* states that at each junction point of branches of a network the total current into the point equals the total current away from the point. Let us now present additional applications of these laws for instantaneous behavior of voltage and current, in setting up differential equations for networks.

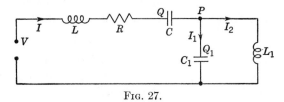

FIG. 27.

An electrical analogue of the Frahm vibration absorber discussed in Sec. 28 is indicated in Fig. 27, where the impressed voltage is

$$V = V_0 \sin \omega t.$$

According to the law of currents, applied at the junction P,

(1) $$I(t) = I_1(t) + I_2(t).$$

We apply the voltage law to the circuit on the left to see that

(2) $$V = LI'(t) + RI(t) + \frac{1}{C} Q(t) + \frac{1}{C_1} Q_1(t),$$

where $Q'(t) = I(t)$ and $Q_1'(t) = I_1(t)$; then to the circuit on the right to see that

(3) $$\frac{1}{C_1} Q_1(t) = L_1 I_2'(t).$$

Let $Q_2(t)$ denote the difference between quantities of charge on the two capacitors, so that

(4) $Q_2(t) = Q(t) - Q_1(t),$ $Q_2'(t) = I(t) - I_1(t) = I_2(t).$

In terms of Q and Q_2 equations (2) and (3) take the form

$$LQ''(t) = -\frac{1}{C}Q(t) + \frac{1}{C_1}[Q_2(t) - Q(t)]$$
(5)
$$\qquad\qquad\qquad - RQ'(t) + V_0 \sin \omega t,$$
$$L_1Q_2''(t) = -\frac{1}{C_1}[Q_2(t) - Q(t)].$$

Except for differences in notation the system (5) of differential equations in $Q(t)$ and $Q_2(t)$ is precisely the system written in Sec. 28 for the displacements $X(t)$ and $X_1(t)$ of the masses m and m_1 in the absorber (Fig. 20). Since all the electrical coefficients here, R, L, etc., are positive constants, the signs of the coefficients in equations (5) match those in the equations for X and X_1. The initial conditions for the network match those chosen for the absorber, and the analogy is complete if

(6) $Q(0) = Q_1(0) = I(0) = I_2(0) = 0.$

Under conditions (6) the transforms of $I(t)$ and $I_2(t)$ are $sq(s)$ and $sq_2(s)$, which correspond to $sx(s)$ and $sx_1(s)$ for the absorber. According to the results found in Sec. 28 therefore, the current $I(t)$ has an undamped component of type $B \sin (\omega t + \alpha)$ unless

(7) $\frac{1}{L_1C_1} = \omega^2.$

But when the elements of the L_1C_1 circuit satisfy condition (7) for a prescribed frequency ω of the impressed voltage V, the current $I(t)$ contains only damped components; thus $I(t) \to 0$ as $t \to \infty$. The currents $I_1(t)$ and $I_2(t)$ in the L_1C_1 circuit, however, do have undamped components of type $B \sin (\omega t + \alpha)$.

Note that equations (1) to (3) with conditions (6) can be solved directly for the currents either by replacing $Q(t)$ by $\int_0^t I(\tau)\,d\tau$ or $q(s)$ by $i(s)/s$, etc. Thus the transformation of equations (2) and (3) gives the equations

$$\left(Ls + R + \frac{1}{Cs}\right)i(s) + \frac{1}{C_1s}i_1(s) = v(s),$$
(8)
$$L_1s\,i(s) - \left(L_1s + \frac{1}{C_1s}\right)i_1(s) = 0.$$

Upon eliminating $i_1(s)$ we find that

(9) $i(s) = v(s)y(s)$ if $y(s) = \dfrac{s(L_1 s^2 + C_1^{-1})}{p(s)}$,

where $p(s)$ is the polynomial introduced in Sec. 28:

$$p(s) = (L_1 s^2 + C_1^{-1})(Ls^2 + Rs + C^{-1} + C_1^{-1}) - C_1^{-2}.$$

The function $y(s)$ depends only upon the characteristics of the network, not upon the impressed voltage. Since the formal transform of the unit impulse symbol $\delta(t)$ is unity, it follows from equation (9) that $y(s) = i(s)$ when $V(t) = \delta(t)$ formally; that is, $Y(t)$ represents the current I produced by the voltage $\delta(t)$. When the network is considered as a system with input $V(t)$ and output $I(t)$, then, in the language of systems analysis, $y(s)$ is the *transfer function* for the system; in view of equation (9) the output corresponding to any input $V(t)$ is given by the formula

(10) $I(t) = V(t) * Y(t)$.

PROBLEMS

1. Show that the network indicated in Fig. 28 represents an electrical analogue of the mechanical system shown in Fig. 25 (Prob. 11, Sec. 29), where Q_1 and Q_2 correspond to the displacements of the two masses.

⊹**2.** If $I_1(0) = I_2(0) = 0$ in the network shown in Fig. 28, while the capacitors have the same initial charge Q_0, show that

$$I_1(t) = I_2(t) = -Q_0 \omega \sin \omega t, \quad \text{where } \omega = (CL)^{-\frac{1}{2}}.$$

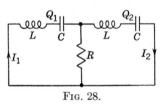

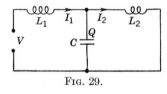

FIG. 28.   FIG. 29.

3. If $I_1(0) = I_2(0) = 0$ in the network shown in Fig. 28 and if $Q_1(0) = a_1$ and $Q_2(0) = a_2$, find the undamped component $\bar{I}_1(t)$ of the current $I_1(t)$, the steady-state current through the first inductance coil.

$\qquad$ *Ans.* $\bar{I}_1 = -\frac{1}{2}(a_1 + a_2)\omega \sin \omega t, \ \omega = (CL)^{-\frac{1}{2}}.$

4. In Fig. 29 the currents $I_1(t)$ and $I_2(t)$ and the charge $Q(t)$ are initially zero. (*a*) Show that the current $I_1(t)$ is unstable under the

impressed voltage $V = V_0 \sin (\omega t + \alpha)$ if $\omega^2 = (L_1C)^{-1} + (L_2C)^{-1}$.
(b) Show that the system indicated in Fig. 23 is a mechanical analogue
to the network here with $X_1(t)$ and $X_2(t)$ corresponding to $Q_1(t)$ and
$Q_2(t)$, where $Q'_1(t) = I_1(t)$, $Q'_2(t) = I_2(t)$, and $Q(t) = Q_1(t) - Q_2(t)$.

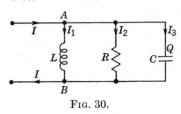

FIG. 30.

5. A prescribed current $I(t)$ is sup-
plied to the network shown in Fig. 30.
The initial values of $I_1(t)$ and $Q(t)$ are
zero. Use the following notation:
$V(t)$ is the resulting potential drop
from the junction A to the junction B,
$\omega_0^2 = (LC)^{-1}$, $2b = (RC)^{-1}$, and
$\omega_1^2 = \omega_0^2 - b^2$, given that $b^2 < \omega_0^2$.

(a) Show that the transfer function from input $I(t)$ to output $I_1(t)$ is

$$y(s) = \frac{\omega_0^2}{s^2 + 2bs + \omega_0^2},$$

thus that $I_1(t) = I(t) * Y(t)$, where $Y(t) = \omega_0^2 \omega_1^{-1} e^{-bt} \sin \omega_1 t$.

(b) Find $V(t)$ when $I(t) = I_0$, a constant.

Ans. $V(t) = I_0(C\omega_1)^{-1} e^{-bt} \sin \omega_1 t$.

6. In a simple LC circuit with inductance coil and capacitor in series,
let the impressed voltage be a periodic function, with period T, of the
type

$$V(t) = a_0 + \sum_{n=1}^{N} (a_n \cos n\omega t + b_n \sin n\omega t),$$

where $\omega = 2\pi/T$. Show that the current $I(t)$ in the circuit is unstable
if the frequency ω of $V(t)$ has any one of the values

$$\omega = \frac{1}{m} \frac{1}{\sqrt{LC}} \qquad (m = 1, 2, \ldots, N),$$

provided that a_m and b_m are not both zero.

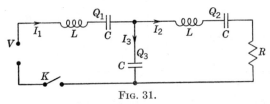

FIG. 31.

7. In the network shown in Fig. 31 all currents and charges are zero
at the instant $t = 0$ when the switch K is closed. If the impressed voltage is given by the equation $V = V_0 \sin \omega t$, where $\omega^2 = 2(LC)^{-1}$, find
the steady-state value $\bar{I}_2(t)$ of the current $I_2(t)$ and note that it is independent of the value of the resistance R. *Ans.* $\bar{I}_2(t) = -V_0 C\omega \cos \omega t$.

8. In the system shown in Fig. 26 apply an exciting force to the first mass and viscous damping to the second mass. Show that the resulting system is a mechanical analogue of the network shown in Fig. 31.

9. Initially the currents and the charge on the capacitor are zero in the network shown in Fig. 32. The voltage drop from A_1 to B_1 caused by the mutual inductance of the two coils is $MI_2'(t)$, and the drop from A_2 to B_2 caused by that mutual inductance is $MI_1'(t)$, where $M^2 < L_1L_2$. The impressed voltage is given by the equation $V = V_0 \cos \omega t$. When the values of C and L_2 are adjusted so that $L_2C = \omega^{-2}$, show that the current $I_1(t)$ in this idealized resistance-free circuit has a simple periodic variation at all times with a frequency greater than ω.

$$Ans. \quad I_1(t) = V_0C\frac{L_2}{L_1}\,\omega_1 \sin \omega_1 t, \quad \omega_1 = \omega \left(\frac{L_1L_2}{L_1L_2 - M^2}\right)^{\frac{1}{2}}.$$

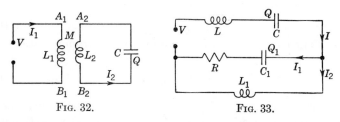

FIG. 32.   FIG. 33.

10. Show that the network in Fig. 33 represents an analogue of the damped absorber discussed in Sec. 29 (Fig. 21) if initial currents and charges are zero, where charges Q and $Q - Q_1$ correspond to displacements X and X_1 and the voltage V corresponds to the force $F_0 \sin \omega t$.

31. Static Deflection of Beams.

Let $Y(x)$ denote the static transverse displacement of a point at distance x from one end

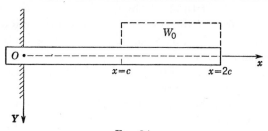

FIG. 34.

of a uniform beam, caused by a load distributed in any manner along the beam (Fig. 34). Under certain idealizing assumptions, primarily that displacements $Y(x)$ and slopes $Y'(x)$ are small, it is shown in mechanics that the internal bending moment $M(x)$

exerted by any span of the beam upon an adjacent span, through their common cross section A_x, is proportional to the curvature of the beam at position x. In fact

(1) $M(x) = EIY''(x),$

where E is Young's modulus of elasticity in tension and compression for the material and I is the moment of inertia of the area A_x with respect to the neutral axis of the cross section, the line in A_x about which A_x turns when the beam bends. Note that $Y''(x)$ is approximately the curvature since $Y'(x)$ is small.

If $F(x)$ denotes the internal shearing force at A_x, it can be seen that $dM(x) = F(x) \, dx$; thus $F(x) = M'(x)$, or

(2) $F(x) = EIY'''(x).$

Let $W(x)$ represent the transverse load per unit length along the beam. Then $W(x) \, dx = dF(x)$, and it follows from equation (2) that

(3) $Y^{(4)}(x) = aW(x)$ $(a^{-1} = EI).$

The shear $F(x)$ is a continuous function except at points where concentrated loads or supports act. When $W(x)$ is sectionally continuous then, in view of equations (2) and (3), $Y'''(x)$ is continuous and $Y^{(4)}(x)$ is sectionally continuous. These are just the continuity conditions that are implied by our formula for the transform, with respect to x, of $Y^{(4)}(x)$.

Although the simple differential equation (3) can be solved by successive integrations, the requirement that the solution $Y(x)$ and its derivatives of the first three orders be continuous at all points often involves tedious labor when $W(x)$ is sectionally continuous. The simplicity of equation (3) enables us to use the Laplace transformation, even though certain Fourier transformations are better adapted to the two-point boundary conditions that accompany that equation.

Let us determine the displacements $Y(x)$ in a beam whose end $x = 0$ is built into a rigid support while the end $x = 2c$ is free, or unsupported (Fig. 34). The load $W(x)$ per unit length is zero over the span $0 < x < c$ and a constant w_0 over the span $c < x < 2c$. The total load W_0 is $w_0 c$. Equation (3) can now be written

(4) $Y^{(4)}(x) = aw_0 S_c(x)$ $(0 < x < 2c),$

where $S_c(x)$ is our unit step function.   The end conditions are

(5) $Y(0) = Y'(0) = 0,$ $Y''(2c) = Y'''(2c) = 0,$

since no bending or shear acts on the end $x = 2c$.

Let $y(s)$ denote the Laplace transform of $Y(x)$ when $Y(x)$ satisfies equation (4) on the semi-infinite range $x > 0$, together with the first pair of boundary conditions (5). In view of the continuity conditions to be satisfied by $Y(x)$ and its derivatives we may expect that

$$s^4 y(s) - s^3(0) - s^2(0) - sY''(0) - Y'''(0) = aw_0 \frac{1}{s} e^{-cs}.$$

We have used a convenient extension, $aw_0 S_c(x)$ when $x > 2c$, of the function $aW(x)$ in the right-hand member of equation (4) where $0 < x < 2c$. The particular extension used is immaterial because we first seek a function $Y(x)$ that satisfies equation (4) when $0 < x < 2c$ and the conditions $Y(0) = Y'(0) = 0$, and contains two arbitrary constants $A = Y''(0)$ and $B = Y'''(0)$. Since

$$y(s) = \frac{A}{s^3} + \frac{B}{s^4} + aw_0 \frac{1}{s^5} e^{-cs},$$

a function that satisfies those requirements is

(6) $Y(x) = \frac{1}{2}Ax^2 + \frac{1}{6}Bx^3 + \frac{1}{24}aw_0(x - c)^4 S_c(x).$

When $x > c$, it follows from equation (6) that

$$Y''(x) = A + Bx + \tfrac{1}{2}aw_0(x - c)^2, \qquad Y'''(x) = B + aw_0(x - c).$$

The last two of conditions (5) are then satisfied if

(7) $A = \tfrac{3}{2}aw_0 c^2,$ $B = -aw_0 c,$

and the displacements in the beam are given by the equation

(8) $Y(x) = aw_0[\tfrac{3}{4}c^2 x^2 - \tfrac{1}{6}cx^3 + \tfrac{1}{24}(x - c)^4 S_c(x)]$ $(0 \leqq x \leqq 2c).$

This function satisfies equations (4) and (5) and the continuity conditions.

Since $Y'''(0) = B = -aw_0 c$, it follows from equation (2) that the shear force at $x = 0$ has the value $-w_0 c$, or $F(0) = -W_0$ as we should expect, since the magnitude of the vertical force exerted by the support must be the same as the total load on the beam.   Actually, the displacements $Y(x)$ for this cantilever beam can be found by first noting that the shear $-Y''''(x)/a$ at each section is the total load on the span to the right of that section. The bending moment at the end $x = 0$ is $Y''(0)/a$ or A/a:

$$M(0) = \tfrac{3}{2}cW_0 \qquad\qquad (W_0 = cw_0).$$

×× If the end $x = 2c$ were pin-supported (hinged or simply supported) so that it can rotate freely about a fixed axis, then the conditions at that end become

$$Y(2c) = Y''(2c) = 0.$$

PROBLEMS

+ **1.** In the above example let the end $x = 2c$ of the beam be pin-supported, rather than free, with no other changes in conditions. Find the vertical force exerted by the beam on the pin, and the vertical force and bending moment exerted on the support at $x = 0$.

$$Ans.\ \tfrac{41}{64}W_0;\ \tfrac{23}{64}W_0;\ \tfrac{7}{32}cW_0.$$

2. Both ends $x = 0$ and $x = 2c$ of a beam are pin-supported. Find the vertical force on each support when a transverse load W_0 is distributed uniformly over the span $c < x < 2c$. $Ans.\ W_0/4;\ 3W_0/4.$

3. Solve Prob. 2 if both ends are built in rather than pin-supported.

$$Ans.\ \tfrac{3}{16}W_0;\ \tfrac{13}{16}W_0.$$

4. The end $x = 0$ of a beam is built in and the end $x = 2c$ is pin-supported. The load per unit length is bx on the span $0 < x < c$, and $b(2c - x)$ on the span $c < x < 2c$. Find the vertical force on each support in terms of the total load W_0 on the beam. $Ans.\ \tfrac{21}{32}W_0;\ \tfrac{11}{32}W_0.$

5. In addition to a distributed load $W(x)$ a single concentrated load W_1 acts between the ends of a beam, at position $x = b$. Then the shear $F(x)$ is continuous except for a jump W_1 at $x = b$. Apply formula (4), Sec. 4, to the function $Y'''(x)$ to show that the transform of equation (3) above is

$$s^4y(s) - s^3Y(0) - s^2Y'(0) - sY''(0) - Y'''(0) - aW_1e^{-bs} = aw(s).$$

Compare this equation in $y(s)$ with the one obtained formally by replacing $W(x)$ in equation (3) by $W(x) + W_1\delta(x - b)$ and transforming as if $Y'''(x)$ were continuous, where $\delta(x)$ is the unit impulse symbol.

32. Evaluation of Integrals.

The transformation can be used to evaluate certain integrals containing a parameter.

Example 1. Evaluate the integral

$$(1) \qquad\qquad F(t) = \int_0^\infty \frac{\cos tx}{x^2 + a^2}\,dx.$$

Let us first proceed formally to transform with respect to t and interchange the order of integration with respect to x and t:

$$(2) \quad f(s) = \int_0^\infty L\{\cos tx\} \frac{dx}{x^2 + a^2} = \int_0^\infty \frac{s \, dx}{(x^2 + a^2)(x^2 + s^2)}$$

$$= \frac{s}{s^2 - a^2} \int_0^\infty \left(\frac{1}{x^2 + a^2} - \frac{1}{x^2 + s^2} \right) dx = \frac{\pi}{2a} \frac{1}{s + a}$$

if $a > 0$ and $s > 0$. Thus the integral has the value

$$(3) \qquad\qquad F(t) = \frac{\pi}{2a} e^{-at} \qquad\qquad (a > 0, t \geqq 0).$$

To see that the formal step (2) is sound, we first note that, whenever T and s are positive constants,

$$(4) \quad \int_0^T e^{-st} \int_0^\infty \frac{\cos tx}{x^2 + a^2} \, dx \, dt = \int_0^\infty \frac{1}{x^2 + a^2} \int_0^T e^{-st} \cos tx \, dt \, dx,$$

because the absolute value of the entire integrand does not exceed $(x^2 + a^2)^{-1}$, a function independent of t whose integral from $x = 0$ to $x = \infty$ exists. The integral $F(t)e^{-st}$ therefore converges uniformly with respect to t when $t \geqq 0$ by the Weierstrass test and, according to equation (11), Sec. 12, the interchange of order of integration with respect to x and t shown in equation (4) is valid.

The final integral in equation (4) can be evaluated by integration by parts and the equation can be written

$$(5) \qquad\qquad \int_0^T e^{-st} F(t) \, dt = \int_0^\infty g(x,T) \, dx,$$

where $\qquad g(x,T) = \dfrac{e^{-sT}(x \sin Tx - s \cos Tx) + s}{(x^2 + a^2)(x^2 + s^2)}.$

This continuous function of x and T has a limit $g(x, \infty)$,

$$g(x, \infty) = \lim_{T \to \infty} g(x,T) = s(x^2 + a^2)^{-1}(x^2 + s^2)^{-1},$$

uniformly with respect to x when $x \geqq 0$ since

$$|g(x,T) - g(x,\infty)| < e^{-sT} \frac{x + s}{(x^2 + a^2)(x^2 + s^2)} \leqq Me^{-sT},$$

where M is the maximum value of the quotient of polynomials in x. To each positive number ϵ there corresponds a number T_ϵ, independent of x, such that $Me^{-sT} < \epsilon$ when $T > T_\epsilon$. Moreover, the second integral in equation (5) converges uniformly with respect to T, according to the Weierstrass test. The limit of the integral (5) as $T \to \infty$ is therefore $\int_0^\infty g(x, \infty)\, dx$ (Prob. 12, Sec. 23), since the latter integral exists; thus equation (2) follows from equation (4).

Example 2.   Evaluate the integral

$$(6) \qquad\qquad F(t) = \int_0^\infty \frac{\sin tx}{x}\, dx.$$

The formal procedure is simple.   When $t > 0$ and $s > 0$

$$(7) \qquad f(s) = \int_0^\infty L\{\sin tx\}\, \frac{dx}{x} = \int_0^\infty \frac{dx}{x^2 + s^2} = \frac{\pi}{2s};$$

hence $F(t) = \pi/2$.   In view of equation (6), $F(t)$ is an *odd function:* $F(-t) = -F(t)$, and $F(0) = 0$.   Therefore

$$F(t) = \frac{\pi}{2} \qquad\qquad (t > 0),$$

$$(8) \qquad\qquad\qquad = -\frac{\pi}{2} \qquad\qquad (t < 0),$$

$$F(0) = 0.$$

In the justification of the formal step (7) the Weierstrass test for uniform convergence does not apply to the integral (6). However, when $t > 0$ we note that

$$F(t) = \int_0^\infty \frac{\sin r}{r}\, dr = \int_0^\pi \frac{\sin r}{r}\, dr + \int_\pi^{2\pi} \frac{\sin r}{r}\, dr + \cdots,$$

where it can be shown that the alternating series here converges and as a consequence that the integral $F(t)$ exists.   Thus to each positive ϵ there corresponds a number R_ϵ such that

$$\left| \int_R^\infty \frac{\sin r}{r}\, dr \right| < \epsilon \qquad\qquad \text{when } R > R_\epsilon.$$

The remainder for the integral (6) then satisfies the condition

$$(9) \qquad \left| \int_X^\infty \frac{\sin tx}{x}\, dx \right| = \left| \int_{tX}^\infty \frac{\sin r}{r}\, dr \right| < \epsilon \quad \text{when } tX > R_\epsilon.$$

If $t_0 > 0$ and $t \geqq t_0$, condition (9) is satisfied when $t_0 X > R_\epsilon$ or $X > R_\epsilon/t_0$, a number independent of t, and the uniform convergence of the integral (6) when $t \geqq t_0$ is established.

The integrand $t \sin (tx)/(tx)$ is continuous in t and x together if we define $\sin r/r$ to be unity when $r = 0$, so that the latter function is continuous for every r. Then (Sec. 12)

$$(10) \quad \int_{t_0}^{T} e^{-st} F(t) \, dt = \int_{0}^{\infty} \int_{t_0}^{T} e^{-st} \sin tx \, dt \, \frac{dx}{x}$$

$$= \int_{0}^{\infty} h(x,T) \, dx - \int_{0}^{\infty} h(x,t_0) \, dx,$$

where $h(x,t)$ is the continuous function

$$h(x,t) = -\frac{e^{-st}}{x^2 + s^2} \left(st \, \frac{\sin r}{r} + \cos r \right) \qquad (r = xt).$$

Now $|\sin r/r| \leqq 1$ for all r and the Weierstrass test applies to show the uniform convergence of the last integral in equations (10) with respect to t_0 when $0 \leqq t_0 \leqq 1$. The limit of that integral as $t_0 \to 0$ is therefore the same as the integral of the limit $h(x,0)$.

If N denotes the maximum value of $(sT + 1)e^{-sT}$, then

$$(11) \quad |h(x,T)| \leqq \frac{N}{x^2 + s^2},$$

$$|h(x,T)| \leqq \frac{1}{s^2} e^{-sT}(sT + 1).$$

The uniform convergence, with respect to T, of the integral of $h(x,T)$ in equations (10) and the fact that $h(x,T) \to 0$ as $T \to \infty$, uniformly with respect to x, follow from conditions (11). Thus we can write $t_0 = 0$ and $T = \infty$ in equations (10) and step (7) is justified.

33. Exponential- and Cosine-integral Functions. The exponential-integral function

$$(1) \quad \text{Ei } t = \int_{-\infty}^{t} \frac{e^r}{r} \, dr \qquad (t < 0)$$

can be written

$$(2) \quad -\text{Ei}(-t) = \int_{t}^{\infty} \frac{e^{-y}}{y} \, dy = \int_{1}^{\infty} \frac{e^{-tx}}{x} \, dx \qquad (t > 0).$$

The transform of the last integral, when $s > 0$, is

$$\int_1^\infty \frac{dx}{x(x+s)} = \frac{1}{s} \int_1^\infty \left(\frac{1}{x} - \frac{1}{x+s} \right) dx = \frac{1}{s} \log \frac{x}{x+s} \Big]_1^\infty.$$

The justification of the formal step here is not difficult (Sec. 32). Thus

$$(3) \qquad\qquad L\{-\operatorname{Ei}(-t)\} = \frac{1}{s} \log (s+1) \qquad\qquad (s > 0).$$

In Sec. 18 we found that the transform of Si t, the sine-integral function, is $s^{-1} \operatorname{arccot} s$. The cosine-integral function is defined as follows.

$$(4) \qquad\qquad \operatorname{Ci} t = - \int_t^\infty \frac{\cos r}{r} dr = - \int_1^\infty \frac{\cos tx}{x} dx \qquad (t > 0).$$

A procedure similar to that used in Example 2, Sec. 32, can be followed to prove that the transform of the final integral in equations (4) has the value

$$-s \int_1^\infty \frac{dx}{x(x^2+s^2)} = -\frac{1}{s} \int_1^\infty \left(\frac{1}{x} - \frac{x}{x^2+s^2} \right) dx$$
$$= -\frac{1}{2s} \log \frac{x^2}{x^2+s^2} \Big]_1^\infty$$

when $s > 0$. Therefore

$$(5) \qquad\qquad L\{\operatorname{Ci} t\} = -\frac{1}{2s} \log (s^2+1) \qquad\qquad (s > 0).$$

Let $H(t)$ denote the function $\cos t \operatorname{Si} t - \sin t \operatorname{Ci} t$, where $t > 0$. Then

$$H(t) = \cos t \int_0^t \frac{\sin r}{r} dr + \sin t \int_t^\infty \frac{\cos r}{r} dr$$
$$= \cos t \int_0^\infty \frac{\sin r}{r} dr - \int_t^\infty \frac{\cos t \sin r - \sin t \cos r}{r} dr.$$

The first integral in the last line has the value $\pi/2$, according to equation (8), Sec. 32. In the second integral we introduce a new variable of integration x, where $r = t(x+1)$:

$$H(t) = \frac{\pi}{2} \cos t - \int_t^\infty \frac{\sin (r-t)}{r} dr = \frac{\pi}{2} \cos t - \int_0^\infty \frac{\sin tx}{x+1} dx.$$

When we transform this last expression for $H(t)$ we obtain the result

$$(6) \qquad L\{\cos t \operatorname{Si} t - \sin t \operatorname{Ci} t\} = \frac{\log s}{s^2 + 1} \qquad (s > 0).$$

Finally, let us evaluate the integral

$$(7) \qquad F(t) = \int_0^\infty \frac{e^{-tx}}{x^2 + 1}\, dx \qquad (t > 0).$$

Its transform is found to be

$$f(s) = \frac{\pi}{2}\frac{s}{s^2 + 1} - \frac{\log s}{s^2 + 1}$$

and therefore, in view of formula (6),

$$(8) \qquad F(t) = \left(\frac{\pi}{2} - \operatorname{Si} t\right)\cos t + \operatorname{Ci} t \sin t.$$

Since the integral (7) is a Laplace integral, this result can be written

$$(9) \qquad L\left\{\frac{1}{t^2 + 1}\right\} = \left(\frac{\pi}{2} - \operatorname{Si} s\right)\cos s + \operatorname{Ci} s \sin s \quad (s > 0).$$

PROBLEMS

1. From the results found in Sec. 33 show that, when $a > 0$ and $s > a$,

(a) $L\{-e^{at} \operatorname{Ei}(-at)\} = \dfrac{\log s - \log a}{s - a}$;

(b) $L\{1 - e^{-at} - at \operatorname{Ei}(-at)\} = \dfrac{a}{s^2}[\log(s + a) - \log a]$;

✗ (c) $L\{\cos at \operatorname{Si} at - \sin at \operatorname{Ci} at\} = a\,\dfrac{\log s - \log a}{s^2 + a^2}$;

✗ (d) $L\{\cos at \operatorname{Ci} at + \sin at \operatorname{Si} at\} = -s\,\dfrac{\log s - \log a}{s^2 + a^2}$.

Derive the following integration formulas, where $t > 0$ and $a > 0$.

2. $\displaystyle\int_0^\infty \frac{\sin tx}{x(x^2 + 1)}\, dx = \frac{\pi}{2}(1 - e^{-t})$.

+ **3.** $\displaystyle\int_{-\infty}^\infty \frac{x \sin tx}{x^2 + a^2}\, dx = \pi e^{-at}$.

✗ **4.** $\displaystyle\int_{-\infty}^\infty \left(\frac{\sin tx}{x}\right)^2 dx = \int_0^\infty \frac{1 - \cos 2tx}{x^2}\, dx = \pi t$.

5. $\int_0^\infty \dfrac{\sin tx}{x + a}\,dx = \left(\dfrac{\pi}{2} - \text{Si } at\right) \cos at + \text{Ci } at \sin at.$ (See Prob. 1.)

6. $\int_0^\infty \dfrac{\cos tx}{x + a}\,dx = \left(\dfrac{\pi}{2} - \text{Si } at\right) \sin at - \text{Ci } at \cos at.$ (See Prob. 1.)

7. $\int_0^\infty \dfrac{e^{-rx^2}}{x^2 + 1}\,dx = \dfrac{\pi}{2} e^r \text{ erfc } \sqrt{r},$ $(r \geqq 0)$;   substitute $t = kx^2$ to derive transformation 111, Appendix 3.

8. $\int_0^\infty \dfrac{e^{-s\tau}}{\tau + a}\,d\tau = L\left\{\dfrac{1}{t + a}\right\} = -e^{as} \text{ Ei } (-as)$ $(s > 0).$

9. $L\left\{\dfrac{1}{(t + a)(t + b)}\right\} = \dfrac{1}{a - b}\left[e^{as} \text{ Ei } (-as) - e^{bs} \text{ Ei } (-bs)\right]$ if $a > 0, b > 0, s > 0,$ and $a \neq b.$ (See Prob. 8.)

10. $L\left\{\dfrac{1}{(t + a)^2}\right\} = \dfrac{1}{a} + se^{as} \text{ Ei } (-as)$ $(s > 0).$ (See Prob. 8.)

11. $\int_0^\infty \dfrac{\sin tx}{\sqrt{x}}\,dx = 2 \int_0^\infty \sin ty^2\,dy = \sqrt{\dfrac{\pi}{2t}}.$ Note   that $y^4 + s^2 = (y^2 + s)^2 - (y\sqrt{2s})^2 = (y^2 - y\sqrt{2s} + s)(y^2 + y\sqrt{2s} + s).$

12. $\int_0^\infty e^{-x^2t} \cos 2atx\,dx = \dfrac{1}{2}\sqrt{\dfrac{\pi}{t}}\, e^{-a^2t}.$

34. The Tautochrone.

We shall now discuss a problem in mechanics that leads to a simple integral equation of the convolution type.

The problem is that of determining a curve through the origin in a vertical xy plane such that the time required for a particle

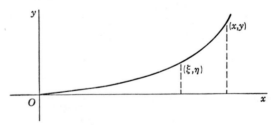

Fig. 35.

to slide down the curve to the origin is independent of the starting position. The particle slides from rest under the action of its weight and the reaction of the curve on which it is constrained to move. The required curve is called the tautochrone.

Let σ denote the length of arc of the curve, measured from the origin O, and let (x,y) be the starting point and (ξ,η) any intermediate point (Fig. 35). Equating the gain in kinetic energy to the loss of potential energy, we have

$$\frac{1}{2} m \left(\frac{d\sigma}{dt}\right)^2 = mg(y - \eta),$$

where m is the mass of the particle and t is time.   Thus

$$d\sigma = - \sqrt{2g} \sqrt{y - \eta} \, dt,$$

and upon separating variables and integrating from $\eta = y$ to $\eta = 0$ we have

$$T \sqrt{2g} = \int_{\eta=0}^{\eta=y} \frac{d\sigma}{\sqrt{y - \eta}},$$

where T is the fixed time of descent.   Now

$$\sigma = H(y),$$

where the function $H(y)$ depends upon the curve, and therefore

$$(1) \qquad T \sqrt{2g} = \int_0^y (y - \eta)^{-\frac{1}{2}} H'(\eta) \, d\eta.$$

This is an integral equation of convolution type in the unknown function $H'(y)$.   We may write it in the form

$$T \sqrt{2g} = y^{-\frac{1}{2}} * H'(y).$$

Let $h(s)$ be the Laplace transform of $H(y)$ with respect to the variable y.   Recalling that $H(0) = 0$ and that the transform of the convolution of two functions is the product of the transforms, it follows formally from equation (1) that

$$T \sqrt{2g} \frac{1}{s} = s \, h(s) L \left\{\frac{1}{\sqrt{y}}\right\} = s \, h(s) \sqrt{\frac{\pi}{s}}.$$

That is,
$$s \, h(s) = T \sqrt{\frac{2g}{\pi}} \frac{1}{\sqrt{s}};$$

hence

$$(2) \qquad H'(y) = \frac{T}{\pi} \sqrt{2g} \frac{1}{\sqrt{y}}.$$

We can see that this function does satisfy our integral equation (1) by substituting it into that equation and performing the integration.

Since $\qquad H'(y) = \dfrac{d\sigma}{dy} = \sqrt{1 + \left(\dfrac{dx}{dy}\right)^2},$

the differential equation of the curve in terms of the variables x and y is, according to equation (2),

$$1 + \left(\frac{dx}{dy}\right)^2 = \frac{2gT^2}{\pi^2 y} = \frac{a}{y},$$

where $a = 2gT^2/\pi^2$. Separating variables here, we have

$$dx = \sqrt{\frac{a - y}{y}}\, dy,$$

and the necessary integration can be performed easily by substituting $y = a \sin^2 \frac{1}{2}\theta$, for we then find that

$$dx = a \cos^2 \frac{1}{2}\, \theta\, d\theta = \frac{a}{2}\, (1 + \cos \theta)\, d\theta.$$

Noting that $x = 0$ when $y = 0$, the parametric equations of the tautochrone are therefore

(3) $\qquad x = \dfrac{a}{2}\, (\theta + \sin \theta), \qquad y = \dfrac{a}{2}\, (1 - \cos \theta).$

These equations represent the cycloid generated by a point P on a circle of radius $\frac{1}{2}a$ as the circle rolls along the lower side of the line $y = a$. The parameter θ is the angle through which the radius drawn to the point P has turned, where the initial position of P is at the origin. Our tautochrone is of course just one arch of this cycloid. Since $a = 2gT^2/\pi^2$, the diameter of the generating circle is determined by the time T of descent.

The above problem can be generalized in various ways so as to lead to other interesting questions; in fact it was a generalization of the problem of the tautochrone that led the great Norwegian mathematician Niels Abel (1802–1829) to introduce the subject of integral equations.[1]

If the time T of descent is a function $F(y)$, for example, our integral equation (1) becomes

(4) $\qquad \sqrt{2g}\, F(y) = \displaystyle\int_0^y (y - \eta)^{-\frac{1}{2}} H'(\eta)\, d\eta.$

---

[1] See Bôcher, M., "Integral Equations," p. 6, 1909.

35. Servomechanisms. Simple integral equations as well as differential equations arise in the theory of automatic control. As a special case we consider servomechanisms that force the angle of turn $\Theta_0(t)$ of a rotating shaft to follow closely the angle of turn $\Theta_i(t)$ of a pointer or indicator, where t denotes time. The shaft and material rigidly attached to it have a total moment of inertia I that is much greater than that of the pointer.

Let $\Phi(t)$ be the angle of deviation between shaft and pointer or the difference between output angle and input angle:

$$(1) \qquad \Phi(t) = \Theta_0(t) - \Theta_i(t).$$

An auxiliary system or servomechanism can be designed to measure $\Phi(t)$ and feed back to the shaft a component of torque that is proportional to the deviation $\Phi(t)$. The servomechanism may contain its own source of power, motors and generators and other electrical equipment. In order to provide damping in the system, let the servo also supply a component of torque proportional to the rate of deviation $\Phi'(t)$. Then, since the product of I by the angular acceleration of the shaft equals the torque applied to the shaft,

$$(2) \qquad I\Theta_0''(t) = -k\Phi(t) - c\Phi'(t),$$

where k and c are positive constants.

If the shaft is initially at rest and its angle of turn is measured from that position, then $\Theta_0(0) = \Theta_0'(0) = 0$. Also, in view of equation (1), $\Phi(0) = -\Theta_i(0)$ and in terms of transforms equation (2) becomes

$$Is^2\theta_0(s) = -(k + cs)\phi(s) - c\Theta_i(0),$$

where we have assumed that $\Theta_0(t)$, $\Theta_0'(t)$, and $\Phi(t)$, and therefore $\Theta_i(t)$, are continuous when $t \geqq 0$. Since $\theta_0(s) = \phi(s) + \theta_i(s)$, it follows that

$$(3) \qquad \phi(s) = -\frac{Is^2\theta_i(s) + c\Theta_i(0)}{Is^2 + cs + k}.$$

Under the input $\Theta_i(t) = At$ it follows from equation (3) that

$$\Phi(t) = -\frac{A}{\omega}e^{-bt}\sin\omega t \qquad \left(b = \frac{c}{2I}, \ \omega^2 = \frac{k}{I} - \frac{c^2}{4I^2}\right).$$

If $k > c^2/(4I)$, the angle of deviation $\Phi(t)$ has a damped oscillation with initial value zero, an oscillation that is small at all times when b is large because $|\sin \omega t/(\omega t)| < 1$ and

$$|\Phi(t)| \leqq |A|te^{-bt} \leqq \frac{|A|}{be}.$$

If in addition to the two components of torque shown in equation (2), a component proportional to the accumulated angle of deviation is produced by the servo, then

$$(4) \qquad I\Theta_0''(t) = -k\Phi(t) - c\Phi'(t) - b\int_0^t \Phi(\tau)\,d\tau,$$

where b is a positive constant. When $\Theta_0(0) = \Theta_0'(0) = 0$ therefore,

$$Is^2[\phi(s) + \theta_i(s)] = -\left(k + cs + \frac{b}{s}\right)\phi(s) - c\Theta_i(0).$$

In terms of the positive numbers B, C, and K, where

$$IC = c, \qquad IK^2 = k, \qquad IB^3 = b,$$

the last equation can be written

$$(5) \qquad \phi(s) = -\frac{s^3\theta_i(s) + Cs\Theta_i(0)}{s^3 + Cs^2 + K^2s + B^3}.$$

In the special case $\Theta_i(t) = At$, $K^2 = BC$, equation (5) becomes

$$(6) \qquad \phi(s) = -\frac{As}{(s + B)[s^2 + (C - B)s + B^2]}$$

and since the polynomials in the numerator and denominator here are of degrees one and three in s, respectively, it follows from our earlier observations (Probs., Sec. 23) that $\Phi(0) = 0$; that is, the initial value of the angle of deviation is zero. When $C > B$, all values of s that make the polynomial in the denominator vanish have negative real parts, and consequently (Sec. 22) $\Phi(t)$ contains only damped components. But when $C < B$, $\Phi(t)$ has an unstable oscillation.

36. Mortality of Equipment. Let the function $F(t)$ denote the number of pieces of equipment on hand at time t, where the number is large enough that we can consider it as a continuous variable instead of a variable that takes on only integral values. The equipment wears out in time, or is lost from service for other reasons, so that, out of n_0 pieces of new equipment introduced at time $t = 0$, the number $N(t)$ in service at time t is given by the formula

$$(1) \qquad\qquad N(t) = n_0 H(t),$$

where $H(t)$ is a function that determines the surviving equipment after t units of time.   Note that $H(0) = 1$, necessarily.

If $R(\tau)$ is the total number of replacements up to time τ, then $R'(\tau)\, d\tau$ is the number of replacements during the time interval from $t = \tau$ to $t = \tau + d\tau$ and the number of survivals at any future time t, out of these replacements, is

$$R'(\tau)H(t - \tau)\, d\tau.$$

The total amount of equipment in service at time t is the sum of these survivals from the replacements during every time interval $d\tau$ between $\tau = 0$ and $\tau = t$, increased of course by the survivals from the new equipment on hand at time $t = 0$. Therefore

$$(2) \qquad F(t) = F(0)H(t) + \int_0^t R'(\tau)H(t - \tau)\, d\tau.$$

We have assumed here that the equipment $F(0)$ on hand at time $t = 0$ is all new; thus we take $R(0) = 0$.

If the amount $F(t)$ that must be in service at each instant is known and if the survival factor $H(t)$ is known, then equation (2) is an integral equation of convolution type in $R'(t)$. Its solution gives the formula by which replacements must be made.

The equation is an integral equation in the survival factor $H(t)$ when $F(t)$ and $R(t)$ are known.

In either case, the transformed equation is

$$(3) \qquad\qquad f(s) = F(0)h(s) + s\, r(s)h(s).$$

Then

$$(4) \qquad\qquad r(s) = \frac{f(s) - F(0)h(s)}{s\, h(s)},$$

and $R(t)$ is the inverse transform of this function.

Suppose the mortality is exponential in character so that

$$H(t) = e^{-kt}$$

and that the amount of equipment on hand is to be a constant,

$$F(t) = b.$$

Then $h(s) = 1/(s + k)$ and $f(s) = b/s$, and it follows from equation (4) that

$$r(s) = bk \frac{1}{s^2}.$$

Therefore replacements must be made at such a rate that the total equipment replaced at each time t is

$$R(t) = bkt,$$

a result that is easily verified as the solution of equation (2). Thus replacements must be made at the rate of bk pieces per unit time.

PROBLEMS

1. In Sec. 34, let the time T of descent be proportional to $\sqrt{y}$, $T\sqrt{2g} = 2B\sqrt{y}$, where $B > 1$. Show that the curve of descent is the line $x = y\sqrt{B^2 - 1}$.

2. If $c = k = 2I$ in equation (2), Sec. 35, find the output angle $\Theta_0(t)$ corresponding to the constant input angle $\Theta_i(t) = 1(t > 0)$, and compare them graphically. Assume that $\Theta_0(0) = \Theta_0'(0) = 0$. Also, note that the value of the output lags behind that of the input until $t = 3\pi/4$.
          Ans. $\Theta_0(t) = 1 - \sqrt{2}\,e^{-t}\sin{(t + \pi/4)}$.

3. For the servomechanism corresponding to equations (4) and (5), Sec. 35, consider this special case: $\Theta_i(t) = At$, $B^3 = CK^2$. If α represents the argument of the complex number $K + Ci$, derive the formula

$$\Phi(t) = \frac{A}{C^2 + K^2}\,[Ce^{-ct} - \sqrt{C^2 + K^2}\sin{(Kt + \alpha)}]$$

for the angle of deviation, and note the undamped component of $\Phi(t)$.

4. Let the servomechanism discussed in Sec. 35 supply only a corrective torque proportional to the deviation angle $\Phi(t)$ while the shaft itself is subject to a damping torque proportional to its angular velocity. If $\Theta_0(0) = \Theta_0'(0) = 0$, show that

$$\theta_0(s) = \frac{k}{Is^2 + cs + k}\,\theta_i(s),$$

where c, k, and I are positive constants. When $\Theta_i(t) = A$, show that $\Theta_0(t)$ approaches A as t increases.

5. When $H(t) = e^{-kt}$, where $H(t)$ is the survival factor in Sec. 36 and k is a positive constant, (a) find the replacement function $R(t)$ corresponding to an arbitrary amount $F(t)$ of equipment on hand; (b) find $R(t)$ when $F(t) = At + B$.   *Ans.* (b) $R(t) = (A + Bk)t + \frac{1}{2}Akt^2$.

6. When $H(t)$ in Sec. 36 is the step function $1 - S_k(t)$ so that every piece of new equipment survives for k units of time, (a) show that the number of replacements $R(t)$ up to time t required to maintain $F(t)$ pieces in service at that time is

$$R(t) = F(t) - F(+0) + F(t - k) + F(t - 2k) + F(t - 3k) + \cdots$$

if we define $F(t)$ to be zero when $t < 0$. (b) When $F(t) = A(t > 0)$, show that $R(t) = A[t/k]$, where $[t]$ is the bracket symbol, and draw the graph of $R(t)$.

7. A particle of mass m moves on a vertical X axis under two forces: the force of gravity and a resistance proportional to the velocity.   If the axis is taken positive downward, the equation of motion is

$$mX''(t) = mg - kX'(t).$$

Show that its solution, under the conditions $X(0) = 0$, $X'(0) = v_0$, is

$$X(t) = \frac{1}{b^2} [(bv_0 - g)(1 - e^{-bt}) + bgt],$$

where $b = k/m$, and discuss the motion.

8. Each one of a set of radioactive elements E_1, E_2, E_3, and E_4 disintegrates into the succeeding one at a rate proportional to the number of atoms present, except for the end product E_4 which is a stable element. If $N_i(t)$, where $i = 1, 2, 3, 4$, denotes the number of atoms of element E_i present at time t and if the distinct positive constants c_1, c_2, and c_3 are the respective coefficients of decay of the first three elements, then

$$N_1'(t) = -c_1 N_1(t), \qquad N_2'(t) = -c_2 N_2(t) + c_1 N_1(t),$$
$$N_3'(t) = -c_3 N_3(t) + c_2 N_2(t), \qquad N_4'(t) = c_3 N_3(t).$$

When only atoms of E_1 are present initially and the number of them is M, find the formula for $N_4(t)$.

CHAPTER 4

PROBLEMS IN PARTIAL DIFFERENTIAL EQUATIONS

37. The Wave Equation. Several functions in physics and engineering satisfy the partial differential equation

a)

(1)
$$\frac{\partial^2 Y}{\partial t^2} = a^2 \frac{\partial^2 Y}{\partial x^2},$$

known as the wave equation in two independent variables x and t. We shall use literal subscripts to indicate partial derivatives; then equation (1) can be written

$$Y_{tt}(x,t) = a^2 Y_{xx}(x,t).$$

Brief derivations of this equation for some elementary physical functions will now be given. The derivations are helpful in writing modifications of the equation and in setting up boundary conditions for specific problems.

First, let $Y(x,t)$ denote the displacement at time t away from the x axis of a point (x,Y) of a string in the xY plane under tension P (Fig. 36). The string is assumed to be flexible enough that all bending moments transmitted between its elements can be neglected; thus each element pulls tangentially on an adjacent element with a force of magnitude P. Suppose further that conditions are such that the magnitude H of the x component of the tension remains essentially constant at all times for all points (x,Y); in particular all displacements $Y(x,t)$ are assumed small compared to the length of the string. Finally let the slope angle α remain small in order that each small element of length of the string may be approximated by the length of its projection Δx on the x axis. All these idealizing assumptions are satisfied, for instance, by strings of musical instruments under ordinary conditions of operation.

The vertical component of tension is the vertical force V

exerted by the part of the string to the left of point (x, Y) on the part to the right of the point. It is proportional to the slope of the string, $-V/H = \tan \alpha$ (Fig. 36); that is,

$$(2) \qquad V(x,t) = -HY_x(x,t).$$

This is the basic formula for deriving the equation of motion.

Now consider an element of length of the string whose projection on the x axis is Δx. If ρ denotes the mass per unit length,

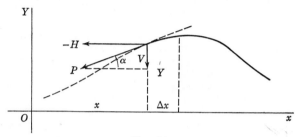

Fig. 36.

the mass of the element is approximately $\rho \, \Delta x$. If no external forces act on the string, the application of Newton's second law to the element gives, in view of formula (2),

$$(3) \qquad \rho \, \Delta x Y_{tt}(x,t) = -HY_x(x,t) + HY_x(x + \Delta x, t)$$

approximately, when Δx is small; that is,

$$Y_{tt}(x,t) = \frac{H}{\rho} \frac{Y_x(x + \Delta x, t) - Y_x(x,t)}{\Delta x}.$$

When we let Δx approach zero, this becomes equation (1), where

$$(4) \qquad a^2 = H/\rho.$$

If in addition to the internal force a force $F(x,t)$ per unit of mass acts in the Y direction along the string, then the additional term $\rho \, \Delta x F(x,t)$ appears on the right in equation (3). The resulting modification of equation (1) is

$$(5) \qquad Y_{tt}(x,t) = a^2 Y_{xx}(x,t) + F(x,t),$$

when the Y axis points vertically upward and the weight of the string is to be taken into account, for instance, $F(x,t) = -g$, where g is the acceleration of gravity.

b)   As another physical example consider the longitudinal displacements in a cylindrical or prismatic elastic bar.   The values of the
variable x are marked on the bar so as to designate the cross
section that is x units from one end when the bar is neither
stretched nor compressed (Fig. 37).   For each value of x the
longitudinal displacement $Y(x,t)$ is measured from a fixed origin
outside the bar, an origin in the plane occupied by the cross
section at x when the bar is unstrained and in some position of
reference.   Thus, if the bar is moved lengthwise as a rigid body,
$Y(x,t)$ is a constant at each time t.

Since $Y(x + \Delta x, t)$ is the displacement of the cross section at
$x + \Delta x$, an element of the bar whose natural length is Δx is

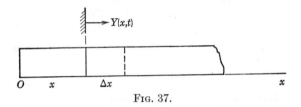

FIG. 37.

stretched by the amount $Y(x + \Delta x, t) - Y(x,t)$ at time t.
According to Hooke's law the force exerted by the bar upon the
left-hand end of the element to produce that extension is

$$-AE \frac{Y(x + \Delta x, t) - Y(x,t)}{\Delta x},$$

where A is the area of the cross section and E is Young's modulus
of elasticity of the material in tension and compression.   When
Δx tends to zero, it follows that the internal force from left to
right at the cross section is

(6) $F(x,t) = -AEY_x(x,t).$

This basic formula corresponds to equation (2) for the string.

Let ρ denote the mass of the material per unit volume.   When
we apply Newton's second law to an element of the bar,

(7) $\rho A \, \Delta x Y_{tt}(x,t) = -AEY_x(x,t) + AEY_x(x + \Delta x, t),$

we find as before that $Y(x,t)$ satisfies equation (1), where

(8) $a^2 = E/\rho.$

When the elastic bar is replaced by a column of air, equation (1) has further applications in acoustics.[1]

c)   Again, the function $Y(x,t)$ may represent the angle of turn of a cross section x units from one end of an elastic cylindrical shaft under torsion (Fig. 38). Let I denote the moment of inertia of the cross section with respect to its axis, E_s the modulus of elasticity of the material in shear, and ρ the density of the

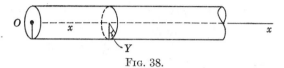

FIG. 38.

material.   Then, by steps analogous to those used above, we find that the internal torque τ acting through a cross section at position x is

(9) $$\tau(x,t) = -I\,E_s Y_x(x,t)$$

and that equation (1) is satisfied by the angle $Y(x,t)$, where

(10) $$a^2 = E_s/\rho.$$

d)   Finally, it should be remarked that equation (1) is a special case of the *telegraph equation*

(11) $$Y_{xx}(x,t) = KLY_{tt}(x,t) + (RK + SL)Y_t(x,t) + RSY(x,t),$$

where $Y(x,t)$ represents either the electric potential or the current at time t at a point x units from one end of a transmission line or cable.[2] Here the elements of resistance, inductance, etc., are *distributed* along the cable or through the circuit, in contrast to the *lumped* elements in elementary circuits (Sec. 30) that lead to ordinary differential equations in the currents.   The cable has resistance R, electrostatic capacity K, leakage conductance S, and self-inductance L, all per unit length.   When R and S are so small that their effect can be neglected, equation (11) reduces to equation (1), where $a^2 = (KL)^{-1}$.

38. Displacements in a Long String.   Let $Y(x,t)$ represent the transverse displacements of the points of a semi-infinite stretched string, a string having one end fixed so far out on the x axis that the end may be considered infinitely far from the origin, and

---

[1] Lord Rayleigh, "Theory of Sound," vols. 1 and 2, Dover, 1945.

[2] A derivation of equation (11) is outlined in Prob. 9, Sec. 83.

having its other end looped around the Y axis. The loop, initially at the origin, is moved in some prescribed manner along the Y axis (Fig. 39) so that $Y = F(t)$ when $x = 0$ and $t \geqq 0$, where $F(t)$ is a prescribed continuous function and $F(0) = 0$. If the string is initially at rest on the x axis, let us find the formula for $Y(x,t)$.

The above conditions on $Y(x,t)$ can be written

(1) $Y_{tt}(x,t) = a^2 Y_{xx}(x,t)$ $(x > 0, t > 0)$,

(2) $Y(x,0) = Y_t(x,0) = 0$ $(x > 0)$,

(3) $Y(0,t) = F(t), \quad \lim_{x \to \infty} Y(x,t) = 0$ $(t \geqq 0)$,

where $a^2 = H/\rho$ (Sec. 37). The equation of motion (1) implies that no external forces act along the string.

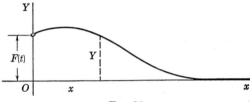

FIG. 39.

A problem composed of such conditions is called a *boundary value problem* in partial differential equations. We shall use a formal procedure to solve the problem and then indicate how our result can be verified as a solution.

If $y(x,s)$ is the Laplace transform of $Y(x,t)$, then, in view of the initial conditions (2), $L\{Y_{tt}\} = s^2 y$. Also,

$$L\{Y_{xx}(x,t)\} = \int_0^\infty \frac{\partial^2}{\partial x^2} [e^{-st} Y(x,t)] \, dt$$

$$= \frac{\partial^2}{\partial x^2} \int_0^\infty e^{-st} Y(x,t) \, dt = y_{xx}(x,s),$$

if the function $e^{-st} Y(x,t)$ satisfies conditions under which the indicated interchange of order of integration with respect to t and differentiation with respect to x is valid (Sec. 12). When both members of the partial differential equation (1) are transformed and conditions (2) are used, we therefore obtain the equation $s^2 y = a^2 y_{xx}$ in the transform of our unknown function.

From conditions (3) we find that $y(0,s) = f(s)$, where $f(s)$ is the transform of $F(t)$, and $\lim_{x \to \infty} y(x,s) = 0$, provided that the order of integrating with respect to t and taking the limit as $x \to \infty$ can be interchanged (Chap. 2). The transformed boundary value problem in $y(x,s)$ is therefore

(4) $$\frac{d^2y}{dx^2} - \frac{s^2}{a^2} y = 0 \qquad\qquad (x > 0),$$

(5) $$y(0,s) = f(s), \qquad \lim_{x \to \infty} y(x,s) = 0.$$

Here we have used the symbol for ordinary rather than partial differentiation because s is only a parameter in the problem; no differentiation with respect to s is involved.

A convenient form of the general solution of equation (4) is

$$y(x,s) = C_1 e^{-sx/a} + C_2 e^{sx/a},$$

where C_1 and C_2 may be functions of s. This solution could of course be obtained by transforming the members of equation (4) with respect to x. We consider s as positive, since Laplace transforms generally exist for all s greater than some fixed number. Then $C_2 = 0$, if $y(x,s)$ is to approach zero as x tends to infinity. The first of conditions (5) is also satisfied if $C_1 = f(s)$, and the solution of the transformed problem is

(6) $$y(x,s) = e^{-(x/a)s} f(s).$$

The translation property (Sec. 10) enables us to write the inverse transform of $y(x,s)$ at once:

(7) $$Y(x,t) = F\left(t - \frac{x}{a}\right) \qquad \text{when } t \geqq \frac{x}{a},$$
$$= 0 \qquad \text{when } t \leqq \frac{x}{a}.$$

Since $F(t)$ is continuous and $F(0) = 0$, we can see that the function $Y(x,t)$ described by formula (7) is continuous when $x \geqq 0$ and $t \geqq 0$, including points on the line $x = at$ in the xt plane. The function clearly satisfies the boundary conditions (2) and (3).

Any function of $t - x/a$ is easily seen to be a solution of the wave equation (1) when its derivative of the second order exists. Let $F(t)$ satisfy these additional conditions: $F'(t)$ and $F''(t)$ are continuous when $t \geqq 0$ except possibly for finite jumps at

$t = t_i$ $(i = 1, 2, \ldots)$. The function $Y(x,t)$ described by formula (7) then satisfies equation (1) except possibly at points (x,t) on the lines $t - x/a = t_i$ and $t - x/a = 0$ in the quadrant $x > 0$, $t > 0$. In this sense then the function (7) is verified as a solution of our boundary value problem [(1) to (3)] *regardless of the validity of formal steps* taken to obtain formula (7). In case $F''(t)$ is continuous for $t \geq 0$ and $F(0) = F'(0) = F''(0) = 0$, the function (7) satisfies equation (1) with no exceptions when $x > 0$ and $t > 0$ and represents a solution of the boundary value problem in the ordinary sense. Note that conditions of exponential order are not involved in the verification of our solution.

According to formula (7), a point of the string x units from the origin remains at rest until the time $t = x/a$. Starting at that time, it executes the same motion as the loop at the left-hand end. The retarding time x/a is the time taken by a disturbance to travel the distance x with velocity a. Since $a = (H/\rho)^{\frac{1}{2}}$, note that it has the physical dimensions of velocity. The vertical force from left to right at a point (Sec. 37) is $-HY_x(x,t)$; thus the vertical force exerted on the loop to make it move in the prescribed manner, as found from formula (7), is

$$V(0,t) = \frac{H}{a} F'(t) = \sqrt{\rho H}\, F'(t).$$

Finally, let us observe instantaneous positions of the string corresponding to the loop movement

$$
(8) \qquad\qquad F(t) = \sin \pi t \qquad \text{when } 0 \leq t \leq 1,
$$
$$
= 0 \qquad\qquad \text{when } t \geq 1;
$$

thus the loop is lifted to the position $Y = 1$ and returned to $Y = 0$, where it remains after time $t = 1$. In this case $F(t - x/a) = 0$ when $t - x/a \geq 1$, that is, when $x \leq a(t - 1)$. Also $F(t - x/a) = \sin \pi(t - x/a)$ when $0 \leq t - x/a \leq 1$, that is, when $a(t - 1) \leq x \leq at$. Then from formula (7) we find that

$$
(9) \quad Y(x,t) = 0 \qquad\qquad \text{when } x \leq a(t - 1) \text{ or when } x \geq at,
$$
$$
= \sin \pi(t - x/a) \qquad \text{when } a(t - 1) \leq x \leq at.
$$

Thus the string coincides with the x axis except on an interval of length a, if $t > 1$, where it forms one arch of a sine curve ending at $x = at$. As t increases the arch moves to the right with velocity a (Fig. 40).

It is interesting to note that for each fixed x in formula (9) the function $Y_t(x,t)$ has a jump π at $t = x/a$ and at $t = 1 + x/a$ and hence $s^2 y(x,s)$ is not the transform of $Y_{tt}(x,t)$. On the other hand it can be shown that $d^2 y/dx^2$ is not the transform of $Y_{xx}(x,t)$, because of the discontinuities of $Y_x(x,t)$; but the transform of $Y_{tt} - a^2 Y_{xx}$ is zero.

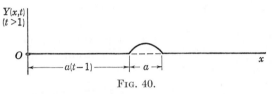

$Y(x,t)$
$(t > 1)$

O

x

$\longleftarrow a(t-1) \longrightarrow \mid \leftarrow a \rightarrow \mid$

FIG. 40.

The function $Y(x,t)$ above can also represent the longitudinal displacements in a semi-infinite elastic bar (Sec. 37), initially at rest and unstrained. The distant end of the bar is held fixed and the end $x = 0$ is displaced in a prescribed manner, $Y(0,t) = F(t)$. When $F(t)$ is given by formula (8), the solution (9) or Fig. 40 shows that at time t the section of the bar from $x = a(t - 1)$ to $x = at$ is strained while the remainder is unstrained and at rest.

39. A Long String under Its Weight. Let the semi-infinite string be stretched along the positive half of a horizontal x axis with its end $x = 0$ fastened at the origin and with its distant end looped around a vertical support that exerts no vertical force

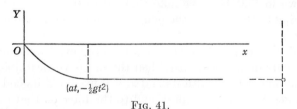

Y

O

x

$(at, -\tfrac{1}{2}gt^2)$

FIG. 41.

on the loop (Fig. 41). In view of formula (2), Sec. 37, for the vertical force at points of the stretched string, $Y_x(x,t)$ vanishes at the distant end. The string is initially supported at rest along the x axis. At the instant $t = 0$ the support is removed and the string moves downward under the action of gravity. Let us find the displacements $Y(x,t)$.

As noted in Sec. 37, equation (5), the equation of motion is

(1) $$Y_{tt}(x,t) = a^2 Y_{xx}(x,t) - g \qquad (x > 0, \, t > 0).$$

The boundary conditions are

(2) $Y(x,0) = Y_t(x,0) = 0$ $(x \geqq 0)$,

(3) $Y(0,t) = 0, \quad \lim_{x \to \infty} Y_x(x,t) = 0$ $(t \geqq 0)$.

The transformed problem is found formally to be

(4) $a^2 y''(x,s) - s^2 y(x,s) = g/s$,

(5) $y(0,s) = 0, \quad \lim_{x \to \infty} y'(x,s) = 0$,

where the primes denote derivatives with respect to x. Since the constant $-g/s^3$ is a particular solution of equation (4), the general solution of that equation is

$$y(x,s) = C_1 e^{-sx/a} + C_2 e^{sx/a} - g/s^3.$$

When conditions (5) are applied, we find that

(6) $y(x,s) = -g \left(\dfrac{1}{s^3} - \dfrac{1}{s^3} e^{-(x/a)s} \right).$

The displacements $Y(x,t)$ can be written in the form

(7) $Y(x,t) = -\dfrac{g}{2a^2} (2axt - x^2)$ when $x \leqq at$,

                $= -\tfrac{1}{2}gt^2$ when $x \geqq at$.

The details of this step and the verification of the solution (7) are left to the problems. An instantaneous position of the string is shown in Fig. 41. We note that up to time t the segment of the string to the right of the point $x = at$ has moved like a freely falling body.

If $Y(x,t)$ in problem (1) to (3) represents longitudinal displacements in an elastic bar, then the bar is vertical, initially at rest and unstrained, with its end $x = 0$ fixed and its end $x = \infty$ free, since $Y_x(\infty,t)$ is proportional to the force on that end.

PROBLEMS

Solve these boundary value problems and verify your result:

1. $Y_x(x,t) + xY_t(x,t) = 0;\ Y(x,0) = 0,\ Y(0,t) = t$.

        Ans. $Y(x,t) = (t - r)S_r(t)$, where $r = x^2/2$.

2. $W_{xx}(x,t) + W_{tx}(x,t) - 2W_{tt}(x,t) = 0$ $(x > 0, t > 0)$;

        $W(x,0) = W_t(x,0) = \lim_{x \to \infty} W(x,t) = 0,\ W(0,t) = F(t)$.

        Ans. $W(x,t) = F(t - 2x)$, where $F(\tau) = 0$ if $\tau < 0$.

3. $W_{xx}(x,t) - 2W_{tx}(x,t) + W_{tt}(x,t) = 0$ $(0 < x < 1, t > 0)$;

$W(x,0) = W_t(x,0) = W(0,t) = 0; W(1,t) = F(t)$ $(t > 0)$.

Ans. $W(x,t) = xF(x + t - 1)$, where $F(\tau) = 0$ if $\tau < 0$.

+4. $xY_x(x,t) + Y_t(x,t) + Y(x,t) = xF(t); Y(x,0) = Y(0,t) = 0$.

$$Ans. \ Y(x,t) = xe^{-2t} \int_0^t e^{2r}F(r) \, dr.$$

5. $Y_x(x,t) + 2xY_t(x,t) = 2x; Y(x,0) = Y(0,t) = 1$.

Ans. $Y(x,t) = 1 + t$ when $t \leq x^2$,

$= 1 + x^2$ when $t \geq x^2$.

6. In the problem on the semi-infinite string falling under its own weight (Sec. 39), (a) give the details in deriving formula (7) for displacements $Y(x,t)$ and verify the result fully; (b) use formula (7) to verify that the vertical force at time t exerted on the string by the support at the origin equals the weight $g\rho at$ of the curved segment of the string.

7. In Sec. 39 let the weight of the string be replaced by a general vertical force of $F(t)$ units per unit mass of string, so that another special case of equation (5), Sec. 37, is involved. Show that the displacements are

$$Y(x,t) = G(t) - G(t - x/a)$$

where $G(t) = \int_0^t \int_0^r F(u) \, du \, dr$ if $t \geq 0$,

$= 0$ if $t \leq 0$.

8. The end $x = 0$ of a semi-infinite stretched string is looped around the Y axis which exerts no vertical force on the loop, and the distant end is fixed on the x axis. The string is displaced into the position $Y = e^{-x}(x \geq 0)$ and released from rest in that position at the instant $t = 0$. If no external forces act on the string, set up the boundary value problem for the displacements $Y(x,t)$ and find its solution in the form

$Y = e^{-x} \cosh at + \sinh (x - at)$ if $x \leq at$,

$= e^{-x} \cosh at$ if $x \geq at$.

Suggestion: Find $A(s)$ so that $A(s)e^{-x}$ is a particular solution of the non-homogeneous equation $a^2y'' - s^2y = -se^{-x}$ in $y(x,s)$.

9. The force per unit area on the end $x = 0$ of a uniform semi-infinite elastic bar (Fig. 42) is $F(t)$: $-EY_x(0,t) = F(t)$. If the infinite end is

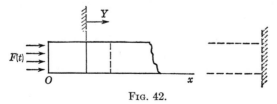

FIG. 42.

fixed and the initial displacement and velocity of each cross section are zero, set up the boundary value problem for longitudinal displacements $Y(x,t)$ and derive the solution

$$Y(x,t) = \frac{a}{E} G\left(t - \frac{x}{a}\right)$$

where
$$G(t) = \int_0^t F(r)\,dr \qquad \text{if } t \geqq 0,$$
$$= 0 \qquad \text{if } t \leqq 0;$$

thus $Y(x,t) = 0$ when $t \leqq x/a$. Note that the displacement of the end $x = 0$ is $Y(0,t) = (a/E)G(t)$.

10. When the pressure $F(t)$ in Prob. 9 is a finite impulse: $F(t) = EF_0$ when $t < t_0$, $F(t) = 0$ when $t > t_0$, show that $Y = 0$ when $t \leqq x/a$, $Y = (at - x)F_0$ when $x/a \leqq t \leqq t_0 + x/a$, and $Y = F_0 a t_0$ when $t \geqq t_0 + x/a$. Study this function $Y(x,t)$ graphically.

11. Under the instantaneous impulse of pressure $F(t) = I\delta(t)$ in Prob. 9 show formally that

$$Y(x,t) = aI/E \qquad \text{when } x < at,$$
$$= 0 \qquad \text{when } x > at.$$

Note that in this hypothetical case a part of the bar is displaced into a region already occupied by another part.

12. When the pressure $F(t)$ in Prob. 9 is constant, units can be chosen so that $F(t) = E$ and $a = 1$. In this case show that $y = s^{-2}e^{-sx}$ and $Y = (t - x)S_x(t)$ and verify this result as a solution of the boundary value problem. Also note the discontinuities in $Y_t(x,t)$ and $Y_x(x,t)$.

13. In Prob. 12, show that

$$L\{Y_{tt}(x,t)\} = s^2 y(x,s) - e^{-sx} = 0,$$

and that $L\{Y_{xx}(x,t)\} = 0$; hence that $y_{xx}(x,s) \neq L\{Y_{xx}(x,t)\}$. In this case then the Laplace integral of $Y(x,t)$ cannot be differentiated twice with respect to x inside the integral sign, because of discontinuities in $Y_x(x,t)$ (cf. Secs. 12, 38).

14. An unstrained semi-infinite elastic bar is moving lengthwise with velocity $-v_0$ when the end $x = 0$ is suddenly brought to rest, the other end remaining free (Fig. 43). Set up and solve the boundary value problem for the longitudinal displacements $Y(x,t)$. Also show that the

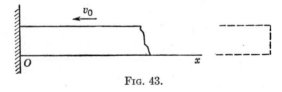

FIG. 43.

force per unit area exerted by the support at $x = 0$ upon the end of the bar is Ev_0/a. *Ans.* $Y = -v_0t$ when $t \leq x/a$, $Y = -v_0x/a$ when $t \geq x/a$.

40. The Long String Initially Displaced. Let the ends of a semi-infinite string stretched along the positive x axis be kept fixed, and let the string be given some prescribed displacement $Y = \Phi(x)$ initially and released from that position with initial velocity zero. Here $\Phi(0) = \Phi(\infty) = 0$. Then the boundary value problem in the transverse displacements $Y(x,t)$ is

(1)
$$\begin{aligned} Y_{tt}(x,t) &= a^2 Y_{xx}(x,t) & (x > 0, t > 0), \\ Y(x,0) &= \Phi(x), \qquad Y_t(x,0) = 0, \\ Y(0,t) &= 0, \qquad \lim_{x \to \infty} Y(x,t) = 0. \end{aligned}$$

The problem in the transform $y(x,s)$ is therefore

(2) $$s^2 y(x,s) - s\Phi(x) = a^2 y_{xx}(x,s) \qquad (x > 0),$$
(3) $$y(0,s) = 0, \qquad \lim_{x \to \infty} y(x,s) = 0.$$

We shall solve the ordinary differential equation (2) by using the Laplace transformation with respect to x. Let $u(z,s)$ denote that transform of $y(x,s)$; that is,

$$u(z,s) = \int_0^\infty e^{-zx} y(x,s) \, dx.$$

Since $y(0,s) = 0$, when we transform both members of equation (2) we obtain the equation

$$s^2 u(z,s) - s\varphi(z) = a^2[z^2 u(z,s) - y_x(0,s)],$$

where $\varphi(z)$ is the transform of $\Phi(x)$. Let the unknown function of s, $y_x(0,s)$ be denoted by C. Then the solution of the last equation can be written

$$u(z,s) = \frac{C}{z^2 - (s^2/a^2)} - \frac{s}{a^2} \varphi(z) \frac{1}{z^2 - (s^2/a^2)},$$

and performing the inverse transformation with respect to z, with the aid of the convolution, we have

(4) $$y(x,s) = \frac{aC}{s} \sinh \frac{sx}{a} - \frac{1}{a} \int_0^x \Phi(\xi) \sinh \frac{s}{a} (x - \xi) \, d\xi.$$

In view of the condition requiring $y(x,s)$ to vanish as x tends to infinity, it is necessary that the coefficient of $e^{sx/a}$ on the right of equation (4) should vanish as x becomes infinite. Writing the hyperbolic sines in terms of exponential functions, we find that coefficient to be

$$\frac{aC}{2s} - \frac{1}{2a} \int_0^x \Phi(\xi)e^{-(s\xi/a)} \, d\xi.$$

Since the limit of this function is to be zero as $x \to \infty$, we have

$$\frac{aC}{s} = \frac{1}{a} \int_0^\infty \Phi(\xi)e^{-(s\xi/a)} \, d\xi.$$

Substituting this into equation (4) we can write the result in the form

$$2ay(x,s) = \int_x^\infty \Phi(\xi)e^{-[s(\xi-x)]/a} \, d\xi - \int_0^\infty \Phi(\xi)e^{-[s(x+\xi)]/a} \, d\xi$$
$$+ \int_0^x \Phi(\xi)e^{-[s(x-\xi)]/a} \, d\xi.$$

The integrals here can be reduced to Laplace integrals. In the first one we substitute $\tau = (\xi - x)/a$, in the second $\tau = (\xi + x)/a$, and in the third $\tau = (x - \xi)/a$ to get

$$(5) \quad 2y(x,s) = \int_0^\infty \Phi(x + a\tau)e^{-s\tau} \, d\tau$$
$$- \int_{x/a}^\infty \Phi(-x + a\tau)e^{-s\tau} \, d\tau + \int_0^{x/a} \Phi(x - a\tau)e^{-s\tau} \, d\tau.$$

In order to combine the last two integrals let $\Phi_1(x)$ represent the odd extension of the function $\Phi(x)$:

$$(6) \qquad\qquad \Phi_1(x) = \Phi(x) \qquad\qquad \text{if } x \geqq 0,$$
$$= -\Phi(-x) \qquad\qquad \text{if } x \leqq 0;$$

thus $\Phi_1(-x) = -\Phi_1(x)$ for all x. Then equation (5) can be written

$$2y(x,s) = L\{\Phi(x + at)\} + L\{\Phi_1(x - at)\}$$

and therefore

$$(7) \qquad Y(x,t) = \tfrac{1}{2}[\Phi(x + at) + \Phi_1(x - at)].$$

Since $x + at \geqq 0$, $\Phi(x + at) = \Phi_1(x + at)$.

The function (7) satisfies all conditions of problem (1). Instantaneous positions of the string can be sketched by adding ordinates as suggested by formula (7). When t is fixed the graph of $\tfrac{1}{2}\Phi_1(x - at)$, for instance, is obtained by translating the graph of the function $\frac{1}{2}\Phi_1(x)$, defined for all real x, to the right through the distance at.

41. A Bar with a Prescribed Force on One End.   Let the end $x = 0$ of an elastic bar of length c be kept fixed, and let $F(t)$ denote a prescribed force per unit area acting parallel to the bar

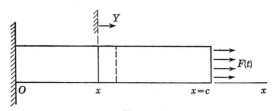

FIG. 44.

at the end $x = c$ (Fig. 44).   If the bar is initially unstrained and at rest, the boundary value problem in the longitudinal displacements $Y(x,t)$ is the following,

$$Y_{tt}(x,t) = a^2 Y_{xx}(x,t) \qquad (0 < x < c, t > 0),$$
$$Y(x,0) = Y_t(x,0) = 0,$$
$$Y(0,t) = 0, \qquad EY_x(c,t) = F(t), \qquad (a^2 = E/\rho).$$

The transform of $Y(x,t)$ therefore satisfies the conditions

$$s^2 y(x,s) = a^2 y_{xx}(x,s),$$
$$y(0,s) = 0, \qquad Ey_x(c,s) = f(s),$$

and the solution of this transformed problem is readily found to be

$$(1) \qquad y(x,s) = \frac{a}{E} f(s) \frac{\sinh (sx/a)}{s \cosh (sc/a)}.$$

Consider first the case of a constant force,

$$(2) \qquad F(t) = F_0.$$

Then

$$(3) \qquad y(x,s) = \frac{aF_0}{E} \frac{\sinh (sx/a)}{s^2 \cosh (sc/a)}$$

and, when $x = c$,

$$y(c,s) = \frac{aF_0}{E} \frac{1}{s^2} \tanh \frac{sc}{a}.$$

In Sec. 19 we found that $s^{-2} \tanh (bs/2)$ is the transform of the triangular wave function $H(b,t)$ of period $2b$ (Fig. 10).   Therefore the displacement of the end $x = c$ is

(4) $$Y(c,t) = \frac{aF_0}{E} H\left(\frac{2c}{a}, t\right);$$

that is, the end moves by jerks as indicated in Fig. 45.

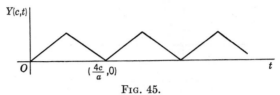

FIG. 45.

To find the displacement of an arbitrary point from formula (3) we may write

$$\frac{\sinh (sx/a)}{\cosh (sc/a)} = \frac{e^{-[(c-x)s]/a} - e^{-[(c+x)s]/a}}{1 + e^{-(2cs/a)}}$$

$$= [e^{-[(c-x)s]/a} - e^{-[(c+x)s]/a}] \sum_{n=0}^{\infty} (-1)^n e^{-(2ncs/a)},$$

since $(1 + z)^{-1} = \sum_{0}^{\infty}(-1)^n z^n$ when $0 < z < 1$. Therefore

$$y(x,s) = \frac{aF_0}{E} \sum_{0}^{\infty} (-1)^n \left\{\frac{1}{s^2} \exp\left[-s\frac{(2n+1)c-x}{a}\right]\right.$$

$$\left. - \frac{1}{s^2} \exp\left[-s\frac{(2n+1)c+x}{a}\right]\right\}.$$

Formally applying the inverse transformation to the terms of the infinite series, we obtain the formula

(5) $$Y(x,t) = \frac{aF_0}{E}\left[\left\{t - \frac{c-x}{a}\right\} - \left\{t - \frac{c+x}{a}\right\}\right.$$

$$- \left\{t - \frac{3c-x}{a}\right\} + \left\{t - \frac{3c+x}{a}\right\} + \left\{t - \frac{5c-x}{a}\right\}$$

$$\left. - \left\{t - \frac{5c+x}{a}\right\} - \cdots\right],$$

where the braces denote the translated function of t:

(6) $$\{t - k\} = (t - k)S_k(t).$$

For any fixed t the series (5) is finite since each of the braces are to be replaced by zero when the quantity inside is negative. The number of nonvanishing terms in the series increases as t increases.

The function (5) can be verified directly as the solution of our problem. Its graph is shown in Fig. 46.

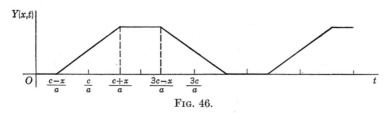

FIG. 46.

Consider now the hypothetical case when the end is given an impulse I at the instant $t = 0$:

(7) $$F(t) = I\delta(t).$$

Then, formally, $f(s) = I$ in formula (1) and

$$Ey(x,s) = aIp(x,s),$$

where

(8) $$p(x,s) = \frac{\sinh (sx/a)}{s \cosh (sc/a)}.$$

The procedure followed above to obtain formula (5) gives the inverse transform of $p(x,s)$ in the form

(9) $$P(x,t) = S_{\frac{c-x}{a}}(t) - S_{\frac{c+x}{a}}(t) - S_{\frac{3c-x}{a}}(t) + S_{\frac{3c+x}{a}}(t) + \cdots$$

and $EY(x,t) = aIP(x,t)$.

The behavior of the end $x = c$ can be seen also by observing that

$$y(c,s) = \frac{aI}{E} \frac{1}{s} \tanh \frac{sc}{a}.$$

The displacement of the end is therefore represented by the square wave function of Sec. 19 (Fig. 9),

(10) $$Y(c,t) = \frac{aI}{E} M \left(\frac{2c}{a}, t\right).$$

Thus the end jumps suddenly back and forth between two fixed positions. It is possible to demonstrate a close approximation to this behavior by substituting for the bar a loosely wound coil spring. If, when the spring is hanging from one end, the free lower end is given a sharp tap, the lower end tends to move as indicated.

In the case of the general forcing function $F(t)$ we can now write equation (1) in terms of the function (8),

$$Ey(x,s) = af(s)p(x,s).$$

Therefore, in terms of the function $P(x,t)$ given by equation (9),

$$(11) \qquad Y(x,t) = \frac{a}{E} \int_0^t F(t - r)P(x,r) \, dr.$$

PROBLEMS

1. A string is stretched between two fixed points $(0,0)$ and $(c,0)$. If it is displaced into the curve $Y = b \sin (\pi x/c)$ and released from rest in that position at time $t = 0$, set up and solve the boundary value problem for the displacements $Y(x,t)$. Verify the result fully and describe the motion of the string.   *Ans.* $Y(x,t) = b \cos (\pi a t/c) \sin (\pi x/c)$.

2. If the initial displacement of the string in Prob. 1 is changed to

$$Y(x,0) = b \sin \frac{n\pi x}{c} \qquad (0 \leqq x \leqq c),$$

where n is any integer, derive the formula

$$Y(x,t) = b \cos \frac{n\pi a t}{c} \cdot \sin \frac{n\pi x}{c}.$$

Note that the sum of two or more of these functions with different values of n and b is a solution of the equation of motion that satisfies all the boundary conditions except one. What is the initial displacement $Y(x,0)$ corresponding to such a superposition of solutions?

3. In Sec. 41, when the force at the end $x = c$ of the bar (Fig. 44) is constant, $F(t) = F_0$, show that the force per unit area exerted by the bar upon the support at the end $x = 0$ is the function shown in Fig. 47. Note that the force becomes twice the applied force during regularly spaced intervals of time.

4. In Sec. 41 (Fig. 44), let the force per unit area on the end $x = c$ be the finite impulse

$$\begin{aligned} F(t) &= F_0 & \text{when } t < 4c/a, \\ &= 0 & \text{when } t > 4c/a. \end{aligned}$$

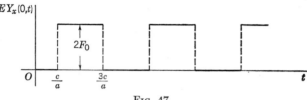

FIG. 47.

Show that the displacement of the end $x = c$ then consists of a single oscillation of duration $t_0 = 4c/a$, namely,

$$Y(c,t) = mt \qquad\qquad (0 \leq t \leq \tfrac{1}{2}t_0),$$
$$= m(t_0 - t) \qquad (\tfrac{1}{2}t_0 \leq t \leq t_0),$$
$$= 0 \qquad\qquad\qquad \text{when } t \geq t_0,$$

where $m = aF_0/E$. Draw the graph of $Y(c,t)$.

5. A constant longitudinal force F_0 per unit area acts upon the end $x = c$ of an elastic bar (Fig. 48). The end $x = 0$ is free, and the bar is initially at rest and unstrained. Set up the boundary value problem for the longitudinal displacements $Y(x,t)$ and find $y(x,s)$.

(*a*) Show that

$$Y_t(0,t) = v_0 \sum_{n=0}^{\infty} S_m(t), \text{ where } m = \frac{c}{a}(2n+1), \quad v_0 = \frac{2aF_0}{E};$$

hence that the end $x = 0$ remains at rest until $t = c/a$, then moves with velocity v_0 until $t = 3c/a$, then with velocity $2v_0$ until $t = 5c/a$, etc.

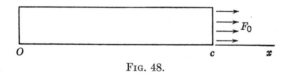

FIG. 48.

(*b*) In terms of the function (6), Sec. 41, show that

$$Y(x,t) = \frac{F_0}{E} \sum_{n=0}^{\infty} [\{at + x - c(2n+1)\} + \{at - x - c(2n+1)\}].$$

6. In Prob. 5, let the force F_0 be replaced by the force

$$F(t) = F_0 \cos \omega t,$$

where $\omega = \pi a/(2c)$. Show that (Sec. 19)

$$\pi EY(c,t) = 2cF_0 \,|\sin \omega t|.$$

7. The end $x = 0$ of a bar or heavy coil spring (Fig. 49) is free. The end $x = c$ is displaced in a prescribed manner, $Y(c,t) = G(t)$. If the bar is initially unstrained and at rest, find the transform $y(x,s)$ of longitudinal displacements.

(a) When $G(t) = F_0 t$, show that the displacement $Y(0,t)$ of the free end is represented by the function obtained by integrating the function $EY_x(0,t)$ in Fig. 47 from 0 to t and show the displacement graphically.

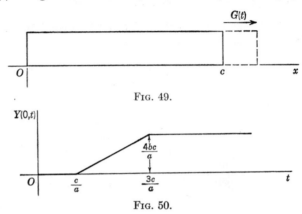

FIG. 49.

FIG. 50.

(b) If $G(t) = bt$ when $t \leqq 4c/a$ and $G(t) = 4bc/a$ when $t \geqq 4c/a$, show that the free end moves with a uniform velocity $2b$ to a new position and remains there, as shown in Fig. 50.

(c) When $G(t)$ is arbitrary, derive the solution

$$Y(x,t) = \sum_{n=0}^{\infty} (-1)^n \{G[t - M_n(-x)] + G[t - M_n(x)]\},$$

where $aM_n(x) = (2n + 1)c + x$, and where $G(t) = 0$ when $t < 0$. Thus the series here is finite for each fixed t.

8. An unstrained elastic bar is moving lengthwise with velocity v_0 when its end $x = c$ is suddenly clamped (Fig. 51). Show that the force on the support at $x = c$ is

$$\frac{v_0 E A}{a} M\left(\frac{2c}{a}, t\right),$$

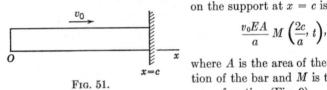

FIG. 51.

where A is the area of the cross section of the bar and M is the square wave function (Fig. 9).

9. A steel bar 10 in. long is moving lengthwise with velocity v_0 when one end strikes a rigid support squarely (Fig. 51). Find the length of time of contact of the end of the bar with the support and note that the time is independent of v_0. For steel take E to be 30×10^6 lb/sq in., and mass per unit volume ρ such that $g\rho = 0.28$ lb/cu in., where $g = 384$ in./sec². (See Prob. 8.) *Ans.* 0.0001 sec.

10. An unstrained cylindrical shaft is rotating with angular velocity ω when its ends $x = \pm c$ are suddenly clamped (Fig. 52). Derive the formula

$$\theta(x,s) = \frac{\omega}{s^2}\left[1 - \frac{\cosh\,(sx/a)}{\cosh\,(sc/a)}\right]$$

for the transform of the angular displacements $\Theta(x,t)$ of the cross sections, where $a^2 = E_s/\rho$ (Sec. 37).

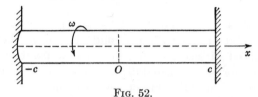

FIG. 52.

(*a*) Show that the displacement of the middle cross section is

$$\Theta(0,t) = \omega t \qquad\qquad \text{when } t \leqq \frac{c}{a},$$
$$= \omega\frac{c}{a} - \omega H\left(\frac{2c}{a}, t - \frac{c}{a}\right) \qquad \text{when } t \geqq \frac{c}{a},$$

where H is the triangular wave function (Fig. 10).

(*b*) Show that the torque acting on the support $x = c$ is

$$\tau(c,t) = \frac{E_s I \omega}{a}\,M\left(\frac{2c}{a}, t\right),$$

where M is the square wave function (Fig. 9).

11. The end $x = 0$ of a cylindrical shaft is kept fixed. The end $x = c$ is rotated through an angle θ_0 and, when all parts have come to rest,

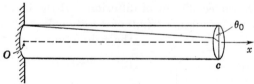

FIG. 53.

this end is released; thus $\Theta = \theta_0 x/c$ when $t = 0$ (Fig. 53). Show that the displacement of the free end at each instant is

$$\Theta(c,t) = \theta_0 - \theta_0\frac{a}{c}\,H\left(\frac{2c}{a}, t\right),$$

where H is the triangular wave function (Fig. 10).

12. An infinite string stretched along the x axis is given a prescribed initial displacement and released from rest in that position. Thus

$$Y_{tt}(x,t) = a^2 Y_{xx}(x,t) \quad (-\infty < x < \infty, t > 0),$$
$$Y(x,0) = \Phi(x), \qquad Y_t(x,0) = 0 \quad (-\infty < x < \infty),$$
$$\lim_{x \to -\infty} Y(x,t) = 0, \qquad \lim_{x \to \infty} Y(x,t) = 0.$$

Derive the formula

$$Y(x,t) = \tfrac{1}{2}[\Phi(x + at) + \Phi(x - at)],$$

and verify this solution.

42. Equations of Diffusion. Let $U(x,y,z,t)$ denote the temperature at a point (x,y,z) within a solid at time t. Let S be a plane or curved surface passed through that point and let the coordinate n represent directed distance along the line normal to S at the point. Then the flux of heat, the quantity of heat per unit area per unit time transferred across S at the point by conduction, is given by the formula

$$(1) \qquad \Phi(x,y,z,t) = -K \frac{d}{dn} U(x,y,z,t),$$

where the coefficient K is the thermal conductivity of the material. The negative sign that appears with this directional derivative of U gives the sense of flow, where positive flux signifies flow in the positive direction of the normal.

Formula (1) is an empirical law or basic postulate for the conduction of heat in solids. It is likewise an empirical law of flux of a substance undergoing simple diffusion into a porous solid if U represents the concentration of the diffusing substance and K the coefficient of diffusion. If the temperature or concentration is a function $U(x,t)$ of x and t only, then the flux in the x direction is

$$(2) \quad \Phi(x,t) = -K U_x(x,t).$$

When the temperature function has the simple form $U(x,t)$, consider a portion of the solid in the shape of a prism parallel to the x axis (Fig. 54). Since there is no temperature variation with respect to distance normal to the lateral surface of the prism, no heat is conducted across that

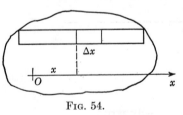

Fig. 54.

surface.   According to formula (2), an element of the prism extending from position x to $x + \Delta x$ receives heat by conduction through its two bases at the rate

$$-AKU_x(x,t) + AKU_x(x + \Delta x, t),$$

where A is the area of the cross section of the prism.   This is the quantity of heat gained by the element per unit time if no heat is generated or lost inside the element.   Another expression for that rate can be written in terms of the coefficient c of *heat capacity per unit volume*, the quantity of heat required to raise the temperature of a unit volume of the material by one degree.   Then when Δx is small $cA \Delta x \, U(x,t)$ is a measure of the instantaneous heat content of the element, and

(3) $cA \Delta x \, U_t(x,t) = A[KU_x(x + \Delta x, t) - KU_x(x,t)].$

If K depends on x, then the first factor K in equation (3) is actually $K(x + \Delta x, t)$ and the second, $K(x,t)$.   When we divide by Δx and let Δx tend to zero, we obtain the partial differential equation

(4) $cU_t (x,t) = [K(x,t)U_x(x,t)]_x.$

When K is either constant or independent of x, the equation becomes

(5) $U_t (x,t) = kU_{xx}(x,t),$

where $k = K/c$ and k is called the thermal diffusivity of the material.   Equation (5) is the simple form of the *heat equation* or the *equation of diffusion*.

When $U(x,t)$ represents the concentration of a diffusing substance in weight per unit volume, equation (3) follows as before if $c = 1$ and K is the coefficient of diffusion.   Thus, when K is constant, $U(x,t)$ satisfies equation (5) where $k = K$.

The heat equation or equation of diffusion for $U(x,y,z,t)$

(6) $U_t = k(U_{xx} + U_{yy} + U_{zz}),$

when coefficients are constant, can be derived in a similar manner by considering a three-dimensional element of volume $\Delta x \, \Delta y \, \Delta z$. Modifications of the equations are easily written.   For example, let $U(x,t)$ represent temperatures in a slender wire along the x axis.   Let heat be generated at a time rate $R(x,t)$ per unit volume of the wire and let heat loss from the lateral surface take place at a rate proportional to the difference between the temperature of the wire and the temperature U_0 of the surroundings. The modification of equation (3) then shows that

$$(7) \qquad U_t(x,t) = kU_{xx}(x,t) + \frac{1}{c} R(x,t) - h[U(x,t) - U_0],$$

where h is a positive coefficient of surface heat transfer.

In our applications we often consider semi-infinite solids, where results are relatively simple. Such bodies are not necessarily large in any absolute sense. In the diffusion of hardening materials into steel, for instance, test bars having a maximum dimension of one inch or less may be represented accurately as semi-infinite solids.

In the problems to follow we assume that the coefficients K, k, etc., are constant.

43. Temperatures in a Semi-infinite Solid. Let us now derive the formula for the temperatures $U(x,t)$ in a semi-infinite solid

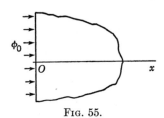

$x \geq 0$, initially at temperature zero, when a constant flux of heat is maintained at the boundary $x = 0$ (Fig. 55). In this idealized case of a thick slab of material, we shall substitute for the thermal condition at the right-hand boundary, the condition that U tends to zero as x tends to in-

Fig. 55.

finity. The boundary value problem is then

$$
\begin{aligned}
(1) \qquad & U_t(x,t) = kU_{xx}(x,t) && (x > 0, \, t > 0), \\
(2) \qquad & U(x,0) = 0 && (x > 0), \\
(3) \qquad & -KU_x(0,t) = \phi_0, \quad \lim_{x \to \infty} U(x,t) = 0 && (t > 0).
\end{aligned}
$$

Let $u(x,s)$ be the transform, with respect to t, of the temperature function $U(x,t)$. Transforming the members of equations (1) and (3), we have the following problem in ordinary differential equations which $u(x,s)$ must satisfy:

$$su(x,s) = ku_{xx}(x,s) \qquad (x > 0),$$

$$-Ku_x(0,s) = \frac{\phi_0}{s}, \quad \lim_{x \to \infty} u(x,s) = 0.$$

The solution of this problem is

$$u(x,s) = \frac{\phi_0 \sqrt{k}}{Ks \sqrt{s}} e^{-x\sqrt{s/k}}.$$

According to formula (5), Sec. 23, we can write

$$L^{-1}\left\{\frac{1}{\sqrt{s}} e^{-x\sqrt{s/k}}\right\} = \frac{1}{\sqrt{\pi t}} e^{-x^2/(4kt)},$$

and in view of the factor $1/s$ in our formula for $u(x,s)$ it follows that

$$U(x,t) = \frac{\phi_0}{K} \sqrt{\frac{k}{\pi}} \int_0^t e^{-x^2/(4k\tau)} \frac{d\tau}{\sqrt{\tau}}$$

$$= \frac{\phi_0 x}{K \sqrt{\pi}} \int_{x/(2\sqrt{kt})}^{\infty} \frac{1}{\lambda^2} e^{-\lambda^2} \, d\lambda,$$

where the second integral is obtained from the first by the substitution $\lambda = x/(2 \sqrt{k\tau})$.   Upon integrating the last integral by parts, we find that

$$U(x,t) = \frac{\phi_0}{K \sqrt{\pi}} \left(2 \sqrt{kt} \, e^{-x^2/(4kt)} - 2x \int_{x/(2\sqrt{kt})}^{\infty} e^{-\lambda^2} \, d\lambda \right).$$

We can therefore write our formula in terms of the complementary error function (Sec. 23) in the form

$$(4) \qquad U(x,t) = \frac{\phi_0}{K}\left[2 \sqrt{\frac{kt}{\pi}} \, e^{-x^2/(4kt)} - x \, \mathrm{erfc}\left(\frac{x}{2 \sqrt{kt}}\right) \right].$$

We can show that the function (4) satisfies all our conditions (1), (2), and (3).   Note, for instance, that

$$U_x(x,t) = \frac{\phi_0}{K}\left[-\frac{x}{\sqrt{\pi kt}} e^{-x^2/(4kt)} - \mathrm{erfc}\left(\frac{x}{2 \sqrt{kt}}\right) + \frac{x}{\sqrt{\pi kt}} e^{-x^2/(4kt)} \right]$$

$$= -\frac{\phi_0}{K} \mathrm{erfc}\left(\frac{x}{2 \sqrt{kt}}\right),$$

and since erfc $0 = 1$ it follows that the first of conditions (3) is satisfied.

Also $\qquad\qquad U_{xx}(x,t) = \frac{\phi_0}{K} \frac{1}{\sqrt{\pi kt}} e^{-x^2/(4kt)},$

and the product of this function by k is the same as $\partial U/\partial t$ found from formula (4). Therefore our function satisfies the heat equation. It is easy to see that the condition (2) in the form $U(x,+0) = 0$ and the second of conditions (3) is satisfied by our function (4).

We observe that

$$U(0,t) = \frac{2\phi_0 \sqrt{k}}{K \sqrt{\pi}} \sqrt{t}.$$

Thus the temperature of the face of the solid must vary as $\sqrt{t}$ in order that the flux of heat through the face shall be constant.

44. The Flux under Variable Surface Temperature. Let the temperature of the face of a semi-infinite solid $x \geq 0$ be a prescribed function $F(t)$ of time. If the initial temperature is zero, the temperature function $U(x,t)$ is the solution of the boundary value problem

$$U_t(x,t) = kU_{xx}(x,t) \qquad (x > 0, t > 0),$$
$$U(x,0) = 0 \qquad (x > 0),$$
$$U(0,t) = F(t), \qquad \lim_{x \to \infty} U(x,t) = 0 \qquad (t > 0).$$

The transform $u(x,s)$ of $U(x,t)$, therefore, satisfies the conditions

$$su(x,s) = ku_{xx}(x,s) \qquad (x > 0),$$
$$u(0,s) = f(s), \qquad \lim_{x \to \infty} u(x,s) = 0,$$

where $f(s)$ is the transform of $F(t)$. It follows that

(1) $$u(x,s) = f(s)\, e^{-x\sqrt{s/k}}.$$

Let us first study the flux of heat through the face of the solid,

$$\Phi(t) = -KU_x(0,t).$$

The transform of this function, $-Ku_x(0,s)$, according to formula (1), is

(2) $$\varphi(s) = \frac{K}{\sqrt{k}} \sqrt{s}\, f(s) = \frac{K}{\sqrt{k}}\, sf(s)\, \frac{1}{\sqrt{s}}.$$

Since $s^{-\frac{1}{2}} = L\{(\pi t)^{-\frac{1}{2}}\}$ and $sf(s) = L\{F'(t)\} + F(+0)$, assuming that $F(t)$ is a continuous function, then

$$\varphi(s) = \frac{K}{\sqrt{k}} \left[\frac{F(+0)}{\sqrt{s}} + L\{F'(t)\}\, \frac{1}{\sqrt{s}} \right]$$

and with the aid of the convolution it follows that

$$(3) \qquad \Phi(t) = \frac{K}{\sqrt{\pi k}} \left[\frac{F(+0)}{\sqrt{t}} + \int_0^t \frac{F'(t-\tau)}{\sqrt{\tau}} \, d\tau \right],$$

when $F(t)$ is continuous.

Whenever $F(+0) \neq 0$, then the flux is infinite initially; in fact it is of the order of $t^{-\frac{1}{2}}$ as t approaches zero. When $F(t)$ is a constant F_0, for example,

$$\Phi(t) = \frac{KF_0}{\sqrt{\pi k}} \frac{1}{\sqrt{t}}.$$

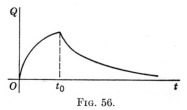

Fig. 56.

The total amount of heat that has been absorbed by the solid through a unit area of the face at time t is

$$Q(t) = \int_0^t \Phi(\tau) \, d\tau.$$

Hence

$$q(s) = \frac{1}{s} \varphi(s) = \frac{K}{\sqrt{k}} \frac{1}{\sqrt{s}} f(s),$$

and therefore

$$(4) \qquad Q(t) = \frac{K}{\sqrt{\pi k}} \int_0^t \frac{F(\tau)}{\sqrt{t-\tau}} \, d\tau = \frac{K}{\sqrt{\pi k}} \int_0^t \frac{F(t-\tau)}{\sqrt{\tau}} \, d\tau.$$

For example, if

$$(5) \qquad\qquad F(t) = F_0 \qquad\qquad \text{when } t < t_0,$$
$$= 0 \qquad\qquad \text{when } t > t_0,$$

it follows from formula (4) that

$$(6) \qquad\qquad Q(t) = \frac{2KF_0}{\sqrt{\pi k}} \sqrt{t} \qquad\qquad \text{when } t \leq t_0,$$
$$= \frac{2KF_0}{\sqrt{\pi k}} (\sqrt{t} - \sqrt{t - t_0}) \qquad \text{when } t \geq t_0.$$

This function is shown in Fig. 56. Its greatest value is

$$2KF_0 \sqrt{t_0/(\pi k)},$$

which is assumed at the instant $t = t_0$.

Returning to formula (1) for $u(x,s)$ and noting that, according to formula (4) of Sec. 23,

$$e^{-x\sqrt{s/k}} = L \left\{ \frac{x}{2 \sqrt{\pi k t^3}} e^{-x^2/(4kt)} \right\},$$

we can write, with the aid of the convolution,

$$U(x,t) = \frac{x}{2 \sqrt{\pi k}} \int_0^t \frac{F(t - \tau)}{\tau^{\frac{3}{2}}} e^{-x^2/(4k\tau)} \, d\tau.$$

Substituting a new variable of integration, we have for the general temperature formula

(7) $$U(x,t) = \frac{2}{\sqrt{\pi}} \int_{\frac{1}{2}x/\sqrt{kt}}^{\infty} F\left(t - \frac{x^2}{4k\lambda^2}\right) e^{-\lambda^2} \, d\lambda.$$

When the temperature of the surface is constant,

(8) $$F(t) = F_0,$$

the temperature within the solid is therefore

(9) $$U(x,t) = F_0 \operatorname{erfc}\left(\frac{x}{2 \sqrt{kt}}\right).$$

Since this is a function of F_0 and $x/\sqrt{kt}$ only, it follows that the rapidity of heating is proportional to k; for if k is increased and t decreased so that kt is unchanged, the temperature at any given distance x from the face is the same. It is also interesting to note that for a fixed k two points x_1 and x_2 will have equal temperatures at times t_1 and t_2 provided $x_1/\sqrt{t_1} = x_2/\sqrt{t_2}$, that is, if

$$\frac{x_1}{x_2} = \sqrt{\frac{t_1}{t_2}}.$$

This is sometimes called the law of times in the conduction of heat in semi-infinite solids.

If F_0 is positive, formula (9) assigns a positive value to $U(x,t)$ for each x and t because the complementary error function has only positive values. At any given interior point of the solid $U(x,t)$ is small when t is small; but $U(x,t)$ does not keep its initial value of zero during any interval of time after $t = 0$.

PROBLEMS

⊢**1.** The initial temperature of a semi-infinite solid $x \geq 0$ is zero. The surface temperature is the step function

$$U(0,t) = F_0 \qquad \text{when } 0 < t < t_0,$$
$$= 0 \qquad \text{when } t > t_0.$$

Obtain the temperature distribution formula

$$U(x,t) = F_0 \operatorname{erfc} \frac{x}{2\sqrt{kt}} \qquad (t \leq t_0)$$

$$= F_0 \left[\operatorname{erf} \frac{x}{2\sqrt{k(t - t_0)}} - \operatorname{erf} \frac{x}{2\sqrt{kt}} \right] \qquad (t \geq t_0).$$

2. A thick slab of iron with thermal diffusivity $k = 0.15$ cgs (centimeter-gram-second) unit is initially at $0°C$ throughout. Its surface is suddenly heated to a temperature of $500°C$ and maintained at that temperature for 5 min, after which the surface is kept chilled to $0°C$. (See Prob. 1.) Find the temperature to the nearest degree at a depth of 10 cm below the surface (a) at the end of 5 min; (b) at the end of 10 min. *Ans.* (a) $146°C$; (b) $82°C$.

3. Solve Prob. 2 if the slab is made of firebrick with diffusivity $k = 0.007$ cgs unit. *Ans.* (a) $0°C$; (b) $0°C$.

4. The surface of a thick slab of concrete for which $k = 0.005$ cgs unit, initially at $0°C$, undergoes temperature changes described in Prob. 2. Show that at each instant the temperature at any depth x_1 in the concrete slab is the same as the temperature at the depth $x_2 = \sqrt{30}\, x_1$ in the iron slab. Generalize this result for materials with diffusivities k_1 and k_2 and any common time interval t_0 of heating the surfaces of the slabs.

5. At time $t = 0$, the brakes of an automobile are applied, bringing the automobile to a stop at time t_0. Assuming that the rate of generating heat at the surface of the brake bands varies linearly with the time, then

$$U_x(0,t) = A(t - t_0),$$

where A is a positive constant and x is the distance from the face of the band. If t_0 is not large, the band can be assumed to be a semi-infinite solid $x \geq 0$. If the initial temperature of the band is taken as zero, show that the temperature at the face is

$$U(0,t) = \frac{2A}{3} \sqrt{\frac{k}{\pi}} \sqrt{t}\, (3t_0 - 2t) \qquad (0 \leq t \leq t_0).$$

Hence show that this temperature is greatest at the instant $t = \frac{1}{2}t_0$ and that this maximum temperature is $\sqrt{2}\, U(0,t_0)$.

6. The initial temperature of a semi-infinite solid $x \geqq 0$ is zero. The inward flux of heat through the face $x = 0$ is a prescribed function $\Phi(t)$ of time and the distant face is kept at temperature zero. Derive the temperature formula

$$U(x,t) = \frac{x}{K\sqrt{\pi}} \int_{\frac{1}{2}x/\sqrt{kt}}^{\infty} \Phi\left(t - \frac{x^2}{4k\lambda^2}\right) \frac{e^{-\lambda^2}}{\lambda^2} d\lambda \qquad (x > 0).$$

Also show that the temperature of the face must be

$$U(0,t) = \frac{1}{K}\sqrt{\frac{k}{\pi}} \int_0^t \Phi(\tau)(t - \tau)^{-\frac{1}{2}} d\tau.$$

7. Let an impulse of heat of quantity Q_0 per unit area be introduced through the face of the solid in Prob. 6 at the instant $t = 0$ and let the face be insulated when $t > 0$, so that $\Phi(t) = Q_0\delta(t)$. Such instantaneous surface heat sources may be realized approximately in burning a layer of highly combustible fuel at the surface. Show formally that the resulting temperatures in the solid are represented by the function

$$U(x,t) = \frac{Q_0}{K}\sqrt{\frac{k}{\pi t}} \, e^{-x^2/(4kt)} \qquad (k = K/c).$$

Verify that this function satisfies the heat equation, the initial condition when $x > 0$ and the end conditions when $t > 0$, and the condition that the total heat content of the solid per unit area of face, $\int_0^{\infty} cU(x,t) \, dx$ relative to the initial heat content, is Q_0. Also observe that $U(x,t) > 0$ whenever $t > 0$, although $U(x,t)$ is very small when t is small and x large.

8. For any solid whose temperatures $U(x,t)$ depend on x and t only, show that the total quantity of heat that passes through a unit area of a plane perpendicular to the x axis is

$$Q(x) = -K \int_0^{\infty} U_x(x,t) \, dt = -K \lim_{s \to 0} u_x(x,s)$$

formally. For the solid in Sec. 44 show that the formal result is

$$Q(x) = \frac{K}{\sqrt{k}} \lim_{s \to 0} \sqrt{s} \, f(s).$$

9. The initial temperature of a semi-infinite solid $x \geqq 0$ is

$$U(x,0) = U_0(x),$$

where the function $U_0(x)$ is prescribed. If the face $x = 0$ is kept at temperature zero $(t > 0)$ and if $U_x(x,t)$ approaches zero as $x \to \infty$, derive the formula

$$U(x,t) = \frac{1}{2\sqrt{\pi kt}} \int_0^{\infty} U_0(\xi)[e^{-(\xi-x)^2/(4kt)} - e^{-(\xi+x)^2/(4kt)}] \, d\xi \qquad (t > 0).$$

10. Show that the sum of the temperature function found in Prob. 9 and of the function (7) of Sec. 44 represents the temperature in the solid $x \geqq 0$ when the temperature of the face is $F(t)$ and the initial temperature is $U_0(x)$.

45. Temperatures in a Slab. The initial temperature of a slab of homogeneous material bounded by the planes $x = 0$ and $x = l$ is u_0. Let us find the formula for the temperatures in this solid after the face $x = 0$ is insulated and the temperature of the face $x = l$ is reduced to zero (Fig. 57).

The temperature function $U(x,t)$ satisfies the following conditions

$$U_t(x,t) = kU_{xx}(x,t) \qquad (0 < x < l, t > 0),$$
$$U(x,0) = u_0 \qquad\qquad (0 < x < l),$$
$$U_x(0,t) = 0, \qquad U(l,t) = 0 \qquad (t > 0).$$

The transform therefore satisfies the conditions

(1) $su(x,s) - u_0 = ku_{xx}(x,s),$

(2) $u_x(0,s) = 0, \qquad u(l,s) = 0.$

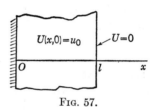

Fig. 57.

The solution of the ordinary differential equation (1) that satisfies the first of the conditions (2) is

$$u(x,s) = \frac{u_0}{s} + C \cosh x \sqrt{\frac{s}{k}},$$

where C is determined by the second of conditions (2). Thus

(3) $$u(x,s) = u_0 \left[\frac{1}{s} - \frac{1}{s} \frac{\cosh x \sqrt{s/k}}{\cosh l \sqrt{s/k}} \right].$$

Let us write $$q = \sqrt{\frac{s}{k}},$$

and note that

$$\frac{\cosh xq}{\cosh lq} = e^{-lq}(e^{xq} + e^{-xq}) \frac{1}{1 + e^{-2lq}}$$

$$= [e^{-(l-x)q} + e^{-(l+x)q}] \sum_0^\infty (-1)^n e^{-2nlq}$$

$$= \sum_{n=0}^\infty (-1)^n \{\exp[-q(ml - x)] + \exp[-q(ml + x)]\},$$

where $m = 2n + 1$. We have seen (Sec. 23) that

$$\frac{1}{s} e^{-\alpha \sqrt{s}} = L \left\{ \operatorname{erfc} \left(\frac{\alpha}{2 \sqrt{t}} \right) \right\} \qquad (\alpha \geq 0).$$

Therefore it follows formally from equation (3) that

$$(4) \quad U(x,t) = u_0 - u_0 \sum_{n=0}^{\infty} (-1)^n \left\{ \operatorname{erfc} \left[\frac{(2n + 1)l - x}{2 \sqrt{kt}} \right] \right.$$
$$\left. + \operatorname{erfc} \left[\frac{(2n + 1)l + x}{2 \sqrt{kt}} \right] \right\}.$$

We shall not take up the verification of this formula since a complete discussion would be lengthy. However, it is not difficult to show with the aid of the ratio test that the series converges uniformly with respect to x and t and that the series can be differentiated term by term. Since the value of the complementary error function here decreases rapidly as n increases, the convergence of the series is rapid, especially when t is small. Moreover the error function is one that is tabulated so that the series is well adapted to computation.

46. A Bar with Variable End Temperature. Let us determine the formula for the temperature $U(x,t)$ in a bar with its lateral surface insulated against the flow of heat when the initial temperature is zero and one end is kept at temperature zero while the temperature of the other end is a prescribed function of t.

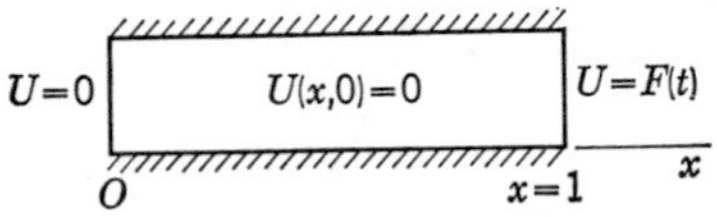

FIG. 58.

If we take the unit of length as the length of the bar (Fig. 58) and select the unit of time such that $(1/k) \partial U/\partial t'$ becomes $\partial U/\partial t$, that is, so that $t = kt'$ where t' is the original and t the new variable, our boundary value problem can be written as follows.

$$U_t(x,t) = U_{xx}(x,t) \qquad (0 < x < 1, t > 0),$$
$$U(x,0) = 0 \qquad (0 < x < 1),$$
$$U(0,t) = 0, \qquad U(1,t) = F(t) \qquad (t > 0).$$

The solution of the transformed problem is found to be

$$u(x,s) = f(s) \frac{\sinh x \sqrt{s}}{\sinh \sqrt{s}}.$$

Proceeding as in the last section, and using the convolution, we find that

$$(1) \quad U(x,t) = \frac{2}{\sqrt{\pi}} \sum_{n=0}^{\infty} \left\{ \int_{\frac{1}{2}(m-x)/\sqrt{t}}^{\infty} F\left[t - \frac{(m-x)^2}{4\lambda^2}\right] e^{-\lambda^2} d\lambda \right.$$

$$\left. - \int_{\frac{1}{2}(m+x)/\sqrt{t}}^{\infty} F\left[t - \frac{(m+x)^2}{4\lambda^2}\right] e^{-\lambda^2} d\lambda \right\} \quad (m = 2n+1).$$

When the temperature of the face $x = 1$ is constant,

$$(2) \qquad\qquad\qquad F(t) = F_0,$$

our formula can be written

$$(3) \quad U(x,t) = F_0 \sum_0^{\infty} \left[\operatorname{erf}\left(\frac{2n+1+x}{2\sqrt{t}}\right) - \operatorname{erf}\left(\frac{2n+1-x}{2\sqrt{t}}\right) \right].$$

Details are left to the problems.

47. A Cooling Fin or Evaporation Plate. A thin semi-infinite plate occupies the space $x \geq 0$, $0 \leq z \leq z_0$, $-\infty < y < \infty$. Heat transfer takes place at the faces $z = 0$ and $z = z_0$, into a medium at temperature zero, according to the linear law of surface heat transfer (Sec. 42); but the thickness z_0 of the plate

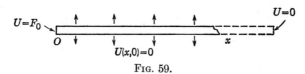

FIG. 59.

is small enough that variations of temperature with z can be neglected. If the initial temperature is zero and the end $x = 0$ is kept at temperature F_0 (Fig. 59), the boundary value problem for the temperature function becomes

$$(1) \quad \begin{array}{c} U_t(x,t) = k U_{xx}(x,t) - h U(x,t) \quad (x > 0, \, t > 0), \\ U(x,0) = 0, \qquad U(0,t) = F_0, \qquad \lim_{x \to \infty} U(x,t) = 0. \end{array}$$

Here $U(x,t)$ may also represent the concentration of moisture in the plate when the plate is initially dry and evaporation takes place into a dry medium, if the concentration at the end $x = 0$ is a constant F_0. In this case $k = K$, the coefficient of diffusion (Sec. 42), and the positive constant h is a coefficient of evaporation.

In terms of transforms, our problem (1) becomes

$$ku_{xx}(x,s) - (s + h)u(x,s) = 0 \qquad (x > 0),$$

$$u(0,s) = \frac{F_0}{s}, \qquad \lim_{x \to \infty} u(x,s) = 0.$$

The solution of this problem is

(2) $$u(x,s) = \frac{F_0}{s} e^{-x\sqrt{(s+h)/k}}.$$

Knowing the inverse transform of $e^{-x\sqrt{s/k}}$ we can write, with the aid of our property on substitution of $s + h$ for s (Sec. 7),

$$L^{-1}\{e^{-x\sqrt{(s+h)/k}}\} = \frac{xe^{-ht}}{2\sqrt{\pi k t^3}} e^{-x^2/(4kt)}.$$

It follows from formula (2) that

$$U(x,t) = \frac{F_0 x}{2\sqrt{\pi k}} \int_0^t e^{-h\tau} e^{-x^2/(4k\tau)} \tau^{-\frac{3}{2}} d\tau$$

(3) $$= \frac{2F_0}{\sqrt{\pi}} \int_{\frac{1}{2}x/\sqrt{kt}}^\infty \exp\left(-\lambda^2 - \frac{hx^2}{4k\lambda^2}\right) d\lambda,$$

where the second integral is obtained by the substitution $\lambda = \frac{1}{2}x/\sqrt{k\tau}$.

The formula (3) can be changed to a more useful form with the aid of the integration formula

(4) $$\frac{4}{\sqrt{\pi}} \int_r^\infty \exp\left(-\lambda^2 - \frac{a^2}{\lambda^2}\right) d\lambda = e^{2a} \operatorname{erfc}\left(r + \frac{a}{r}\right)$$

$$+ e^{-2a} \operatorname{erfc}\left(r - \frac{a}{r}\right).$$

This formula can be verified by noting that its two members have the same derivative with respect to the parameter r and that both members vanish as r tends to infinity. With the aid of formula (4) the solution (3) of our problem becomes

(5) $$U(x,t) = \frac{F_0}{2}\left[e^{bx} \operatorname{erfc}\left(\frac{x}{2\sqrt{kt}} + \sqrt{ht}\right)\right.$$

$$\left. + e^{-bx} \operatorname{erfc}\left(\frac{x}{2\sqrt{kt}} - \sqrt{ht}\right)\right],$$

where $b = \sqrt{h/k}$. Note that $U(x,t) > 0$ for each x whenever $t > 0$, if $F_0 > 0$.

In obtaining equation (5) we have found a desirable form of the inverse transform of the function (2). The verification of our formal solution of problem (1) is left to the problems.

48. Temperatures in a Composite Solid. Let us write the formula for temperatures $U(x,t)$ in a solid $x \geqq 0$, composed of a layer $0 < x < a$ of material initially at uniform temperature A in perfect thermal contact with a semi-infinite solid $x > a$ of another material initially at temperature zero, when the face $x = 0$ is kept insulated (Fig. 60).

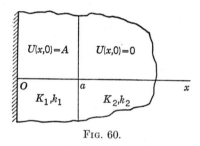

FIG. 60.

If the thermal conductivity and diffusivity are K_1 and k_1, respectively, in the first part and K_2 and k_2 in the second part, the boundary value problem is the following one:

(1) $$U_t(x,t) = k_1 U_{xx}(x,t) \quad (0 < x < a, t > 0),$$
(2) $$U_t(x,t) = k_2 U_{xx}(x,t) \quad (x > a, t > 0),$$
(3) $$U(x,0) = A (0 < x < a), \quad U(x,0) = 0 \quad (x > a),$$
(4) $$U_x(0,t) = 0, \quad \lim_{x \to \infty} U(x,t) = 0 \quad (t > 0),$$
(5) $$U(a - 0, t) = U(a + 0, t) \quad (t > 0),$$
(6) $$K_1 U_x(a - 0, t) = K_2 U_x(a + 0, t) \quad (t > 0).$$

Condition (5) states that the temperature at the interface $x = a$ is the same after $t = 0$ when the point approaches the interface from either direction. Condition (6) states that the flux of heat out of the first part through the interface must be equal to the flux into the second part, at each instant.

The problem in the transform of $U(x,t)$ is then

(7) $$su(x,s) - A = k_1 u_{xx}(x,s) \quad (0 < x < a),$$
(8) $$su(x,s) = k_2 u_{xx}(x,s) \quad (x > a),$$

(9)
$$u_x(0,s) = 0, \qquad \lim_{x \to \infty} u(x,s) = 0,$$

(10)
$$u(a - 0, s) = u(a + 0, s),$$
$$K_1 u_x(a - 0, s) = K_2 u_x(a + 0, s).$$

The solution of equation (7) that satisfies the first of conditions (9) is

$$u(x,s) = C_1 \cosh x \sqrt{\frac{s}{k_1}} + \frac{A}{s} \qquad (0 \le x < a),$$

and the solution of (8) that satisfies the second of conditions (9) is

$$u(x,s) = C_2 e^{-x\sqrt{s/k_2}} \qquad (x > a).$$

By applying the conditions (10) to these functions, the values of C_1 and C_2 are easily found. The formulas for $u(x,s)$ can then be written

(11) $$u(x,s) = \frac{A}{s} \left[1 - \frac{1 - \lambda}{2} \frac{e^{-\sigma(a-x)} + e^{-\sigma(a+x)}}{1 - \lambda e^{-2\sigma a}} \right] \qquad (0 < x < a),$$

(12) $$u(x,s) = \frac{A(1 + \lambda)}{2s} \frac{e^{-\sigma\mu(x-a)} - e^{-\sigma(2a+\mu x-\mu a)}}{1 - \lambda e^{-2\sigma a}} \qquad (x > a),$$

where

$$\sigma = \sqrt{\frac{s}{k_1}}, \qquad \mu = \sqrt{\frac{k_1}{k_2}}, \qquad \lambda = \frac{K_1 \sqrt{k_2} - K_2 \sqrt{k_1}}{K_1 \sqrt{k_2} + K_2 \sqrt{k_1}},$$

and therefore $\sigma\mu = \sqrt{s/k_2}$ and $|\lambda| < 1$.

Equation (11) can be written in the form

$$\frac{u(x,s)}{A} = \frac{1}{s} - \frac{1 - \lambda}{2} \sum_{n=0}^{\infty} \frac{\lambda^n}{s} [e^{-\sigma(ma-x)} + e^{-\sigma(ma+x)}] \qquad (0 < x < a),$$

where $m = 2n + 1$, and (12) can be written

$$\frac{u(x,s)}{A} = \frac{1 + \lambda}{2} \sum_{n=0}^{\infty} \frac{\lambda^n}{s} [e^{-\sigma(2na+\mu x-\mu a)} - e^{-\sigma(2na+2a+\mu x-\mu a)}] \qquad (x > a).$$

It therefore follows that

(13) $$U(x,t) = A - A \frac{1 - \lambda}{2} \sum_{0}^{\infty} \lambda^n \left\{ \text{erfc} \left[\frac{(2n + 1)a - x}{2\sqrt{k_1 t}} \right] \right.$$
$$\left. + \text{erfc} \left[\frac{(2n + 1)a + x}{2\sqrt{k_1 t}} \right] \right\} \qquad (0 < x < a),$$

$$(14) \quad U(x,t) = A \frac{1 + \lambda}{2} \sum_{0}^{\infty} \lambda^n \left\{ \operatorname{erfc} \left[\frac{2na + \mu(x - a)}{2 \sqrt{k_1 t}} \right] \right.$$
$$\left. - \operatorname{erfc} \left[\frac{(2n + 2)a + \mu(x - a)}{2 \sqrt{k_1 t}} \right] \right\} \quad (x > a).$$

From these formulas we can see that as $t \to \infty$, $U(x,t) \to 0$ in both parts of the solid.   Thus if $U(x,t)$ is interpreted as the concentration of a diffusing substance in a composite porous medium, so that K_1 and K_2 are the coefficients of diffusion and $k_1 = K_1$ and $k_2 = K_2$, then the equilibrium concentrations here are equal.   The equilibrium concentrations in adjacent layers of different materials generally have some ratio α, where $\alpha \neq 1$, in which case the interface condition (5) is replaced by the condition

$$(15) \qquad U(a + 0, t) = \alpha U(a - 0, t).$$

PROBLEMS

1. Complete the derivation of formula (1), Sec. 46.

2. When $x = 1$, show that the general term of the series in formula (3), Sec. 46, becomes

$$\frac{2}{\sqrt{\pi}} \int_{n/\sqrt{t}}^{(n+1)/\sqrt{t}} e^{-\lambda^2} \, d\lambda,$$

and hence that $U(1,t) = F_0$.

3. In Sec. 47, verify the solution (5) of problem (1).

4. In the problem (1) of Sec. 47, show that the flux into the plate at the end $x = 0$ is given by the formula

$$\Phi(0,t) = KF_0 \left(\frac{1}{\sqrt{\pi k t}} e^{-ht} + \sqrt{\frac{h}{k}} \operatorname{erf} \sqrt{ht} \right).$$

5. In the problem (1) of Sec. 47, make the substitution

$$V(x,t) = e^{ht} U(x,t)$$

and show that the resulting problem in $V(x,t)$ is a special case of one solved in Sec. 44.

6. The faces $x = 0$ and $x = 1$ of a slab of material for which $k = 1$ are kept at temperatures $U = 0$ and $U = 1$ respectively until the temperature distribution becomes $U = x$.   After time $t = 0$ both faces are held at temperature $U = 0$.   Derive the temperature formula

$$U(x,t) = x - \sum_{n=0}^{\infty} \left(\mathrm{erfc}\, \frac{2n + 1 - x}{2\sqrt{t}} - \mathrm{erfc}\, \frac{2n + 1 + x}{2\sqrt{t}} \right) \qquad (t > 0).$$

7. In Prob. 6, let the face $x = 1$ be insulated when $t > 0$ while $U = 0$ as before at the face $x = 0$.   Find the flux of heat outward through the

face $x = 0$.   *Ans.* $K \left[1 - 2 \sum_{n=0}^{\infty} (-1)^n \, \mathrm{erfc}\, \frac{2n + 1}{2\sqrt{t}} \right].$

8. Heat is generated in a long bar $x \geqq 0$ at a rate $R(t)$ units per unit volume [Sec. 42, equation (7)], and the lateral surface of the bar is

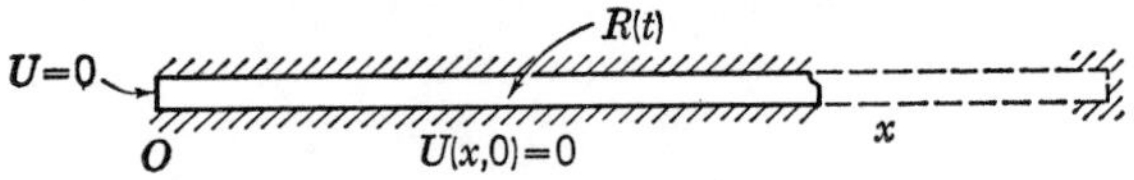

Fig. 61.

insulated.   If the initial temperature is zero and the end $x = 0$ is kept at that temperature while the infinite end is insulated (Fig. 61), derive the temperature formula

$$U(x,t) = Q(t) - \frac{2}{\sqrt{\pi}} \int_{\frac{1}{2}x/\sqrt{kt}}^{\infty} Q\left(t - \frac{x^2}{4k\lambda^2} \right) e^{-\lambda^2} \, d\lambda,$$

where $$Q(t) = \frac{1}{c} \int_0^t R(\tau) \, d\tau.$$

9. In Prob. 8, let the rate of generation of heat be a constant B and show that

$$U(x,t) = \frac{B}{c} \int_0^t \mathrm{erf}\, \frac{x}{2\sqrt{k\tau}} \, d\tau.$$

10. The lateral surface of a bar of unit length is insulated while its ends $x = 0$ and $x = 1$ are kept at temperature zero.   Heat is generated throughout the bar at a constant rate of B units per unit volume.   If the initial temperature is $B(x - x^2)/(2K)$, derive the temperature formula

$$U(x,t) = \frac{B}{2K} (x - x^2).$$

11. Units of time and distance are chosen so that $k = 1$ and a given bar has unit length.   The lateral surface and the end $x = 0$ are insulated.   The initial temperature of the bar is zero and the end $x = 1$ is kept at that temperature.   If heat is generated throughout the bar at a rate of $R(t)$ units per unit volume, derive the temperature formula

$$cU(x,t) = \int_0^t R(\tau)\, d\tau - \int_0^t R(t - \tau) E(x,\tau)\, d\tau,$$

where

$$E(x,t) = \sum_0^\infty (-1)^n \left[\operatorname{erfc} \left(\frac{2n + 1 + x}{2 \sqrt{t}} \right) + \operatorname{erfc} \left(\frac{2n + 1 - x}{2 \sqrt{t}} \right) \right].$$

12. Let the semi-infinite evaporation plate (Sec. 47, Fig. 59) have a uniform initial concentration of moisture $U(x,0) = u_0$, and let the end $x = 0$ be kept dry, $U(0,t) = 0$, while the infinite end is impervious to moisture.   Derive this formula for the concentration:

$$U(x,t) = u_0 e^{-ht} \operatorname{erf} \frac{x}{2 \sqrt{Kt}}.$$

13. A long radiating wire $(x \geqq 0)$ contains a constant source of heat so that the heat equation has the form (Sec. 42)

$$V_t(x,t) = k V_{xx}(x,t) - h V(x,t) + F_0 \quad (x > 0,\, t > 0).$$

If the initial temperature $V(x,0)$ is zero and if the end $x = 0$ is kept at that temperature while the distant end is insulated, derive the temperature formula

$$hV(x,t) = F_0 \left(1 - e^{-ht} \operatorname{erf} \frac{x}{2 \sqrt{kt}} \right) - U(x,t),$$

where $U(x,t)$ is given by formula (5), Sec. 47.

14. The entire surface of a long porous cylinder is impervious to moisture.   The cylinder consists of two semi-infinite parts, the first

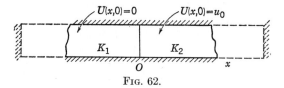

FIG. 62.

$(-\infty < x < 0)$ of material with a coefficient of diffusion of moisture K_1, and the second $(0 < x < \infty)$ with coefficient K_2 (Fig. 62).   Initially, the concentration of moisture is zero in the part $x < 0$ and u_0 in the part $x > 0$.   Let α be the ratio of equilibrium concentrations in the two parts so that, as indicated in Sec. 48, the concentration $U(x,t)$ satisfies the conditions

$$U(+0,t) = \alpha U(-0,t), \qquad K_2 U_x(+0,t) = K_1 U_x(-0,t)$$

at the interface $x = 0$.   Derive the formula

$$U(x,t) = \frac{u_0}{\alpha + \beta}\, \mathrm{erfc}\left(\frac{-x}{2\,\sqrt{K_1 t}}\right) \qquad \text{when } x < 0,$$

$$= \frac{u_0}{\alpha + \beta}\left(\alpha + \beta\, \mathrm{erf}\, \frac{x}{2\,\sqrt{K_2 t}}\right) \qquad \text{when } x > 0,$$

where $\beta = \sqrt{K_1/K_2}$. Show that the ratio of the limiting concentrations, as $t \to \infty$, in the two parts is α.

49. Observations on the Method.   All the problems treated in this chapter involve partial differential equations and boundary conditions that are *linear*, that is, of first degree in the unknown function and its derivatives.   The limitation of our operational method to the treatment of such linear boundary value problems is a natural one, since we have presented no formula giving the Laplace transform of the product of two functions in terms of the transforms of the individual functions.   It is known that the transform of the product of two arbitrary functions can be expressed by a convolution integral of the two transforms, where the integration is one in the complex plane of s.   But it is safe to say that no advantage can be anticipated in replacing nonlinear differential forms by complex nonlinear integral forms.

We have solved problems with constant coefficients.   If the coefficients are functions of t, the variable with respect to which the transformation is made, the transformed problem is not likely to be simpler than the original one.   For even when the coefficients are polynomials in t, the transformed problem involves derivatives with respect to s in place of the derivatives with respect to t present in the original one.   If the coefficients are not functions of t, the transformed problem will be simpler.

We have made the transformation with respect to time t in all our problems in partial differential equations.   If the physical problem involved the first derivative U_t, the initial value $U(x,0)$ was prescribed; if it involved Y_{tt}, then $Y(x,0)$ and $Y_t(x,0)$ were both prescribed.   Consequently, when we applied the formula for the transformation of these derivatives, $u(x,s)$ or $y(x,s)$ was the only unknown function arising.   But suppose the transformation with respect to x had been applied in the temperature problems.   Then if $L\{U(x,t)\} = u(z,t)$,

$$L\{U_{xx}(x,t)\} = z^2 u(z,t) - z U(0,t) - U_x(0,t),$$

and not both of the functions $U(0,t)$ and $U_x(0,t)$ could be prescribed, since both the temperature and the flux of heat at the surface $x = 0$ cannot be prescribed. Thus one of these unknown functions must be determined with the aid of other boundary conditions, and the procedure becomes unwieldy.

In case there are more than two independent variables, say x, y, and t, a transformation of the equation with respect to t still leaves us with a partial differential equation in the independent variables x and y. This may be attacked by one of the classical methods, such as the method of separation of variables, by one of the Fourier transformations or other transformations with respect to x or y, or by a Laplace transformation with respect to x or y. The choice should depend on the particular problem, as we shall see in the final chapter. As the problems in the present chapter have indicated, transformation methods help to show whether the number and type of boundary conditions used with a given partial differential equation are adequate to determine a unique solution of the boundary value problem.

The operational method of solving partial differential equations is of course not limited to equations of the second order. We shall soon take up a more powerful method of obtaining inverse transforms, and then we can attack problems whose solutions depend upon more involved inverse transformations than those in this chapter.

Finally, it is worth noting that the operational method is well adapted to the solution of problems in differential equations in which some of the given functions or their derivatives are discontinuous. This has been illustrated in the last two chapters. It is one of the remarkable features of the method.

CHAPTER 5

FUNCTIONS OF A COMPLEX VARIABLE

For the reader's convenience, we present in this chapter a synopsis of some important definitions and theorems that are needed in the further development of the theory of the Laplace transformation. For a more extensive study of these topics and for proofs of the theorems, the reader may refer to books on the theory of functions of a complex variable.[1]

50. Complex Numbers. A complex number z is an ordered pair of real numbers x, y that satisfies certain rules of operation specified below. It is written in either of the forms

$$z = x + iy = x + yi,$$

where i is the imaginary unit. As these forms suggest, z reduces to the real number x when $y = 0$, and to the imaginary unit i when $x = 0$ and $y = 1$. The real part x and the coefficient y of the imaginary part of z are written

$$\Re(z) = x, \qquad \Im(z) = y.$$

The first rule of operation is this: two complex numbers

$$z_1 = x_1 + iy_1, \qquad z_2 = x_2 + iy_2$$

are equal if and only if $x_1 = x_2$ and $y_1 = y_2$. In particular, $z = 0$ implies that $x = y = 0$. Further rules define the operations of addition, subtraction, multiplication, and division of complex numbers:

$$(x_1 + iy_1) \pm (x_2 + iy_2) = (x_1 \pm x_2) + i(y_1 \pm y_2),$$
$$(x_1 + iy_1)(x_2 + iy_2) = (x_1x_2 - y_1y_2) + i(x_1y_2 + x_2y_1),$$
$$\frac{x_1 + iy_1}{x_2 + iy_2} = \frac{(x_1 + iy_1)(x_2 - iy_2)}{x_2{}^2 + y_2{}^2} = \frac{x_1x_2 + y_1y_2}{x_2{}^2 + y_2{}^2} + \frac{x_2y_1 - x_1y_2}{x_2{}^2 + y_2{}^2}\, i,$$

[1] See R. V. Churchill "Introduction to Complex Variables and Applications," 1948. A bibliography on the subject will be found in Appendix 1 of that book. Also see L. V. Ahlfors, "Complex Analysis," 1953.

except that division by zero is not defined. It follows that $i^2 = -1$, and that the above rules can be written down by formally applying rules for real binomials to $x + iy$ and replacing i^2 by -1.

The less elementary operations on z, such as z^c where c is a complex number, are still to be defined. But from the rules above it follows that complex numbers obey the usual commutative and associative laws of addition and multiplication, as well as the distributive law

$$z_1(z_2 + z_3) = z_1z_2 + z_1z_3.$$

A complex number $z_1 = x_1 + iy_1$ is represented geometrically either by the point (x_1,y_1) or by the vector whose x component is x_1 and whose y component is y_1 (Fig. 63). The rule for addition shows that the sum $z_1 + z_2$ is represented by the vector sum of the two vectors that represent the complex numbers z_1 and z_2.

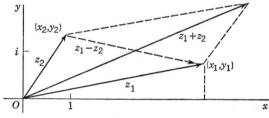

FIG. 63.

The length of the vector representing z is called the absolute value of z,

$$|z| = \sqrt{x^2 + y^2} = \sqrt{z\bar{z}},$$

where $\bar{z}$ is the conjugate of the complex number z, $\bar{z} = x - iy$. The distance from the point z_1 to the point z_2 is $|z_1 - z_2|$ (Fig. 63).

Let (r, θ) be the polar coordinates of the point (x,y). Then $|z| = r$ and

$$z = x + iy = r(\cos \theta + i \sin \theta).$$

For two complex numbers in polar form, it can be shown that

$$z_1z_2 = r_1r_2[\cos (\theta_1 + \theta_2) + i \sin (\theta_1 + \theta_2)],$$

$$\frac{z_1}{z_2} = \frac{r_1}{r_2} [\cos (\theta_1 - \theta_2) + i \sin (\theta_1 - \theta_2)].$$

As noted earlier (Sec. 22), θ is called the argument of z: $\theta = \arg z$.

If $m = p/q$ where p and q are integers, and if z^m is defined as a number w such that $w^q = z^p$, then

$$z^m = r^m(\cos m\theta + i \sin m\theta),$$

where r^m is the positive number $\sqrt[q]{r^p}$. It follows that

$$|z_1 z_2| = |z_1|\,|z_2|, \qquad \left|\frac{z_1}{z_2}\right| = \frac{|z_1|}{|z_2|}, \qquad |z^m| = |z|^m.$$

The triangle inequalities

(1) $\qquad |z_1 \pm z_2| \leq |z_1| + |z_2|, \qquad |z_1 \pm z_2| \geq |\,|z_1| - |z_2|\,|$

follow from elementary geometry. Note that neither of the statements $z_1 > z_2$ nor $z_1 < z_2$ has a meaning unless z_1 and z_2 are both real.

The conjugate operation has the distributive properties

(2) $\qquad \overline{z_1 \pm z_2} = \bar{z}_1 \pm \bar{z}_2, \qquad \overline{z_1 z_2} = \bar{z}_1 \bar{z}_2, \qquad \overline{(z_1/z_2)} = \bar{z}_1/\bar{z}_2.$

When ϵ is a positive number, the two-dimensional circular region consisting of points z such that $|z - z_0| < \epsilon$ is called a *neighborhood* of z_0.

51. Analytic Functions. Let w be a complex variable whose value is uniquely determined by the value of the variable $z = x + iy$; that is, w is a single-valued function of z,

$$w = f(z) = u(x,y) + iv(x,y),$$

where u and v are real functions. Thus if $w = z^2$, then

$$f(z) = (x + iy)^2 = (x^2 - y^2) + 2xyi,$$

so that $u = x^2 - y^2$ and $v = 2xy$.

The definition of the limit of $f(z)$ as z approaches z_0 and the theorems on limits of sums, products and quotients correspond to those in calculus for functions of a real variable. But the neighborhoods involved are now two-dimensional circular regions of the type defined at the end of the preceding section. Let u_0 and v_0 denote real numbers and write $z_0 = x_0 + iy_0$. Then it turns out that the condition

$$\lim_{z \to z_0} f(z) = u_0 + iv_0$$

on the function $f(z) = u(x,y) + iv(x,y)$ is satisfied if and only if the two dimensional limits of the real functions $u(x,y)$ and $v(x,y)$, as $x \rightarrow x_0$ and $y \rightarrow y_0$, have the values u_0 and v_0, respectively. Also, $f(z)$ is continuous when $z = z_0$ if and only if $u(x,y)$ and $v(x,y)$ are both continuous at (x_0,y_0).

The derivative of w at a point z is

$$\frac{dw}{dz} = f'(z) = \lim_{\Delta z \to 0} \frac{\Delta w}{\Delta z} = \lim_{\Delta z \to 0} \frac{f(z + \Delta z) - f(z)}{\Delta z},$$

provided this limit exists. But here $\Delta z = \Delta x + i\,\Delta y$ and the value of the limit must be independent of the direction of the vector representing Δz (Fig. 64). Suppose, for instance, that $\Delta y = 0$ so that $\Delta z = \Delta x$. Then, since $\Delta w = \Delta u + i\,\Delta v$,

$$\frac{dw}{dz} = \lim_{\Delta x \to 0} \left(\frac{\Delta u}{\Delta x} + i\frac{\Delta v}{\Delta x} \right) = \frac{\partial u}{\partial x} + i\frac{\partial v}{\partial x}.$$

But if $\Delta x = 0$ so that $\Delta z = i\,\Delta y$, then

$$\frac{dw}{dz} = -i\frac{\partial u}{\partial y} + \frac{\partial v}{\partial y}.$$

If the two values of dw/dz so found are to be the same, it is therefore necessary that u and v satisfy the two conditions

$$\frac{\partial u}{\partial x} = \frac{\partial v}{\partial y}, \qquad \frac{\partial v}{\partial x} = -\frac{\partial u}{\partial y}.$$

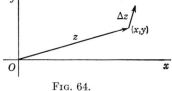

FIG. 64.

These are known as the *Cauchy-Riemann* conditions.

Let u and v, together with their partial derivatives u_x, u_y, v_x and v_y, be continuous functions of x and y in some neighborhood of a point (x_0,y_0). Then in order that the function $f(z) = u + iv$ have a derivative $f'(z)$ at a point z in that neighborhood, where $z = x + iy$, it is necessary and sufficient that u and v satisfy the Cauchy-Riemann conditions at that point.

A function $f(z)$ is said to be *analytic* at a point z_0 if its derivative $f'(z)$ exists *at every point* of some neighborhood of z_0. It is analytic in a specified region if it is analytic at every point of that region. Analyticity implies continuity, but not conversely. The function $\bar{z} = x - iy$ is everywhere continuous, for instance, but since the first Cauchy-Riemann condition is satisfied nowhere, $\bar{z}$ is nowhere analytic.

Formulas for derivatives of sums, products, quotients, and powers of functions and of composite functions $g[f(z)]$ correspond to those in calculus. Consequently the sum, product, or quotient of two analytic functions is analytic except, in the case of the quotient, at those points where the denominator vanishes. An analytic function $g(w)$ of an analytic function $w = f(z)$ is analytic for values of z in a region R where w is analytic and where the values of w are interior to a region where $g(w)$ is analytic.

An *entire function* is one that is analytic for all finite values of z. Every polynomial in z is an entire function.

The function $f(z) = 1/z$ is analytic except **at $z = 0$.** Its derivative is $-1/z^2$, where $z \neq 0$.

The function $f(z) = |z|^2 = x^2 + y^2$ is continuous for all z since $u = x^2 + y^2$ and $v = 0$. Although u and v are continuous and have continuous partial derivatives everywhere, they satisfy the Cauchy-Riemann conditions only at $z = 0$. Hence $f'(z)$ exists only at the origin, where $f'(0) = u_x(0,0) + iv_x(0,0) = 0$, not throughout any neighborhood. Consequently $|z|^2$ is nowhere analytic. The functions $\Re(z) = x$ and $\Im(z) = y$ are further examples of continuous functions that are nowhere analytic.

52. Exponential and Trigonometric Functions. The exponential function with imaginary exponent, written exp (iy) or e^{iy}, may be defined by the equation

$$(1) \qquad e^{iy} = \cos y + i \sin y,$$

where y is the radian measure of the argument of the trigonometric functions. This definition is suggested when iy is substituted formally for t in the power series expansion for e^t. When the exponent is complex, we extend the definition thus:

$$(2) \qquad e^z = \exp (x + iy) = e^x(\cos y + i \sin y).$$

Here u and v and their partial derivatives are continuous everywhere and satisfy the Cauchy-Riemann conditions. Therefore the derivative of e^z exists everywhere and the derivative of this entire function is

$$(3) \qquad \frac{d}{dz} e^z = u_x + iv_x = e^z.$$

The polar form (Sec. 50) of z can now be written

$$z = r(\cos \theta + i \sin \theta) = re^{i\theta}.$$

According to the definition (1),

$$e^{-iy} = \cos y - i \sin y,$$

and from this equation and equation (1) we find that

$$\cos y = \frac{e^{iy} + e^{-iy}}{2} = \cosh iy,$$

$$\sin y = \frac{e^{iy} - e^{-iy}}{2i} = -i \sinh iy,$$

where, by definition,

(4) $$\cosh z = \frac{e^z + e^{-z}}{2}, \qquad \sinh z = \frac{e^z - e^{-z}}{2}.$$

Since $\exp(\pm z)$ are entire functions, it follows that $\cosh z$ and $\sinh z$ are entire. These hyperbolic functions can be written

$$\cosh z = \cosh x \cos y + i \sinh x \sin y,$$
$$\sinh z = \sinh x \cos y + i \cosh x \sin y.$$

Each of the remaining hyperbolic functions of z,

$$\tanh z = \frac{\sinh z}{\cosh z}, \qquad \coth z = \frac{1}{\tanh z},$$

$$\operatorname{sech} z = \frac{1}{\cosh z}, \qquad \operatorname{csch} z = \frac{1}{\sinh z},$$

is analytic except at those points where the denominator on the right-hand side vanishes.

The circular functions of z can be defined as follows:

(5) $$\cos z = \frac{e^{iz} + e^{-iz}}{2}, \qquad \sin z = \frac{e^{iz} - e^{-iz}}{2i}, \qquad \tan z = \frac{\sin z}{\cos z},$$

the remaining three being the reciprocals of these. The functions $\cos z$ and $\sin z$ are entire. In view of these definitions, it follows that

$$\cos iz = \cosh z, \qquad \sin iz = i \sinh z.$$

All trigonometric identities for the functions with real arguments can be extended without change of form to the functions with complex arguments; for example,

$$\sin^2 z + \cos^2 z = 1,$$
$$\sin(z_1 + z_2) = \sin z_1 \cos z_2 + \cos z_1 \sin z_2.$$

The same is true for the relations between the six hyperbolic functions. Furthermore, the formulas for the derivatives of all these functions retain the same form when the variable is complex as they have when the variable is real. Thus for all z in a region where $w(z)$ is analytic, the composite functions $\sin w(z)$ and $\cos w(z)$ are analytic functions of z and

$$\frac{d}{dz} \sin w = \cos w \frac{dw}{dz}, \qquad \frac{d}{dz} \cos w = -\sin w \frac{dw}{dz}.$$

The absolute values of $\sin z$ and $\cos z$ are not bounded for all complex z. It is left to the problems to show that

(6) $|\sin z|^2 = \sin^2 x + \sinh^2 y, \qquad |\cos z|^2 = \cos^2 x + \sinh^2 y,$

(7) $|\sinh z|^2 = \sinh^2 x + \sin^2 y, \qquad |\cosh z|^2 = \sinh^2 x + \cos^2 y.$

PROBLEMS

1. Establish geometrically the triangle inequalities (1), Sec. 50.

2. If $z_1, z_2, \ldots, z_m$ are complex numbers, show that

$$\left| \sum_{n=1}^{m} z_n \right| \leq \sum_{n=1}^{m} |z_n|.$$

3. If $|z_2| \neq |z_3|$, show that

$$\left| \frac{z_1}{z_2 + z_3} \right| \leq \frac{|z_1|}{\left| |z_2| - |z_3| \right|}.$$

4. When n is a positive integer and $z \neq 0$, show that $z^{1/n}$ has n distinct values.

5. If a_n and b_n are real numbers, show that the function

$$f(z) = a_1 x + b_1 y + c_1 + i(a_2 x + b_2 y + c_2)$$

is an entire function if and only if the coefficients are such that

$$f(z) = (a_1 - ib_1)z + c_1 + ic_2.$$

6. Prove that the function $f(z) = x^2 + iy^2$ is nowhere analytic.

7. Show why the functions $\sin e^z$ and $\exp(\cos z)$ are entire.

8. Show that

(a) $|e^z| = e^x$;   (b) $e^{-z} = \dfrac{1}{e^z}$;   (c) $e^{(z_1+z_2)} = e^{z_1}e^{z_2}$;

also note that $|e^{-z}|$ is not bounded for all complex z.

9. Establish the identities (6), Sec. 52.

10. Establish the identities (7), Sec. 52.

11. Prove (a) that the zeros of sin z, that is, all values of z for which the function is zero, are $z = \pm n\pi$ ($n = 0, 1, 2, \ldots$); (b) that the zeros of sinh z are $z = \pm n\pi i$.

12. Show that tanh z is analytic except at the points

$$z = \frac{\pm(2n - 1)\pi i}{2} \qquad (n = 1, 2, \ldots).$$

53. Integrals. Let C denote either an arc of a curve

(1) $$x = \phi(t), \qquad y = \psi(t),$$

where ϕ and ψ are single-valued functions of a parameter t, with continuous derivatives $\phi'(t)$ and $\psi'(t)$, or a curve formed by joining a finite number of such arcs endwise. If $f(z)$ is a continuous function, the line integral of $f(z)$ over C, defined as a limit of a sum, exists and has the property

(2) $$\left| \int_C f(z)\, dz \right| \leqq \int_C |f(z)|\, |dz| \leqq ML,$$

where $|dz|^2 = dx^2 + dy^2$ so that $|dz|$ represents an element of arc length of C, and where L is the length of C and M is the maximum value of $|f(z)|$ for all points z on C.

When we write $f(z) = u(x,y) + iv(x,y)$, the integral can be written in terms of real line integrals,

(3) $$\int_C f(z)\, dz = \int_C [u(x,y)\, dx - v(x,y)\, dy]$$
$$+ i \int_C [u(x,y)\, dy + v(x,y)\, dx],$$

a result that follows formally by writing $dz = dx + i\, dy$. The real line integrals can be written as definite integrals with respect to t with the aid of the parametric equations (1) of the curve C.

Now let C be a closed curve, one forming a closed loop, interior to a region R in which $f(z)$ is analytic. If the region R is *simply connected*, that is, if every closed curve in R encloses only points of R, then

(4) $$\int_C f(z)\, dz = 0.$$

This basic theorem is the *Cauchy integral theorem*. It can be extended to apply to the integral over the entire boundary of a multiply connected region if $f(z)$ is analytic within and on the boundary of the region. In the integration the boundary is then described in such a direction that the region lies to the left.

The value of a function $f(z)$, analytic in a simply connected region R, is determined at a point z_0 by the values of $f(z)$ at the points on any closed curve C interior to R and enclosing z_0 (Fig. 65):

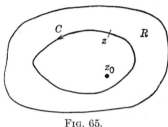

FIG. 65.

$$(5) \quad f(z_0) = \frac{1}{2\pi i} \int_C \frac{f(z)}{z - z_0} \, dz,$$

where z traverses C in the counterclockwise (positive) direction. This is *Cauchy's integral formula*. Note that the integrand of the integral (5) is not analytic at the point $z = z_0$. Here again the formula applies when R is multiply connected if C is the entire boundary of a region of analyticity of $f(z)$ with z_0 as an interior point.

Derivatives of the integral (5) with respect to z_0 can be shown to exist and to be given by the integral of the derivative; in particular,

$$(6) \qquad f''(z_0) = \frac{1}{\pi i} \int_C \frac{f(z)}{(z - z_0)^3} \, dz.$$

Consequently the derivative $f'(z)$ of a function $f(z)$ that is analytic in a region is itself analytic there. It follows that the derivative of any order $f^{(n)}(z)$ is analytic.

If z_0 and z are two points in a simply connected region R in which $f(z)$ is analytic, it follows from formula (4) that the line integral

$$F(z) = \int_{z_0}^{z} f(\xi) \, d\xi$$

is independent of the path C from z_0 to z as long as C is within R. Moreover $F'(z)$ exists and equals $f(z)$, so that $F(z)$ is analytic in R. Except for the addition of an arbitrary constant, $F(z)$ is the only function whose derivative is the given function $f(z)$. In terms of the antiderivative we find that, if z_1 is also in R,

$$\int_{z_0}^{z_1} f(z) \, dz = F(z_1) - F(z_0).$$

54. Power Series. Let $f(z)$ be analytic interior to a circle $|z - z_0| = r_0$. Then at each interior point z it is true that

$$(1) \qquad f(z) = f(z_0) + \sum_{n=1}^{\infty} \frac{f^{(n)}(z_0)}{n!} (z - z_0)^n;$$

that is, *Taylor's series* converges whenever $|z - z_0| < r_0$ and it converges to $f(z)$. This important theorem is a consequence of Cauchy's integral formula.

The region of convergence of a power series

$$(2) \qquad \sum_{n=0}^{\infty} a_n(z - z_0)^n,$$

where a_n are complex constants, is always a circle about the point z_0, $|z - z_0| < r_0$, unless the series converges only when $z = z_0$. For some series $r_0 = \infty$. Let $f(z)$ denote the sum of the series. If the series is differentiated or integrated termwise the result is a series that converges, within the circle, to the derivative or integral of $f(z)$. Thus the series (2) represents an analytic function within its circle of convergence. Only one power series representation (2) of a given function $f(z)$ can exist when $|z - z_0| < r_0$, and consequently the series (2) is Taylor's series for $f(z)$; that is,

$$a_0 = f(z_0), \qquad a_n = \frac{1}{n!} f^{(n)}(z_0) \quad (n = 1, 2, \ldots).$$

The convergence of the power series is always absolute and uniform, with respect to z, in each interior circle $|z - z_0| \leqq r_1$, where $r_1 < r_0$.

Since e^z is an entire function, *Maclaurin's* series ($z_0 = 0$) represents this function for all z:

$$(3) \qquad e^z = 1 + \sum_{n=1}^{\infty} \frac{z^n}{n!} \qquad (|z| < \infty).$$

Consequently the function $g(z) = \exp (z^2)$ has the power series representation

$$g(z) = e^{z^2} = 1 + \sum_{n=1}^{\infty} \frac{z^{2n}}{n!} \qquad (|z| < \infty),$$

which is the Maclaurin series for $g(z)$ and hence $g^{(2n)}(0) = (2n)!/n!$, $g^{(2n-1)}(0) = 0$.

With the aid of power series it can be shown that *the zeros of each analytic function are isolated;* that is, if $f(z_0) = 0$ and $f(z)$ is analytic at z_0, then there is some neighborhood of z_0 throughout which $f(z) \neq 0$ except at z_0 itself, unless f is identically zero.

A further consequence of Cauchy's integral formula follows. If $f(z)$ is analytic in an annulus R, $r_1 < |z - z_0| < r_0$, it is represented in R by the *Laurent series:*

$$(4) \qquad f(z) = \sum_{n=-\infty}^{\infty} A_n(z - z_0)^n \quad (r_1 < |z - z_0| < r_0),$$

where, if C is any closed curve counterclockwise around the annulus (Fig. 66),

$$(5) \qquad A_n = \frac{1}{2\pi i} \int_C \frac{f(z)}{(z - z_0)^{n+1}}\, dz \quad (n = 0, \pm 1, \pm 2, \ldots).$$

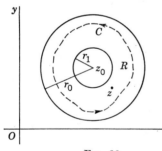

FIG. 66.

We note, in particular, that

$$A_{-1} = \frac{1}{2\pi i} \int_C f(z)\, dz.$$

Again, the representation of a given function in the annulus R by series of type (4) is unique. Consequently the values of the integrals (5) can be seen from the series representation. From the expansion (3), for instance, this Laurent series representation follows:

$$(6) \qquad e^{1/z} = 1 + \frac{1}{z} + \frac{1}{2!}\frac{1}{z^2} + \frac{1}{3!}\frac{1}{z^3} + \cdots \qquad (|z| > 0).$$

Here $A_{-1} = 1$, $A_{-2} = \frac{1}{2}$, and $z_0 = 0$. According to formula (5) then

$$\int_C e^{1/z}\, dz = 2\pi i, \qquad \int_C z e^{1/z}\, dz = \pi i,$$

for any closed curve C described counterclockwise around the origin.

Series of types (2) or (4) can be added, multiplied, or divided to produce series of those types that converge to the corresponding combinations of their sums, under natural restrictions on the regions. The region of convergence of a series of type (4) is always an annulus with center at z_0, and the sum is analytic interior to the region.

55. Singular Points and Residues. If a function is analytic at some point in every neighborhood of a point z_0, but not at z_0 itself, then z_0 is called a *singular point* of the function. If the function is analytic at all points except z_0, in some neighborhood of z_0, then z_0 is an *isolated singular point*. The function $(z^2 + 1)^{-1}$, for example, is everywhere analytic except for the two isolated singular points $z = \pm i$.

About an isolated singular point z_0 a function always has a Laurent series representation:

$$(1)\quad f(z) = \frac{A_{-1}}{z - z_0} + \frac{A_{-2}}{(z - z_0)^2} + \cdots$$
$$+ A_0 + A_1(z - z_0) + \cdots \quad (0 < |z - z_0| < r_0),$$

where r_0 is the radius of the neighborhood in which $f(z)$ is analytic except at z_0. The coefficients A_n are given by formula (5), Sec. 54, where the inner radius r_1 of the annulus, around which C is described, is now zero. In particular,

$$(2)\qquad\qquad A_{-1} = \frac{1}{2\pi i} \int_C f(z)\, dz,$$

where C can be any closed curve, described counterclockwise, containing z_0 in its interior and such that, except for z_0, $f(z)$ is analytic within and on C.

The complex number A_{-1}, the coefficient of $(z - z_0)^{-1}$ in the expansion (1), is called the *residue* of $f(z)$ at the isolated singular point z_0; $2\pi i A_{-1}$ is the value of the integral of $f(z)$ in the positive direction around a path that encloses no other singular points but z_0. The expansion (6), Sec. 54, for instance, shows that the residue of the function $\exp(1/z)$ at the point $z = 0$ has the value $A_{-1} = 1$.

If C_0 is a closed curve within and on which $f(z)$ is analytic except for a finite number of singular points $z_1, z_2, \ldots, z_m$, interior to the region bounded by C_0, the *residue theorem* states that

$$(3)\qquad\qquad \int_{C_0} f(z)\, dz = 2\pi i(\rho_1 + \rho_2 + \cdots + \rho_m),$$

where ρ_n denotes the residue of $f(z)$ at z_n and where the integration is in the positive direction around C_0. Note that the singular points z_n are necessarily isolated because of their finite number.

In the representation (1) the series of negative powers of $(z - z_0)$ is called the *principal part* of $f(z)$ about the isolated singular point z_0. The point z_0 is an *essential singular point* of $f(z)$ if the principal part has an infinite number of nonvanishing terms. It is a *pole of order m* if $A_{-m} \neq 0$ and $A_{-n} = 0$ when $n > m$. It is called a *simple pole* when $m = 1$; thus, if z_0 is a simple pole, a number r_0 exists such that

$$(4) \qquad f(z) = \frac{A_{-1}}{z - z_0} + \sum_{n=0}^{\infty} A_n (z - z_0)^n$$
$$(A_{-1} \neq 0, \, 0 < |z - z_0| < r_0).$$

The function $\exp(1/z)$ has an essential singular point at the origin, in view of its representation (6), Sec. 54. The function

$$\frac{\cos z}{z^2} = \frac{1}{z^2} \sum_{n=0}^{\infty} \frac{(-1)^n}{(2n)!} z^{2n} = \frac{1}{z^2} - \frac{1}{2!} + \frac{z^2}{4!} + \cdots \qquad (|z| > 0)$$

has a pole of order 2 at $z = 0$, where the residue of the function is zero.

If a function is not analytic at z_0 but can be made so by merely assigning a suitable value to the function at that point, then z_0 is a *removable singular point* of the function. Thus the function

$$\frac{\sin z}{z} = 1 - \frac{z^2}{3!} + \frac{z^4}{5!} - \cdots \qquad (|z| > 0)$$

is analytic when $z \neq 0$. If we define its value to be unity when $z = 0$, the function is represented by the above convergent power series for all z and is therefore entire. Consequently $z = 0$ is a removable singular point of $z^{-1} \sin z$.

When $f(z)$ has a pole of order m at z_0, let us write

$$(5) \qquad \phi(z) = (z - z_0)^m f(z) \qquad (0 < |z - z_0| < r_0).$$

From the Laurent expansion (1) of $f(z)$ about z_0 it follows that z_0 is a removable singular point of $\phi(z)$, that $\phi(z)$ is analytic at z_0

if we make the definition

$$(6) \qquad \phi(z_0) = A_{-m}.$$

Then $\phi(z)$ is represented by Taylor's series when $|z - z_0| < r_0$, and it can be seen from equation (5) that

$$(7) \qquad A_{-1} = \frac{\phi^{(m-1)}(z_0)}{(m-1)!}.$$

This is a useful formula for the residue of $f(z)$ at a pole. For a simple pole ($m = 1$) it becomes

$$(8) \qquad A_{-1} = \phi(z_0) = \lim_{z \to z_0} (z - z_0)f(z).$$

We also note that $|f(z)| \to \infty$ as $z \to z_0$ whenever z_0 is a pole.

Conversely, for a given $f(z)$, suppose that a positive integer m exists such that the function $\phi(z)$, defined by equation (5), is analytic at z_0 when $\phi(z_0)$ is suitably defined and that this value $\phi(z_0) \neq 0$. Then Taylor's series for $\phi(z)$ shows that $f(z)$ has a pole of order m at z_0 and that the residue of $f(z)$ there is given by formula (7), or by (8) if $m = 1$. For example, if

$$f(z) = \frac{e^{-z}}{z^2 + \pi^2} = \frac{e^{-z}}{z + \pi i}\frac{1}{z - \pi i}$$

then corresponding to the singular point $z = \pi i$,

$$\phi(z) = \frac{e^{-z}}{z + \pi i}.$$

and $m = 1$, so that πi is a simple pole. Here $\phi(\pi i) = e^{-\pi i}/(2\pi i)$; thus the residue of $f(z)$ at this pole is $i/(2\pi)$.

Let functions $p(z)$ and $q(z)$ be analytic at z_0, where $p(z_0) \neq 0$. Then the function

$$(9) \qquad f(z) = \frac{p(z)}{q(z)}$$

has a simple pole at z_0 if and only if $q(z_0) = 0$ and $q'(z_0) \neq 0$. The residue of $f(z)$ at the simple pole is given by the formula

$$(10) \qquad A_{-1} = \frac{p(z_0)}{q'(z_0)}.$$

If $q(z_0) = q'(z_0) = 0$ and $q''(z_0) \neq 0$, then z_0 is a pole of $f(z)$ of order 2, and conversely. Similarly for poles of higher order

Since formulas for residues in terms of p and q are awkward when $m > 1$, we rely on formula (7) or the Laurent expansion instead.

PROBLEMS

1. When C is the boundary of a square with opposite vertices at the points $z = 0$ and $z = 1 + i$, evaluate the integral $\int_C z^2 \, dz$ directly in terms of real line integrals to show that its value is zero.

2. When C is the circle $|z| = 2$ described counterclockwise, use Cauchy's integral theorem or Cauchy's integral formula to prove that

(a) $\displaystyle \int_C \frac{z}{z^2 + 9} \, dz = 0;$ (b) $\displaystyle \int_C \sec \frac{z}{2} \, dz = 0;$

(c) $\displaystyle \int_C \frac{z^2 + 4}{z - 1} \, dz = 10\pi i;$ (d) $\displaystyle \int_C \frac{\sinh z}{2z + \pi i} \, dz = \pi.$

3. Establish these expansions in the regions indicated:

(a) $\displaystyle \frac{1}{1 + z} = \sum_{n=0}^{\infty} (-1)^n z^n$ $(|z| < 1);$

(b) $\displaystyle \frac{1}{1 - z^2} = \sum_{n=0}^{\infty} z^{2n}$ $(|z| < 1);$

(c) $\displaystyle \sinh z = \sum_{n=1}^{\infty} \frac{z^{2n-1}}{(2n - 1)!}$ $(|z| < \infty);$

(d) $\displaystyle \frac{z}{z - 1} = \sum_{n=0}^{\infty} \frac{1}{z^n}$ $(|z| > 1).$

4. Show that the function $\tan z$ is analytic except for simple poles at $z = \pm(2n - 1)\pi/2$ and that its integral around the square bounded by the lines $x = \pm 2$, $y = \pm 2$ has the value $-4\pi i$.

5. Show that the integral of $\tanh z$ around the circle $r = \pi$ has the value $4\pi i$.

6. Show that the functions $\sin (1/z)$ and $\cos (1/z)$ are analytic except at $z = 0$ and that $z = 0$ is an essential singular point. Find the residues there.   *Ans.* 1; 0.

7. Find the residues of these functions at their isolated singular points:

(a) $\displaystyle \frac{z + 1}{z - 1};$ (b) $\displaystyle \frac{1}{\sin z};$ (c) $\displaystyle \frac{\cos z}{(z - z_0)^2};$ (d) $z^3 \cosh \dfrac{1}{z^2}.$

$\qquad\qquad$ *Ans.* (a) 2; (b) ± 1; (c) $-\sin z_0$; (d) $\frac{1}{2}$.

8. Show that the singular point $z = 0$ of the function

$$f(z) = \frac{1}{\sin (\pi/z)}$$

is not isolated.

9. Using the Cauchy-Riemann conditions, show that if a function $f(z) = u + iv$ is analytic at a point then u and v satisfy Laplace's equation in two variables there,

$$\frac{\partial^2 u}{\partial x^2} + \frac{\partial^2 u}{\partial y^2} = 0, \qquad \frac{\partial^2 v}{\partial x^2} + \frac{\partial^2 v}{\partial y^2} = 0.$$

56. Branches of Multiple-valued Functions. The argument θ of a given complex number $z = re^{i\theta}$ is not single-valued unless the range of θ is restricted. When $z \neq 0$ the function

$$(1) \quad z^{\frac{1}{2}} = \sqrt{r}\left(\cos\frac{\theta}{2} + i\sin\frac{\theta}{2}\right)$$

has one value corresponding to a particular choice of θ and a second value when that argument is increased by 2π. Those two values of $z^{\frac{1}{2}}$, which differ only in algebraic sign, are the

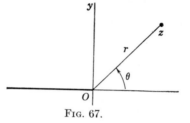

Fig. 67.

only possible values for a given z; thus the function (1) is double-valued.

A *branch* of a multiple-valued function $f(z)$ is a single-valued function that is analytic in some region and whose value at each point there coincides with one of the values of $f(z)$ at the point. The function

$$(2) \qquad f_1(z) = \sqrt{r}\left(\cos\frac{\theta}{2} + i\sin\frac{\theta}{2}\right) \quad (-\pi < \theta < \pi, r > 0),$$

for example, is a branch of the double-valued function (1). The definition of the derivative can be used to show that $f_1(z)$ is analytic everywhere except at the origin and points on the negative real axis. Since $f_1(z)$ tends to $i\sqrt{r}$ when $\theta \to \pi$ and to $-i\sqrt{r}$ when $\theta \to -\pi$, the function has no limit as $z \to -r$ $(r > 0)$. Thus $f_1(z)$ cannot be defined on the negative real axis so as to make the function continuous there, and the ray $\theta = \pi$ must be excluded from the region of analyticity (Fig. 67).

The negative real axis is called a *branch cut* of $f_1(z)$, a boundary that is needed to define the branch in the greatest possible region. Note that each point of the branch cut is a singular point of $f_1(z)$ that is not isolated. The origin is a *branch point*, a point associated with the multiple-valued function in this way: each branch of the function has a branch cut running from that point. Since the function (1) is double-valued unless the range of θ is limited to the value 2π or less, its branches must have cuts running out from the origin.

A second branch of the function (1) with the same cut as $f_1(z)$ is

$$(3) \qquad f_2(z) = \sqrt{r}\left(\cos\frac{\theta}{2} + i\sin\frac{\theta}{2}\right) \quad (\pi < \theta < 3\pi, r > 0).$$

Here $f_2(z) = -f_1(z)$. The number of branches is unlimited. A branch with the positive real axis as its branch cut is

$$(4) \qquad f_3(z) = \sqrt{r}\left(\cos\frac{\theta}{2} + i\sin\frac{\theta}{2}\right) \quad (0 < \theta < 2\pi, r > 0);$$

one that has the positive y axis as a cut is the function (1) with the restriction $\pi/2 < \theta < 5\pi/2, r > 0$; etc.

A branch of the n-valued function $z^{1/n}$ $(n = 2, 3, \ldots)$ with a ray $\theta = \theta_0$ as the branch cut is described by the conditions

$$(5) \qquad z^{1/n} = \sqrt[n]{r}\left(\cos\frac{\theta}{n} + i\sin\frac{\theta}{n}\right) \quad (\theta_0 < \theta < \theta_0 + 2\pi, r > 0).$$

For this function it can be shown that

$$\frac{d}{dz}\left(z^{1/n}\right) = \frac{1}{n}\,z^{(1/n)-1}$$

The function $\log z$, the inverse of the exponential function, is infinitely multiple-valued. It can be written

$$(6) \qquad \log z = \log\,(re^{i\theta}) = \operatorname{Log} r + i\theta,$$

where $\operatorname{Log} r$ denotes the real natural logarithm of the positive number r. The branch known as the principal value of $\log z$ is the function

$$(7) \qquad \operatorname{Log} z = \operatorname{Log} r + i\theta \quad (-\pi < \theta < \pi, r > 0),$$

whose branch cut is the negative real axis. Its derivative is $1/z$.

When c is a complex constant, the multiple-valued function z^c is defined as exp $(c \log z)$.

The inverse trigonometric and hyperbolic functions are further simple examples of multiple-valued functions.

57. Analytic Continuation. If a function is single-valued and analytic throughout a region, it is uniquely determined throughout the region by its values over an arc, or over a subregion, within the given region. This theorem can be proved with the aid of Taylor's series.

Let $f_1(z)$ denote a given function analytic in a region R_1, and let R be a greater region containing R_1. A function $f(z)$, analytic throughout R and equal to $f_1(z)$ whenever z is in R_1, may exist. If so, there is only one such function in view of the foregoing theorem. The function $f(z)$ is called the *analytic continuation* of $f_1(z)$ into the larger region R.

As an example, let $f_1(z)$ be defined by this power series:

$$f_1(z) = \sum_{n=0}^{\infty} z^n \qquad\qquad (|z| < 1).$$

Then $f_1(z)$ is analytic in the region $|z| < 1$, the circle of convergence of the series; but the function is undefined for all other values of z because the series diverges whenever $|z| \geqq 1$. The series is the Maclaurin series representing the function $(1 - z)^{-1}$ in the region; thus $f_1(z) = (1 - z)^{-1}$ when $|z| < 1$. This second representation of $f_1(z)$ discloses the analytic continuation

$$f(z) = \frac{1}{1 - z} \qquad\qquad (z \neq 1)$$

of $f_1(z)$ into the entire z plane, excluding the point $z = 1$, because $f(z)$ is everywhere analytic except at that point and $f(z) = f_1(z)$ when $|z| < 1$.

As another example, consider the Laplace transform

$$f_1(z) = \int_0^{\infty} e^{-zt}\, dt = \int_0^{\infty} e^{-xt} \cos yt\, dt - i \int_0^{\infty} e^{-xt} \sin yt\, dt.$$

The Laplace integral here exists only if $x > 0$, where its value is $1/z$. Thus $f_1(z) = 1/z$ $(x > 0)$ and the function is analytic in that right half plane. But since $1/z$ is analytic everywhere except at the origin, the analytic continuation of $f_1(z)$ out of the half plane is the function

$$f(z) = \frac{1}{z} \qquad\qquad (z \neq 0).$$

We also note that if the Laplace integral were known to represent an analytic function in the half plane and to have the value $1/x$ when $z = x$ there, then the integral represents $1/z$ there because the latter function is analytic and has the values $1/x$ on the x axis.

Finally, consider the branch (2), Sec. 56, of the function $z^{\frac{1}{2}}$. In the half plane $y > 0$ it is given by the conditions

$$f_1(z) = \sqrt{r}\left(\cos\frac{\theta}{2} + i\sin\frac{\theta}{2}\right) \quad (0 < \theta < \pi, r > 0).$$

It is not analytic on the negative real axis. The function

$$f(z) = \sqrt{r}\left(\cos\frac{\theta}{2} + i\sin\frac{\theta}{2}\right) \quad (0 < \theta < 2\pi, r > 0)$$

is analytic except on the positive real axis, and its values coincide with those of $f_1(z)$ in the half plane $y > 0$. Thus $f(z)$ is the analytic continuation of $f_1(z)$ downward across the negative real axis.

The following *principle of reflection* is easily established with the aid of the Cauchy-Riemann conditions. Let a function $w = f(z)$ be analytic in some region R that includes a segment of the x axis and is symmetric with respect to that axis. If $f(x)$ is real when x is a point on that segment, then

(1) $f(\bar{z}) = \bar{w}$

whenever z is in R. Conversely, if condition (1) is satisfied, then $f(x)$ is real. Condition (1) can be written $f(\bar{z}) = \overline{f(z)}$, or $\overline{f(\bar{z})} = f(z)$.

As examples, the entire functions z^2, e^z, and $\sin z$ are real when z is real, and the complex conjugate of each function is the same as the function of $\bar{z}$. But the functions iz and $z^2 + i$ are not real when $z = x$; their conjugates are different from $i\bar{z}$ and $\bar{z}^2 + i$.

58. An Extension of Cauchy's Integral Formula. In Sec. 53 we noted that the value of an analytic function $f(z)$ at any point z_0 inside a closed curve C is given in terms of the value of the function on C by Cauchy's integral formula

$$f(z_0) = \frac{1}{2\pi i} \int_C \frac{f(z)\, dz}{z - z_0}.$$

In the next chapter we shall need an extension of this formula to the case in which C is replaced by a straight line parallel to the axis of imaginaries and z_0 is any point to the right of that line.

To establish such an extension of the theorem, let us first introduce the notion of order of a function of a complex variable. A function $f(z)$ is of the order of z^k as $|z|$ tends to infinity, written

$$f(z) = O(z^k) \quad \text{as } |z| \to \infty,$$

if some positive numbers M and r_0 exist such that $|z^{-k} f(z)| < M$ when $|z| > r_0$; that is, if

$$|f(z)| < M |z|^k$$

for all $|z|$ sufficiently large.

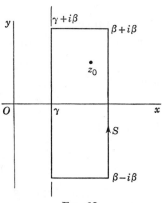

Fig. 68.

Theorem. *Let the function $f(z)$ be analytic when $\Re(z) \geqq \gamma$ and of the order $O(z^{-k})$ as $|z| \to \infty$ in that half plane, where γ and k are real constants and $k > 0$. Then if z_0 is any complex number such that $\Re(z_0) > \gamma$,*

$$(1) \qquad f(z_0) = -\frac{1}{2\pi i} \lim_{\beta \to \infty} \int_{\gamma - i\beta}^{\gamma + i\beta} \frac{f(z)\, dz}{z - z_0}.$$

The notation here is intended to imply that the integration takes place along the line $x = \gamma$, where $z = x + iy$, from the point $\gamma - i\beta$ to $\gamma + i\beta$. The limit of this integral as $\beta \to \infty$ is called the Cauchy *principal value* of the integral from $y = -\infty$ to $y = \infty$ along the line.

Consider the rectangle (Fig. 68) with vertices $\gamma \pm i\beta$, $\beta \pm i\beta$, where $\beta > |\gamma|$ and β is large enough that the fixed point z_0 lies inside the rectangle. Let S denote the path consisting of the open rectangle obtained by removing the left-hand side of our rectangle, where z traverses S in the counterclockwise direction. Applying Cauchy's integral formula to the closed rectangle, we can write

$$(2) \qquad \frac{1}{2\pi i}\left[\ \cdots\ \int_{\gamma-i\beta}^{\gamma+i\beta}\frac{f(z)\,dz}{z-z_0}+\int_S\frac{f(z)\,dz}{z-z_0}\right]=\ f(z_0).$$

In view of the order condition on $f(z)$ the absolute value of the integrand of the second integral here satisfies the condition

$$\left|\frac{f(z)}{z-z_0}\right|<\frac{M}{|z|^k|z-z_0|}=\frac{M}{|z|^{k+1}|1-(z_0/z)|}.$$

Here the points z are on S, so that $|z|\geqq\beta$. We take β large enough, $\beta>2|z_0|$, that $|z_0|<\tfrac{1}{2}|z|$ or $|z_0/z|<\tfrac{1}{2}$; then

$$|1-(z_0/z)|\geqq 1-|z_0/z|>\tfrac{1}{2}.$$

Therefore

$$\left|\frac{f(z)}{z-z_0}\right|<\frac{2M}{\beta^{k+1}}.$$

It follows that

$$\left|\int_S\frac{f(z)\,dz}{z-z_0}\right|<\frac{2M}{\beta^{k+1}}\int_S|dz|=\frac{2M}{\beta^k}\left(4-\frac{2\gamma}{\beta}\right),$$

since the length of S is $4\beta-2\gamma$. Since $k>0$, the expression on the right vanishes as $\beta\to\infty$.

The number $f(z_0)$ in equation (2) is independent of β. Consequently the limit as β tends to infinity of the product of $(2\pi i)^{-1}$ and the first integral in that equation exists and equals $f(z_0)$. This completes the proof of the theorem.

Under the conditions of the theorem the integrand of the integral (1) is a continuous function of the variable of integration y that is of the order of $y^{-(k+1)}$ as $|y|\to\infty$. Thus the improper integral itself exists and is the same as its principal value, and formula (1) can be written

$$(3) \qquad f(z_0)=-\frac{1}{2\pi}\int_{-\infty}^{\infty}\frac{f(\gamma+iy)}{\gamma+iy-z_0}\,dy.$$

In the proof of the theorem, circular arcs $|z-\gamma|=\beta$, $x\geqq\gamma$, or $|z|=\beta$, $x\geqq\gamma$, can be used in place of the open rectangles S. These variations in the proof are suggested as exercises for the reader.

CHAPTER 6

THE INVERSION INTEGRAL

We shall now extend our theory of the Laplace transformation by letting the letter s in the transform $f(s)$ represent a complex variable. As before $F(t)$ represents a real-valued function of the positive real variable t; but the transform $f(s)$ can assume complex values. We shall see that the properties of the transformation already obtained by assuming that s is real carry over to the case in which s is complex.

59. Analytic Transforms. When s is the complex variable

$$s = x + iy,$$

the Laplace transform of the real-valued function $F(t)$,

$$(1) \qquad f(s) = \int_0^\infty e^{-st} F(t)\, dt = \int_0^\infty e^{-xt} e^{-iyt} F(t)\, dt,$$

can be written in the form

$$(2) \qquad f(s) = u(x,y) + iv(x,y),$$

where the components u and v are real integrals:

$$(3) \qquad \begin{aligned} u(x,y) &= \int_0^\infty e^{-xt} \cos yt\, F(t)\, dt, \\ v(x,y) &= -\int_0^\infty e^{-xt} \sin yt\, F(t)\, dt. \end{aligned}$$

Since the integrands of the integrals (3) are the real and imaginary coefficients of the integrand $e^{-st} F(t)$ of the Laplace integral (1), we note that

$$(4) \qquad \begin{aligned} |e^{-xt} \cos yt\, F(t)| &\leq |e^{-st} F(t)|, \\ |-e^{-xt} \sin yt\, F(t)| &\leq |e^{-st} F(t)|. \end{aligned}$$

These inequalities will be useful in discussing the convergence of the integral (1).

Under broad conditions on $F(t)$ the transform $f(s)$ is analytic in a right half plane. Let $F(t)$ be sectionally continuous in each interval $0 \leq t \leq T$ and of exponential order as t tends to infinity. Then constants M and x_0 exist such that

$$|F(t)| < Me^{x_0 t} \qquad\qquad (t \geq 0)$$

and consequently, whenever $x \geq x_1$, where $x_1 > x_0$,

$$(5) \qquad |e^{-st}F(t)| = e^{-xt}|F(t)| < Me^{-(x-x_0)t} \leq Me^{-(x_1-x_0)t}.$$

The integrands of the real integrals (3) are continuous functions of x, y, and t except for the finite jumps of $F(t)$; their absolute values do not exceed $M \exp[-(x_1 - x_0)t]$ when $x \geq x_1$, in view of inequalities (4) and (5). According to the Weierstrass test then the integrals (3) converge uniformly with respect to x and y in the half plane $x \geq x_1$. They also represent continuous functions $u(x,y)$ and $v(x,y)$ in that half plane (Sec. 12).

When $F(t)$ is of the order of $\exp(x_0 t)$ we noted earlier (Sec. 16) that $tF(t)$ is of the order of $\exp[(x_0 + \epsilon)t]$ for each positive number ϵ. It follows that

$$(6) \qquad u_x(x,y) = \int_0^\infty e^{-xt}\cos yt(-t)F(t)\,dt$$

because the integral here converges uniformly with respect to x when $x \geq x_1$. Also, $u_x(x,y)$ is a continuous function in that half plane. From the second of equations (3) we see that the integral in formula (6) also represents $v_y(x,y)$; hence u and v satisfy the first Cauchy-Riemann condition in the half plane $x > x_0$. In the same manner we find that the second condition $u_y = -v_x$ is satisfied there. These conditions, together with the continuity of u and v and their partial derivatives, show that $f(s)$ is analytic in the half plane $x > x_0$ (Sec. 51).

Now $f'(s) = u_x + iv_x$ when $f(s)$ is analytic; thus

$$f'(s) = -\int_0^\infty te^{-xt}(\cos yt - i\sin yt)F(t)\,dt = L\{-tF(t)\}$$
$$(x > x_0).$$

Since $tF(t)$ is also sectionally continuous and of exponential order, our result applies as well to that function, so that

$$f''(s) = L\{t^2 F(t)\} \qquad\qquad (x > x_0),$$

and so on for $f^{(n)}(s)$. Moreover, $f(s)$ is real when $s = x$ because

$F(t)$ is real. It follows from the principle of reflection (Sec. 57), or directly from equations (2) and (3), that $\overline{f(s)} = f(\bar{s})$. Our results can be stated as follows.

Theorem 1. *Let the real-valued function $F(t)$ be sectionally continuous in each finite interval and of the order $O(e^{x_0 t})$, when $t \geqq 0$. Then the Laplace transform of $F(t)$*

$$f(s) = \int_0^\infty e^{-st} F(t)\, dt = L\{F(t)\} \qquad (s = x + iy)$$

is an analytic function of s in the half plane $x > x_0$. The Laplace integral is absolutely convergent there; it is uniformly convergent with respect to x and y in each half plane $x \geqq x_1$, where $x_1 > x_0$. The derivatives of $f(s)$ are given by the formula

$$(7) \qquad f^{(n)}(s) = L\{(-t)^n F(t)\} \qquad (n = 1, 2, \ldots ; x > x_0).$$

Moreover, the complex conjugate of $f(s)$ can be written

$$(8) \qquad \overline{f(s)} = f(\bar{s}) \qquad (x > x_0).$$

Formula (7) was derived in Sec. 16 (Theorem 6) for the special case in which s is a real variable.

The conditions in Theorem 1 can be relaxed. For instance, let $F(t)$ satisfy the conditions as stated, except that it becomes infinite at $t = t_0$ in such a way that $|(t - t_0)^k F(t)|$ remains bounded as $t \to t_0$, where $k < 1$. Then the conclusions in the theorem are still valid. As an example, the transform of $F(t) = t^{-\frac{1}{2}}$ is analytic in the half plane $x > 0$, and formula (7) applies to it.

60. Permanence of Forms. We have seen that the Laplace integral of $F(t)$ leads to a function $f(s)$ that is analytic in the half plane $x > x_0$, where $s = x + iy$. If the integration is performed when $s = x$, a real function $\phi(x)$ is obtained that is identical to $f(s)$ to the right of x_0 along the real axis; that is, $\phi(x) = f(x)$ when $x > x_0$. If $\phi(s)$ is an analytic function in the half plane, then it must be identical to $f(s)$, since two different analytic functions cannot be identical along a line (Sec. 57).

It follows that transforms can be found by carrying out the integration as if s were a real variable. That the function $f(s)$ so found is analytic when $\Re(s) > x_0$ can be seen in the particular cases; but it is true in general because the integration formulas are the same whether the parameter in the integral is complex or real. The transform of $F(t) = t^2$, for instance, was found to be $2s^{-3}$ when s is real. Now t^2 is of the order $O(e^{x_0 t})$ for any positive x_0, and $2s^{-3}$ is analytic except at $s = 0$. Therefore $L\{t^2\} = 2s^{-3}$ for all complex s in the half plane $x > 0$.

All our transforms of particular functions, tabulated in Appendix 3, are valid when s is complex. We seldom need the value of x_0 which determines the half plane in which s lies; the existence of the number x_0 usually suffices.

The operational properties of the transformation developed in the first two chapters and tabulated in Appendix 2 are likewise valid when s is a complex variable in the half plane $x > x_0$. For the sake of simplicity, we may make an exception of operation 10, Appendix 2:

$$L\left\{\frac{1}{t} F(t)\right\} = \int_s^\infty f(\lambda)\, d\lambda$$

and agree that s is real here.

The permanence of the forms of those properties is again a consequence of the fact that the steps used in their derivations are independent of the real or complex character of the parameter s. However, the derivations could be rewritten when $s = x + iy$ by taking the corresponding steps with the real integrals (3), Sec. 59, that represent $u(x,y)$ and $v(x,y)$.

61. Order Properties of Transforms. We shall now show that the behavior of $f(s)$, as either $|s|$ or $\Re(s)$ increases, is restricted.

Theorem 2. *Let $F(t)$ be sectionally continuous in each finite interval and of the order $O(e^{x_0 t})$, when $t \geqq 0$. Then $|f(s)|$ and $|xf(s)|$ are bounded in each half plane $x \geqq x_1$, where $x_1 > x_0$, and $f(s) \to 0$ as $|y| \to \infty$ for each fixed $x(x > x_0)$; that is,*

(1) $|f(x + iy)| < M,$ $|xf(x + iy)| < M$ $(x \geqq x_1 > x_0),$

(2) $\lim\limits_{y \to \pm\infty} f(x + iy) = 0$ $(x > x_0),$

where the constant M may depend on the value chosen for x_1.

The second of conditions (1) states that $f(s)$ is of the order $O(1/x)$ for all s in each half plane $x \geqq x_1$, uniformly with respect to y, and consequently

(3) $\lim\limits_{x \to \infty} f(x + iy) = 0,$

uniformly with respect to y. Thus a constant other than zero cannot be the transform of any function that is sectionally continuous and of exponential order. The function e^{-cs}, where c is a real constant, fails to satisfy condition (2); therefore it is not the transform of any function of the above class.

We write $f(s) = u + iv$. To establish conditions (1) we first observe that, owing to the exponential order of $F(t)$, a constant M_0 exists such that, whenever $x > x_0$,

$$|u(x,y)| = \left| \int_0^\infty \Re[e^{-st}F(t)]\,dt \right| < M_0 \int_0^\infty e^{-(x-x_0)t}\,dt;$$

similarly for $|v(x,y)|$. Therefore

$$|u(x,y)| < \frac{M_0}{x - x_0}, \qquad |v(x,y)| < \frac{M_0}{x - x_0} \qquad (x > x_0)$$

and consequently

(4) $$|f(s)| < \frac{2M_0}{x - x_0} \qquad (x > x_0).$$

When $x \geq x_1 > x_0$, it follows that $|f(s)| < M$, where M is any number not less than $2M_0/(x_1 - x_0)$.

From the inequality (4) we see that

$$|xf(s)| < \frac{2M_0|x|}{x - x_0} = \frac{2M_0}{(x/|x|) - (x_0/|x|)} < 4M_0$$

if x is sufficiently large and positive, say $x \geq x_2$. Since $|f(s)|$ is bounded in the half plane $x \geq x_1$, then $|xf(s)|$ is bounded in the strip $x_1 \leq x \leq x_2$. Therefore $|xf(s)|$ is bounded for all s in the half plane $x \geq x_1$ consisting of the strip and the region $x \geq x_2$, and the inequalities (1) are established.

We use a basic theorem in the theory of Fourier series to prove statement (2) in Theorem 2. If $G(t)$ is a sectionally continuous function on an interval $a \leq t \leq b$, then

(5) $$\lim_{y \to \infty} \int_a^b G(t) \cos yt\,dt = \lim_{y \to \infty} \int_a^b G(t) \sin yt\,dt = 0.$$

Clearly these limits, known as *Dirichlet integrals*, can be taken also as $y \to -\infty$. Equations (5) are plausible when considered in terms of areas represented by the integrals; their proof is not difficult.[1] Let us write the equations in the form

(6) $$\lim_{|y| \to \infty} \int_0^T e^{-iyt}G(t)\,dt = 0,$$

where $G(t)$ is sectionally continuous on the interval $0 \leq t \leq T$.

---

[1] See, for instance, R. V. Churchill, "Fourier Series and Boundary Value Problems," pp. 67, 68, 1941.

Now let $G(t)$ be sectionally continuous on each bounded interval $0 \leq t \leq T$. We can show that

$$(7) \qquad \lim_{|y| \to \infty} \int_0^\infty e^{-iyt} G(t)\, dt = 0,$$

provided the improper integral is uniformly convergent with respect to y for all real y. To prove this special case of the *Riemann-Lebesgue lemma* for Fourier integrals, we first use a consequence of the uniform convergence. To each positive number ϵ there corresponds a number T_ϵ, independent of y, such that

$$\int_0^\infty e^{-iyt} G(t)\, dt = \int_0^{T_\epsilon} e^{-iyt} G(t)\, dt + R(y, T_\epsilon),$$

where $|R(y, T_\epsilon)| < \epsilon/2$. In view of equation (6) a number y_ϵ exists such that

$$\left| \int_0^{T_\epsilon} e^{-iyt} G(t)\, dt \right| < \frac{\epsilon}{2} \qquad \text{when } |y| > y_\epsilon.$$

It follows that

$$\left| \int_0^\infty e^{-iyt} G(t)\, dt \right| \leq \left| \int_0^{T_\epsilon} e^{-iyt} G(t)\, dt \right| + |R(y, T_\epsilon)| < \epsilon$$

when $|y| > y_\epsilon$, and therefore equation (7) is true.

When $G(t) = e^{-xt} F(t)$, the integral in equation (7) is the Laplace integral of $F(t)$. Under the conditions stated in Theorem 2 the integral is uniformly convergent with respect to y for each fixed $x(x > x_0)$, according to Theorem 1; also, $G(t)$ is sectionally continuous. Thus the result (2) follows from equation (7).

Theorem 3. *If $F(t)$ is continuous and $F'(t)$ is sectionally continuous in each interval $0 \leq t \leq T$ and if both functions are $O(e^{x_0 t})$, then $|f(s)|$ is $O(1/s)$ in each half plane $x \geq x_1 > x_0$; that is, corresponding to a given value of x_1, a constant M exists such that*

$$(8) \qquad\qquad |sf(s)| < M \qquad\qquad (x \geq x_1 > x_0).$$

Under the conditions stated we know that

$$L\{F'(t)\} = sf(s) - F(0) \qquad\qquad (x > x_0),$$

and that $|L\{F'(t)\}|$ is bounded in the half plane $x \geq x_1$ (Theorem 2). Since $F(0)$ is a constant, the term $sf(s)$ must be bounded, and Theorem 3 is proved.

As illustrations, the functions $F(t) = 1$, $F(t) = \cos t$, and $F(t) = t$ satisfy the conditions in Theorem 3 when $x_0 > 0$. Their transforms $1/s$, $s/(s^2 + 1)$, and $1/s^2$ are $O(1/s)$ in each half plane $x \geqq x_1 > 0$. In fact, the last transform is $O(1/s^2)$, a conclusion that follows from properties of the function $F(t) = t$ with the aid of the following extension of Theorem 3.

Theorem 4. *If $F(t)$ and $F'(t)$ are continuous and $F''(t)$ is sectionally continuous, on each interval $0 \leqq t \leqq T$, and if all three functions are $O(e^{x_0 t})$, then*

$$(9) \qquad\qquad |s^2 f(s) - sF(0)| < M \qquad\qquad (x \geqq x_1 > x_0);$$

the additional condition $F(0) = 0$ is necessary and sufficient for $|f(s)|$ to be $O(1/s^2)$ in the half plane $x \geqq x_1$.

Since our formula for the transform of $F''(t)$ is valid here, then

$$L\{F''(t)\} + F'(0) = s^2 f(s) - sF(0) \qquad\qquad (x > x_0).$$

According to Theorem 2, $|L\{F''(t)\}|$ is bounded when $x \geqq x_1$, and condition (9) follows. If $F(0) = 0$, then $|s^2 f(s)| < M$ according to (9). Conversely, if $|s^2 f(s)|$ is bounded ($x \geqq x_1$), it follows from condition (9) that $|sF(0)|$ must be bounded; but this is so only if $F(0) = 0$.

Extensions of Theorem 4 are evident. For instance, $|f(s)|$ is $O(1/s^3)$ when $x \geqq x_1 > x_0$ if $F(t)$, $F'(t)$, and $F''(t)$ are continuous and $F'''(t)$ is sectionally continuous, and if all four functions are $O(e^{x_0 t})$, provided that $F(0) = F'(0) = 0$.

In Theorem 3 the condition that $F(t)$ be continuous is introduced to simplify the proof; $|f(s)|$ is $O(1/s)$ under somewhat more relaxed conditions on $F(t)$.

PROBLEMS

1. When $s = x + iy$, write the real and imaginary components of $L\{F'(t)\}$ and derive the formula for $L\{F'(t)\}$, using the real integrals involved.

2. A function $F(t)$ is sectionally continuous on a finite interval $T_1 \leqq t \leqq T_2 (T_1 \geqq 0)$ and $F(t) = 0$ for all other positive values of t. What values can be assigned to x_0 in order that $|F(t)|$ be $O(e^{x_0 t})$? Show why the transform $f(s)$ of such a function must be an entire function (Theorem 1).

3. The step function $1 - S_1(t)$ is an example of the function $F(t)$

considered in Prob. 2. Show directly that its transform is

$$f(s) = \frac{1 - e^{-s}}{s} \qquad (s \neq 0), \qquad [f(0) = 1],$$

and verify that $f(s)$ is an entire function of the complex variable s.

4. Determine an order property of $f(s)$ from the character of the function $F(t)$ in each of the following cases, and verify your conclusion by writing $f(s)$.

(a) $F(t) = \sin kt$;   (b) $F(t) = \cosh t$;   (c) $F(t) = t \sin t$;

(d) $F(t) = S_k(t)$;   (e) $F(t) = (t - 1)S_1(t)$.

5. Show that the function $s^{-k} \exp(-s^2)$, where $k \geqq 0$, cannot be the transform of any sectionally continuous function of exponential order.

6. Prove Theorem 3 when the continuity condition on $F(t)$ is replaced by the condition that $F(t)$ is continuous when $t \geqq 0$ except for finite jumps $J(t_n)$ at a finite number of points t_n $(n = 1, 2, \ldots, m)$.

62. The Inversion Integral. According to our extension of Cauchy's integral formula (Sec. 58), a function $f(s)$ that is analytic and of order $O(s^{-k})$ in a half plane $x \geqq \gamma$, where $k > 0$, can be expressed in terms of its values on the boundary by a line integral:

$$f(s) = \frac{1}{2\pi i} \lim_{\beta \to \infty} \int_{\gamma - i\beta}^{\gamma + i\beta} \frac{f(z)\ dz}{s - z} \qquad [\Re(s) > \gamma].$$

If we formally apply the inverse Laplace transformation to the functions of s on either side of this equation, and interchange the order of the operation L^{-1} and the integration, we find that

$$(1) \qquad F(t) = \frac{1}{2\pi i} \lim_{\beta \to \infty} \int_{\gamma - i\beta}^{\gamma + i\beta} e^{zt} f(z)\ dz.$$

The expression on the right here is called the *complex inversion integral* for the Laplace transformation. We use the symbol L_i^{-1} here for the linear integral transformation of $f(s)$ represented by the inversion integral; that is,

$$(2) \qquad L_i^{-1}\{f(s)\} = \frac{1}{2\pi i} \lim_{\beta \to \infty} \int_{\gamma - i\beta}^{\gamma + i\beta} e^{zt} f(z)\ dz.$$

The symbol is intended to suggest an integration as well as an inverse Laplace transformation.

We assume that $f(\bar{s}) = \overline{f(s)}$, a condition that is satisfied by transforms of real-valued functions $F(t)$ (Sec. 59). Although the inversion integral is an integral in the complex plane along the line $x = \gamma$ (Fig. 69), we can write it as a real improper integral. Since $z = \gamma + iy$, where γ is fixed, the integral in equation (2) can be written as

$$ie^{\gamma t} \left[\int_{-\beta}^{0} e^{iyt} f(\gamma + iy)\, dy + \int_{0}^{\beta} e^{iyt} f(\gamma + iy)\, dy \right].$$

When the variable of integration in the first integral here is replaced by $-y$, the expression inside the brackets becomes

$$\int_{0}^{\beta} [e^{-iyt} f(\gamma - iy) + e^{iyt} f(\gamma + iy)]\, dy.$$

The integrand of this last integral is $2\Re[e^{iyt} f(\gamma + iy)]$, since the complex conjugate of $e^{iyt} f(\gamma + iy)$ is $e^{-iyt} f(\gamma - iy)$. We write

$$f(x + iy) = u(x,y) + iv(x,y);$$

then

$$\Re[e^{iyt} f(\gamma + iy)] = u(\gamma,y) \cos yt - v(\gamma,y) \sin yt$$

and therefore

$$(3) \quad L_i^{-1}\{f(s)\} = \frac{e^{\gamma t}}{\pi} \int_{0}^{\infty} [u(\gamma,y) \cos yt - v(\gamma,y) \sin yt]\, dy.$$

When $f(s)$ satisfies certain conditions, we shall see that the value of the real integral (3) is independent of γ for all values of γ greater than a prescribed number. In view of the form (3) we see that the inversion integral is subject to the rules of operation for real integrals. But even for simple functions $f(s)$ the integrations involved in this real form are generally difficult. To evaluate the inversion integral we shall use the complex form (2) in conjunction with the theory of residues or changes in the path of integration.

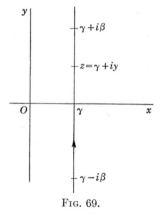

FIG. 69.

In the sections to follow, conditions on either $f(s)$ or $F(t)$ will be established under which the inversion integral represents the inverse transform $F(t)$ of $f(s)$, so that equation (1) becomes an explicit formula for $F(t)$ in terms of $f(s)$.

Other formulas for the inverse transformation are known.[1]
The inversion integral (2), however, has greater general utility
than any of the others.

63. Conditions on $f(s)$. The following theorem gives conditions on a function $f(s)$ sufficient to guarantee that a function
$F(t)$ exists whose transform is $f(s)$, and that $F(t)$ is given by the
inversion integral.   Certain properties of $F(t)$ are also noted.

   Theorem 5.   *Let $f(s)$ be any function of the complex variable s
that is analytic and of order $O(s^{-k})$ for all s ($s = x + iy$) in a half
plane $x \geqq x_0$, where $k > 1$; also let $f(x)$ be real ($x \geqq x_0$).   Then
the inversion integral of $f(s)$ along any line $x = \gamma$, where $\gamma \geqq x_0$,
converges to a real-valued function $F(t)$ that is independent of γ,*

$$(1) \qquad\qquad F(t) = L_i^{-1}\{f(s)\} \qquad (-\infty < t < \infty),$$

whose Laplace transform is the given function $f(s)$:

$$(2) \qquad\qquad L\{F(t)\} = f(s) \qquad\qquad (x > x_0).$$

Furthermore $F(t)$ is $O(e^{x_0 t})$, it is continuous ($-\infty < t < \infty$), and

$$(3) \qquad\qquad\qquad F(t) = 0 \qquad\qquad when\ t \leqq 0.$$

The integrand $e^{zt}f(z)$ of the inversion integral is everywhere a
continuous function of y and t, where $z = \gamma + iy$ and $\gamma \geqq x_0$,
because $f(z)$ is analytic when $x \geqq x_0$.   From the order condition
on $f(s)$ it follows that positive numbers M and y_0 exist such that

$$(4) \qquad\qquad |f(\gamma + iy)| < \frac{M}{(\gamma^2 + y^2)^{\frac{1}{2}k}} \leqq \frac{M}{|y|^k} \qquad (|y| > y_0).$$

Since $f(s)$ is analytic and $f(x)$ is real in the half plane $x \geqq x_0$,
then $f(\bar{s}) = \overline{f(s)}$ there, according to the principle of reflection,
and the inversion integral takes the real form (3), Sec. 62, which
we now write

$$(5) \qquad \pi e^{-\gamma t}L_i^{-1}\{f(s)\} = \int_0^{y_0} g(t,y)\ dy + \int_{y_0}^\infty g(t,y)\ dy,$$

$$(6) \qquad\qquad g(t,y) = u(\gamma,y)\cos yt - v(\gamma,y)\sin yt.$$

In view of condition (4), $|g(t,y)| < 2M|y|^{-k}$, where $k > 1$ and
M is independent of t, hence the improper integral in equation (5)
converges uniformly with respect to t ($-\infty < t < \infty$).   But
$g(t,y)$ is continuous for all t and y, so that both integrals repre-

---

[1] See books by Doetsch or Widder listed in Appendix 1.

sent continuous functions of t. Both are also bounded functions of the variable t, if $\gamma = x_0$, as we can see by observing that $|g(t,y)|$ is not greater than $2|f(x_0 + iy)|$, which is independent of t and integrable.

We have now shown that the inversion integral of $f(s)$ represents a continuous function $F(t)$ when $\gamma \geqq x_0$ and that a number M_0, independent of t, exists such that $F(t)$ has the exponential order property

$$(7) \qquad\qquad e^{-x_0 t}|F(t)| < M_0 \qquad\qquad (-\infty < t < \infty).$$

To show that $F(t)$ is independent of γ we use any second path $x = \gamma'$, where $\gamma' > \gamma$. Since $e^{zt}f(z)$ is analytic when $x \geqq \gamma$, the integral of that function around the boundary of the rectangle $ABCD$ (Fig. 70) is zero, according to Cauchy's integral theorem. On the side BC, $z = x + i\beta$ and, since $|f(z)| < M|z|^{-k}$,

$$|e^{zt}f(z)| < e^{xt}\frac{M}{\beta^k}.$$

Consequently the integral along that side satisfies the condition

$$\left| \int_{\gamma+i\beta}^{\gamma'+i\beta} e^{zt}f(z)\, dz \right| < \frac{M}{\beta^k} \int_{\gamma}^{\gamma'} e^{xt}\, dx$$

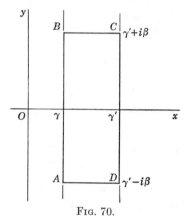

FIG. 70.

and the integral vanishes as $\beta \to \infty$. The same argument applies to the integral along AD. We have used only the fact that $k > 0$ here.

Since the sum of the integrals over the four sides is zero, then

$$\lim_{\beta \to \infty} \left[\int_{\gamma-i\beta}^{\gamma+i\beta} e^{zt}f(z)\, dz + \int_{\gamma'+i\beta}^{\gamma'-i\beta} e^{zt}f(z)\, dz \right] = 0.$$

When $k > 1$, we have seen that the limit of each integral exists; hence

$$\lim_{\beta \to \infty} \int_{\gamma-i\beta}^{\gamma+i\beta} e^{zt}f(z)\, dz = \lim_{\beta \to \infty} \int_{\gamma'-i\beta}^{\gamma'+i\beta} e^{zt}f(z)\, dz.$$

The function defined by equation (1) is therefore independent of γ.

Now let t have any fixed nonpositive value ($t \leqq 0$) and select a positive number for γ. The function

$$\phi(z) = e^{zt}f(z)(z - z_1) \qquad [\Re(z_1) > \gamma]$$

is analytic in the half plane $x \geqq \gamma$ and of the order of $|z|^{-(k-1)}$ there since $|e^{zt}| \leqq 1$, where $k > 1$, and hence $k - 1 > 0$. The extension of Cauchy's integral formula therefore represents $\phi(z_1)$ in the form

$$\phi(z_1) = -\frac{1}{2\pi i} \lim_{\beta \to \infty} \int_{\gamma - i\beta}^{\gamma + i\beta} \frac{\phi(z) \, dz}{z - z_1} = -L_i^{-1}\{f(s)\}$$

and, since $\phi(z_1) = 0$, property (3) of $F(t)$ is established.

Finally, the transform of our function (1) must exist since we have shown that $F(t)$ is continuous and of exponential order. We write $s = a + ib$, where $a > x_0$, and $z = x_0 + iy$. Then

$$L\{F(t)\} = \lim_{T \to \infty} \int_0^T e^{-st} \frac{1}{2\pi} \int_{-\infty}^{\infty} e^{zt}f(z) \, dy \, dt,$$

and in view of the uniform convergence of the inversion integral, with respect to t, the order of integration can be interchanged. Thus

$$(8) \qquad L\{F(t)\} = \frac{1}{2\pi} \lim_{T \to \infty} \int_{-\infty}^{\infty} f(z) \int_0^T e^{-(s-z)t} \, dt \, dy.$$

The improper integral here converges uniformly with respect to T because its integrand satisfies the conditions

$$\left| f(z) \int_0^T e^{-(s-z)t} \, dt \right| < \frac{M}{|y|^k} \frac{1 - e^{-(a-x_0)T}}{a - x_0} < \frac{M}{a - x_0} \frac{1}{|y|^k}$$

when $|y| > y_0 > 0$, where M is independent of T and $k > 1$. The limit of the integrand, as $T \to \infty$, can be written

$$f(z) \int_0^{\infty} e^{-(s-z)t} \, dt = \frac{f(z)}{s - z},$$

and the improper integral of this function of y exists. That limit is approached uniformly with respect to $y(-\infty < y < \infty)$ because for each positive ϵ there is a number T_ϵ, independent of y, such that

$$\left| f(z) \int_T^{\infty} e^{-(s-z)t} \, dt \right| < \frac{M_1}{a - x_0} e^{-(a-x_0)T} < \epsilon$$

when $T > T_\epsilon$, where M_1 is an upper bound of $|f(z)|$. We have now justified writing the limit in equation (8) inside the first integral sign (Prob. 12, Sec. 23). Thus

$$L\{F(t)\} = \frac{1}{2\pi} \int_{-\infty}^{\infty} \frac{f(z)}{s - z} \, dy = f(s),$$

where the last step follows from our extension of Cauchy's integral formula. The proof of Theorem 5 is now complete.

64. Conditions on $F(t)$. Uniqueness of the Inversion. The foregoing conditions under which the inversion integral formula is valid are severe. They are not satisfied, for example, by the function $f(s) = 1/s$, since this function is not of the order of $1/s^k$, where $k > 1$. Hence Theorem 5 does not ensure the convergence of the inversion integral in this case to the function $F(t)$. By using a Fourier integral theorem and qualifying the function $F(t)$ instead of $f(s)$, we can relax the conditions so that the inversion integral formula can be seen to apply in nearly all cases of interest to us. In fact, we shall see that our formula is only a modified form of the Fourier integral formula.

Let $G(t)$ be a function defined for all real values of t, sectionally continuous over each finite interval of the t axis, and let its values when $|t|$ is large be such that the integral

$$\int_{-\infty}^{\infty} |G(t)| \, dt$$

exists. Also let $G'(t)$ be sectionally continuous on each finite interval. We agree to define $G(t)$ at each point t_0, where it is discontinuous as the mean value of its limits from the right and left at t_0; that is,

(1) $$G(t_0) = \tfrac{1}{2}[G(t_0 + 0) + G(t_0 - 0)].$$

Any such function is represented by the *Fourier integral formula*[1]

(2) $$G(t) = \frac{1}{\pi} \int_0^{\infty} \int_{-\infty}^{\infty} G(\tau) \cos y(t - \tau) \, d\tau \, dy \quad (-\infty < t < \infty).$$

Thus

$$G(t) = \frac{1}{2\pi} \lim_{\beta \to \infty} \int_0^{\beta} \int_{-\infty}^{\infty} G(\tau)[e^{iy(t-\tau)} + e^{-iy(t-\tau)}] \, d\tau \, dy$$

---

[1] See, for instance, Churchill, *op. cit.*, pp. 89 ff.

and, since the integral of $|G(\tau)|$ exists, the iterated integral here can be written as the sum

$$\int_0^\beta e^{iyt} \int_{-\infty}^\infty G(\tau)e^{-iy\tau}\, d\tau\, dy + \int_{-\beta}^0 e^{iyt} \int_{-\infty}^\infty G(\tau)e^{-iy\tau}\, d\tau\, dy.$$

Hence the Fourier integral formula has the exponential form

$$(3) \quad G(t) = \frac{1}{2\pi} \lim_{\beta \to \infty} \int_{-\beta}^\beta e^{iyt} \int_{-\infty}^\infty G(\tau)e^{-iy\tau}\, d\tau\, dy \quad (-\infty < t < \infty).$$

Now let $F(t)$ be a function that is defined when $t \geqq 0$ and of exponential order $O(e^{x_0 t})$, and let $F(t)$ and $F'(t)$ be sectionally continuous on each interval $0 \leqq t \leqq T$. If we write

$$\begin{aligned} G(t) &= 0 && \text{when } t < 0, \\ &= e^{-\gamma t}F(t) && \text{when } t > 0, \end{aligned}$$

where $\gamma > x_0$, then $G(t)$ satisfies the sufficient conditions stated above for the representation (3). Therefore

$$(4) \quad G(t) = \frac{1}{2\pi} \lim_{\beta \to \infty} \int_{-\beta}^\beta e^{iyt} \int_0^\infty e^{-(\gamma+iy)\tau}F(\tau)\, d\tau\, dy$$
$$(-\infty < t < \infty).$$

The inner integral represents $f(\gamma + iy)$, where $f(s)$ is the Laplace transform of $F(t)$. If $z = \gamma + iy$ it follows that, for all t,

$$(5) \quad e^{\gamma t}G(t) = \frac{1}{2\pi i} \lim_{\beta \to \infty} \int_{\gamma-i\beta}^{\gamma+i\beta} e^{zt}f(z)\, dz = L_i^{-1}\{f(s)\}.$$

When $t < 0$, $G(t) = 0$ and therefore $L_i^{-1}\{f(s)\} = 0$.

When $t > 0$, $e^{\gamma t}G(t) = F(t)$ and equation (5) represents $F(t)$ as the inversion integral $L_i^{-1}\{f(s)\}$. But since the function $G(t)$ represented by formula (4) has the mean value (1) at each point t_0 of discontinuity, the inversion integral converges to $F(t_0)$ at a point t_0 where $F(t)$ has a jump, provided we agree that

$$(6) \qquad F(t_0) = \tfrac{1}{2}[F(t_0 + 0) + F(t_0 - 0)] \qquad (t_0 > 0).$$

When $t = 0$ the value of the inversion integral is $\frac{1}{2}[F(+0) + 0]$.

Note that the original form of the inversion integral, the principal value (5) of the improper integral from $\gamma - i\infty$ to $\gamma + i\infty$, involving the limit as $\beta \to \infty$, is used here. Our results can be stated as follows.

Theorem 6. *If* $f(s)$ *is the transform of any function* $F(t)$ *of order* $O(e^{x_0 t})$, *where* $F(t)$ *and* $F'(t)$ *are sectionally continuous in each interval* $0 \leqq t \leqq T$, *then the inversion integral of* $f(s)$ *along any line* $x = \gamma$, *where* $\gamma > x_0$, *exists and represents* $F(t)$:

$$(7) \qquad\qquad L_i^{-1}\{f(s)\} = F(t) \qquad\qquad (t > 0).$$

At any point t_0, *where* $F(t)$ *is discontinuous, the inversion integral represents the mean value* (6) *of* $F(t)$; *when* $t = 0$ *it has the value* $\frac{1}{2}F(+0)$, *and when* $t < 0$ *it has the value zero.*

In order to make a simple analysis of uniqueness of the inverse Laplace transformation we define a *class* $\mathcal{E}(x_0)$ *of real-valued functions.* A function $F(t)$ belongs to the class $\mathcal{E}(x_0)$ if it is defined whenever $t \geqq 0$, of exponential order $O(e^{x_0 t})$, if $F(t)$ and $F'(t)$ are sectionally continuous on each finite interval in the range $t \geqq 0$, and if $F(t_0)$ is defined as its mean value (6) at each point t_0 of discontinuity of $F(t)$ while $F(0)$ is defined as $\frac{1}{2}F(+0)$.

Each function $F(t)$ of that class has just one transform $f(s)$, where $s = x + iy$ and $x > x_0$ (Theorem 1). According to Theorem 6, $L_i^{-1}\{f(s)\}$ has the value $F(t)$ when $t \geqq 0$, regardless of which line $x = \gamma$ is used for the inversion integral as long as $\gamma > x_0$. Suppose that a function $G(t)$ belongs to a class $\mathcal{E}(x_1)$ and that its transform is also $f(s)$, where $x > x_1$. Then $L_i^{-1}\{f(s)\} = G(t)$ when $t \geqq 0$, where $\gamma > x_1$. In both inversion integrals γ can be taken as a number greater than x_0 and greater than x_1; thus $G(t) = F(t)$.

Theorem 7. *Among all functions of any of the classes* $\mathcal{E}(x_0)$, *for all finite* x_0, *no two distinct functions can have the same transform.*

The function $F(t) = e^{kt}$, for example, is of class $\mathcal{E}(x_0)$ if we define $F(0)$ to be $\frac{1}{2}$. It is the only function of such a class that has the transform $(s - k)^{-1}$; in particular, e^{kt} is the only function that is continuous and of exponential order ($t \geqq 0$) and has that transform.

The inverse transform is unique under somewhat broader conditions than those stated above. It is known that any two functions with the same transform can differ at most by a null function, that is, by a function $N(t)$ such that

$$\int_0^t N(\tau)\, d\tau = 0 \qquad \text{for every positive } t.$$

The function $N(t)$ cannot differ from zero over any interval of positive length along the t axis. If the two functions are continuous, they must be identical for all positive t. The proof of these statements, known as Lerch's theorem, can be found in the more theoretical books on the transformation.[1]

65. Derivatives of the Inversion Integral. When the solution of a boundary value problem is found in the form of an inversion integral $L_i^{-1}\{f\}$, it is often possible to verify completely that solution by examining the function f. The two theorems in this section are useful for that purpose. Their proofs follow at once from Theorem 5 and the properties of uniformly convergent improper integrals (Sec. 12).

When the inversion integral is differentiated with respect to t under the integral sign, we obtain $L_i^{-1}\{sf(s)\}$:

$$(1) \quad \frac{1}{2\pi i} \lim_{\beta \to \infty} \int_{\gamma-i\beta}^{\gamma+i\beta} \frac{\partial}{\partial t} [e^{zt}f(z)] \, dz = \frac{1}{2\pi i} \lim_{\beta \to \infty} \int_{\gamma-i\beta}^{\gamma+i\beta} e^{zt}zf(z) \, dz.$$

If the function $sf(s)$ as well as $f(s)$ satisfies the conditions imposed upon the function $f(s)$ in Theorem 5, the integral (1) converges uniformly with respect to t and represents the derivative, with respect to t, of $L_i^{-1}\{f(s)\}$. That derivative satisfies the continuity conditions stated for the function $F(t)$ in Theorem 5. The additional condition needed on $f(s)$ here is that $sf(s)$ be $O(s^{-k})$ where $k > 1$, or that $f(s)$ be of order $O(s^{-k-1})$.

By replacing $f(s)$ in the last paragraph by the function $sf(s)$, it follows that the second derivative with respect to t of $L_i^{-1}\{f(s)\}$ is $L_i^{-1}\{s^2f(s)\}$, and so on. Thus we have the following theorem:

Theorem 8. *Let $f(s)$ be any function of the complex variable s that is analytic and of order $O(s^{-k-m})$, in some half plane $\Re(s) \geq x_0$ where $k > 1$ and m is a positive integer. Then the inversion integral along any line $x = \gamma$ where $\gamma \geq x_0$ converges to the inverse transform $F(t)$ of $f(s)$,*

$$(2) \qquad L_i^{-1}\{f(s)\} = F(t),$$

and the derivatives of this function are given by the formula

$$(3) \qquad F^{(n)}(t) = L_i^{-1}\{s^nf(s)\} \quad (n = 1, 2, \ldots, m);$$

furthermore $F(t)$ and each of its derivatives (3) are continuous functions of $t(t \geq 0)$ of order $O(e^{x_0 t})$, and they vanish at $t = 0$,

$$(4) \qquad F(0) = F'(0) = \cdots = F^{(m)}(0) = 0.$$

[1] See books by Doetsch or Widder listed in Appendix 1.

It follows from this theorem, for example, that the inverse transform of the function

$$f(s) = \frac{1}{(s^2 + a^2)^{\frac{3}{2}}},$$

which is of the order $O(s^{-3})$ in a right half plane, is the transform of a function $F(t)$ represented by the inversion integral, that $F'(t)$ is continuous $(t \geqq 0)$, and that

$$F(0) = F'(0) = 0.$$

The function $F(t)$ here is given in terms of a Bessel function in Appendix 3, transform 57.

It will be recalled that formula (3) cannot hold true without rather severe restrictions on either $F(t)$ or $f(s)$. For according to our basic property of the transformation of derivatives,

$$F^{(n)}(t) = L^{-1}\{s^n f(s) - s^{n-1}F(0) - \cdots - F^{(n-1)}(0)\},$$

when $F^{(n)}(t)$ is sectionally continuous and $F^{(n-1)}(t)$ is continuous and the functions here are of exponential order. If $F^{(n)}(t)$ is to be the inverse transform of $s^n f(s)$, it is essential that $F(0)$, $F'(0)$, . . . , $F^{(n-1)}(0)$ all vanish.

Of course the function f in the above theorem may involve constants or variables independent of s provided the statements in the theorem are understood to apply for fixed values of those parameters. Concerning differentiation and continuity with respect to such a parameter r, the following theorem can be seen from the properties of uniformly convergent infinite integrals.

Theorem 9. *Let $f(r,s)$ be a continuous function of its two variables, analytic with respect to s in some half plane $\Re(s) \geqq x_0$, and let $|f(r,s)|$ be less than $M|s|^{-k}$ $(k > 1)$ in that half plane, where the constant M is independent of r. Then the inverse transform of $f(r,s)$ with respect to s is*

$$F(r,t) = L_i^{-1}\{f(r,s)\},$$

where the path of integration $x = \gamma$ is such that $\gamma \geqq x_0$, and $F(r,t)$ is a continuous function of its two variables r, t when $t \geqq 0$. If the parameter has an infinite range $r > r_0$ and $f(r,s) \to \phi(s)$ as $r \to \infty$, uniformly with respect to s on the line $x = \gamma$, then

(5) $$\lim_{r \to \infty} F(r,t) = L_i^{-1}\{\phi(s)\}.$$

If $\partial/\partial r \,[f(r,s)]$ also satisfies the conditions imposed on $f(r,s)$, then

(6) $$\frac{\partial}{\partial r} F(r,t) = L_i^{-1} \left\{ \frac{\partial}{\partial r} f(r,s) \right\}.$$

The theorem can be applied to $\partial/\partial r \,[f(r,s)]$ to obtain corresponding results for $\partial^2/\partial r^2 \,[F(r,t)]$, and so on for derivatives of higher order. Applications of these theorems are presented in the next chapter.

66. Representation by Series of Residues. Throughout this and the following section, $f(s)$ denotes a function that is analytic for all finite values of the complex variable s except for a set of isolated singular points

$$s_1, s_2, \ldots , s_n, \ldots$$

confined to some left half plane $\mathfrak{R}(s) < \gamma$. We assume also that $f(s)$ satisfies conditions under which its inversion integral along the line $x = \gamma$ converges to the inverse transform $F(t)$, say the conditions in either Theorem 5 or 6. Then $F(t)$ can be represented formally by a series, finite or infinite depending on the number of singular points, and we shall establish practical conditions in the following section under which the representation is valid.

Since e^{zt} is an entire function of z, the singular points $z = s_n$ of $f(z)$ are the singular points of the integrand $e^{zt}f(z)$ of the inversion integral. Let $\rho_n(t)$ denote the residue of the integrand, for any fixed t, at the isolated singular point s_n:

(1) $$\rho_n(t) = \text{the residue of } e^{zt}f(z) \text{ at } z = s_n.$$

According to the residue theorem the integral of $e^{zt}f(z)$ around a path enclosing the points $s_1, s_2, \ldots , s_N$ has the value

$$2\pi i[\rho_1(t) + \rho_2(t) + \cdots + \rho_N(t)].$$

Let the path be made up of the line segment joining the points $\gamma - i\beta_N$, $\gamma + i\beta_N$, and some curve C_N beginning at the second and ending at the first of these two points and lying in the half plane $x \leqq \gamma$ (Fig. 71). Then

(2) $$\frac{1}{2\pi i} \int_{\gamma-i\beta_N}^{\gamma+i\beta_N} e^{zt}f(z) \, dz + \frac{1}{2\pi i} \int_{C_N} e^{zt}f(z) \, dz = \sum_{n=1}^{N} \rho_n(t).$$

As $\beta_N \to \infty$ the value of the first integral here tends to $L_i^{-1}\{f(s)\}$ since the inversion integral is the limit of the corresponding integral involving β, as $\beta \to \infty$ in any manner. Let the numbers β_N $(N = 1, 2, \ldots)$ be selected so that $\beta_N \to \infty$ as $N \to \infty$, and let the curves C_N together with the line $x = \gamma$ enclose the points $s_1, s_2, \ldots, s_N$, if the number of singular points is infinite. If the number is finite, let all of them be enclosed when N is greater than some fixed number. Then if $f(z)$ and C_N satisfy additional conditions under which

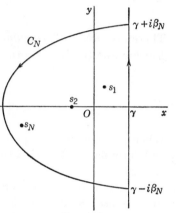

$$(3) \quad \frac{1}{2\pi i} \lim_{N \to \infty} \int_{C_N} e^{zt} f(z) \, dz = 0,$$

it follows, by letting $N \to \infty$ in equation (2), that

$$L_i^{-1}\{f(s)\} = \sum_{n=1}^{\infty} \rho_n(t).$$

The series on the right is necessarily convergent since the limit,

FIG. 71.

as $N \to \infty$, of the left-hand member of equation (2) exists. If the number of poles is finite, there is only a finite number of terms in the series.

Since the inversion integral represents $F(t)$ by hypothesis, the inverse transform of $f(s)$ is represented as the series of residues of $e^{zt}f(z)$:

$$(4) \qquad\qquad F(t) = \sum_{n=1}^{\infty} \rho_n(t).$$

It is not essential that the line $x = \gamma$ and the curve C_N enclose exactly N of the poles, of course. For example, if two poles are included in the ring between C_N and C_{N+1}, the residues at these two poles are simply grouped as a single term in the series.

When a pole s_n is a simple pole, the residue can be written, according to Sec. 55, as

$$(5) \qquad \rho_n(t) = \lim_{z \to s_n} (z - s_n) e^{zt} f(z) = e^{s_n t} \lim_{z \to s_n} (z - s_n) f(z).$$

If in particular $f(z)$ has the fractional form

$$(6) \qquad f(z) = \frac{p(z)}{q(z)},$$

where $p(z)$ and $q(z)$ are analytic at $z = s_n$ and $p(s_n) \neq 0$, the residue at the simple pole s_n is

$$(7) \qquad \rho_n(t) = \frac{p(s_n)}{q'(s_n)} e^{s_n t}.$$

Therefore, *when all singular points of $f(s)$ are simple poles* and $f(s)$ has the fractional form (6), the representation (4) becomes

$$(8) \qquad F(t) = L^{-1}\left\{\frac{p(s)}{q(s)}\right\} = \sum_{n=1}^{\infty} \frac{p(s_n)}{q'(s_n)} e^{s_n t}.$$

When $p(s)$ and $q(s)$ are polynomials the number of poles is finite and formula (8) becomes the Heaviside expansion formula (4), Sec. 20.

It is often convenient to use the series representation (4) or its special case (8) directly and formally, without regard to conditions under which the inversion integral represents $F(t)$ and the integral over C_N tends to zero. The function $F(t)$ so found may be such that its transform can be shown to be $f(s)$, or such that it satisfies all conditions in a problem whose solution was sought by the transformation method. As we shall see in the problems at the end of this chapter, however, there are simple cases in which such a formal procedure leads to incorrect results.

If s_n is a pole of $f(s)$, of order m, the function

$$\phi_n(z) = (z - s_n)^m f(z)$$

is analytic at s_n, provided $\phi_n(s_n)$ is properly defined (Sec. 55). Then $\phi_n(z)e^{zt}$ is analytic there and $f(z)e^{zt}$ has a pole of order m at s_n. The residue of the integrand of the inversion integral at the pole is therefore given by the formula

$$(9) \qquad \rho_n(t) = \frac{\Phi_n(s_n)}{(m-1)!}, \qquad \text{if} \qquad \Phi_n(z) = \frac{\partial^{m-1}}{\partial z^{m-1}}[\phi_n(z)e^{zt}].$$

Another formula for the residue in this case can be written from the Laurent series that represents $f(z)$ about the pole s_n,

$$(10) \quad f(z) = \frac{A_{-1}}{z - s_n} + \cdots + \frac{A_{-m}}{(z - s_n)^m} + \sum_{j=0}^{\infty} A_j (z - s_n)^j,$$

where $0 < |z - s_n| < r_0$, and where r_0 and the A's depend on s_n. The product of that series and Taylor's series expansion of e^{zt}, about s_n,

$$e^{zt} = e^{s_n t} \left[1 + t(z - s_n) + \cdots + \frac{t^{m-1}}{(m - 1)!} (z - s_n)^{m-1} + \cdots \right]$$

gives the Laurent series for $e^{zt} f(z)$ about s_n. The coefficient of $(z - s_n)^{-1}$ in the product of the two series or the residue of $e^{zt} f(z)$ at the pole s_n of order m is

$$(11) \quad \rho_n(t) = e^{s_n t} \left[A_{-1} + t A_{-2} + \cdots + \frac{t^{m-1}}{(m - 1)!} A_{-m} \right].$$

Note that this residue is just the inverse transform of the principal part of $f(s)$ about s_n, the part corresponding to the negative powers of $(z - s_n)$ in the Laurent series (10).

Suppose that two of the singular points of $f(z)$ are *simple poles* of the type

$$(12) \qquad\qquad z = \pm i\omega,$$

where ω is real. We assume that $f(x)$ is real; thus $f(\bar{z}) = \overline{f(z)}$. For convenience in applying formula (5) we write

$$\phi_1(z) = (z - i\omega)f(z), \qquad \phi_2(z) = (z + i\omega)f(z).$$

These functions are analytic at $\pm i\omega$, respectively. The number

$$(13) \qquad\qquad \lim_{z \to i\omega} \phi_1(z) = \phi_1(i\omega) = r_1 e^{i\theta_1} \qquad\qquad (r_1 > 0)$$

is the residue of $f(z)$ at the pole $i\omega$. Now

$$\phi_2(\bar{z}) = (\bar{z} + i\omega)f(\bar{z}) = \overline{\phi_1(z)},$$

and therefore the sum of the residues of $e^{zt} f(z)$ at the poles (12),

$$\lim_{z \to i\omega} e^{zt} \phi_1(z) + \lim_{z \to -i\omega} e^{zt} \phi_2(z),$$

can be written

$$\lim_{z \to i\omega} [e^{zt} \phi_1(z) + e^{\bar{z}t} \phi_2(\bar{z})] = \lim_{z \to i\omega} [e^{zt} \phi_1(z) + \overline{e^{zt} \phi_1(z)}].$$

That is,

$$\rho_1(t) + \rho_2(t) = 2 \lim_{z \to i\omega} \Re[e^{zt}\phi_1(z)] = 2\Re[e^{i\omega t}\phi_1(i\omega)].$$

In terms of the residue (13) then the component of $F(t)$ that corresponds to the poles (12) is the periodic function

$$(14) \qquad \rho_1(t) + \rho_2(t) = 2r_1 \cos(\omega t + \theta_1).$$

In case all singular points of $f(z)$ consist of the simple poles

$$z = \pm in\omega \qquad (n = 1, 2, \ldots),$$

the series (4) for $F(t)$ represents a periodic function of t with angular frequency ω.

When the poles (12) of $f(z)$ are of *second order*, we write

$$\phi_1(z) = (z - i\omega)^2 f(z), \qquad \phi_1(i\omega) = r_1 e^{i\theta_1}, \qquad \phi_1'(i\omega) = r_1' e^{i\theta_1'},$$

where $r_1 > 0$ and $r_1' \geqq 0$. The terms in $F(t)$ corresponding to the poles $\pm i\omega$, found with the aid of formula (9), are

$$(15) \qquad 2[r_1' \cos(\omega t + \theta_1') + r_1 t \cos(\omega t + \theta_1)].$$

Details of the derivation are left to the problems. The second term here, a term of *resonance type*, represents an *unstable* component of $F(t)$. Its coefficient r_1 does not vanish.

Similarly, if the poles (12) are of order m, then $F(t)$ contains a term $t^{m-1} \cos(\omega t + \theta)$ whose coefficient is not zero.

67. Validity of the Representation by Series. We now establish conditions on $f(z)$ under which the integrals of $e^{zt}f(z)$, over certain useful types of paths C_N, tend to zero as N tends to infinity, as assumed in Sec. 66, equation (3). Since the integrals must exist, the paths should not pass through singular points, nor should they pass arbitrarily close to the points when N is large if the limit of the integrals is to exist. The ease of finding the order of $|f(z)|$ when z is on C_N depends upon the particular function $f(z)$ and the type of paths chosen for C_N.

The order properties of some types of functions on horizontal and vertical lines are easily determined. In such cases it is convenient to let C_N be an open rectangle with sides along the lines $y = \pm\beta_N$ and $x = -\beta_N$, as indicated in Fig. 72, where $\beta_N \to \infty$ as $N \to \infty$. For the function $f(z)$, suppose that the numbers β_N can be selected so that

$$|f(x \pm i\beta_N)| < \delta_N \qquad (-\beta_N < x < \gamma),$$

where $\delta_N \to 0$ as $N \to \infty$; that is, $|f(z)| \to 0$ uniformly with respect to x on the upper and lower sides of C_N as $N \to \infty$. Then $|e^{zt}f(z)| < \delta_N e^{xt}$ there, and the absolute value of the integral over each side is less than

$$\delta_N \int_{-\beta_N}^{\gamma} e^{xt}\,dx, \quad\text{or}\quad \frac{\delta_N}{t}(e^{\gamma t} - e^{-\beta_N t}) \qquad (t > 0).$$

Thus the integrals over those sides vanish as $N \to \infty$ when $t > 0$.

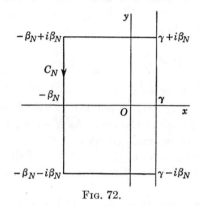

FIG. 72.

Suppose further that $|f(z)|$ is uniformly bounded on the third side of all the open rectangles:

$$|f(-\beta_N + iy)| < M \qquad (-\beta_N < y < \beta_N),$$

where the constant M is independent of N. Then the absolute value of the integral of $e^{zt}f(z)$ along that side of C_N is less than

$$M e^{-\beta_N t} \int_{-\beta_N}^{\beta_N} dy, \quad\text{or}\quad 2M\beta_N e^{-\beta_N t},$$

which vanishes as $N \to \infty$ if $t > 0$. Thus when $f(z)$ satisfies the above conditions

$$(1) \qquad \lim_{N \to \infty} \int_{C_N} e^{zt}f(z)\,dz = 0 \qquad (t > 0).$$

For some types of functions $f(z)$ involving $z^{\frac{1}{2}}$ it is convenient to use arcs of parabolas having the origin as their common focus and with vertices on the negative real axis, so that the equation of C_N in polar coordinates is

$$(2) \qquad r = \frac{2R_N}{1 - \cos\theta} = R_N \csc^2 \frac{\theta}{2} \qquad (x = r\cos\theta \leqq \gamma).$$

The curve C_N resembles the one shown in Fig. 71. When $N \to \infty$, we agree that $R_N \to \infty$ and hence $\beta_N \to \infty$, where $(\gamma, \pm\beta_N)$ are the end points of C_N.

Suppose $f(z)$ is such that numbers R_N can be found for which

$$(3) \qquad |f(z)| < \frac{M}{|z|^k} = \frac{M}{r^k} \text{ when } z \text{ is on } C_N \qquad (k > 0),$$

where the constants M and k are independent of N. When $\gamma > 0$ and z is any point of either arc of C_N on the right-hand side of the y axis, then

$$|e^{zt}f(z)| < \frac{M}{r^k} e^{xt} \leqq \frac{M}{2^k} e^{\gamma t} \frac{1}{R_N{}^k} = \frac{M_1(t)}{R_N{}^k},$$

since $2R_N$ is the least value of r there. The absolute value of the integral of $e^{zt}f(z)$ over either arc is less than $M_1(t)R_N{}^{-k}L_N$, where L_N is the length of the arc. As $N \to \infty$, $L_N \to \gamma\sqrt{2}$ and the integral therefore tends to zero.

Let C'_N denote the part of C_N on the left of the y axis, whether γ is positive or negative. When z is on C'_N, we find that

$$z = re^{i\theta} = R_N e^{i\theta} \csc^2 \frac{\theta}{2}, \qquad |dz| = r \left| \csc \frac{\theta}{2} \right| |d\theta|.$$

Since $\cos \theta \leqq 0$ and $1 \leqq \csc^2 \tfrac{1}{2}\theta \leqq 2$ and $R_N \leqq r \leqq 2R_N$, it follows that

$$(4) \qquad \left| \int_{C'_N} e^{zt}f(z)\,dz \right| < 2M \int_{\pi/2}^{\pi} e^{tr\cos\theta} \left| \csc \frac{\theta}{2} \right| \frac{r\,d\theta}{r^k}$$

$$< \frac{M'}{R_N{}^k} \int_{\pi/2}^{\pi} e^{tR_N\cos\theta} R_N\,d\theta,$$

where $M' = 4\sqrt{2}\,M$. When we substitute $\phi = \theta - \pi/2$ and observe from the graph of $\sin\phi$ that $\sin\phi > 2\phi/\pi$ when $0 < \phi < \pi/2$, we can write for the final member of inequalities (4)

$$\frac{M'}{R_N{}^k} \int_0^{\pi/2} e^{-tR_N\sin\phi} R_N\,d\phi < \frac{M'}{R_N{}^k} \int_0^{\pi/2} e^{-2tR_N\phi/\pi} R_N\,d\phi.$$

When we evaluate the elementary integral in the last member, we find that the member vanishes as $N \to \infty$, if $t > 0$. Therefore condition (1) is established for the parabolic arcs C_N.

The proof is simpler when C_N are circular arcs $r = R_N$. It is left to the problems; but we include the result in the following theorem.

Theorem 10. *Let $f(s)$ be a function for which the inversion integral along a line $x = \gamma$ represents the inverse transform $F(t)$ of $f(s)$, and let $f(s)$ be analytic except for isolated singular points s_n $(n = 1, 2, \ldots)$ in the half plane $x < \gamma$. Then the series of residues $\rho_n(t)$ of $e^{zt}f(z)$ at $z = s_n$ converges to $F(t)$ for each positive t,*

$$(5) \qquad\qquad F(t) = \sum_{n=1}^{\infty} \rho_n(t) \qquad\qquad (t > 0),$$

if the terms in the series corresponding to points s_n within the ring between successive curves C_N and C_{N+1} are grouped as a single term, provided $f(z)$ satisfies one of the following three sets of conditions.

(a) C_N are the open rectangles (Fig. 72) in which $\beta_N \to \infty$ as $N \to \infty$, and numbers δ_N and M exist, where M is independent of N, such that

$$(6) \qquad |f(x \pm i\beta_N)| < \delta_N, \qquad |f(-\beta_N + iy)| < M,$$

when $-\beta_N < x < \gamma$ and $|y| < \beta_N$, and $\delta_N \to 0$ as $N \to \infty$.

(b) C_N are the parabolic arcs (2), and constants k and M, independent of N, exist such that whenever z is on C_N

$$(7) \qquad\qquad |f(z)| < \frac{M}{|z|^k} \qquad\qquad (k > 0).$$

(c) C_N are circular arcs

$$(8) \qquad\qquad |z| = R_N \qquad\qquad (x \leqq \gamma),$$

and $f(z)$ satisfies condition (7) whenever z is on C_N.

If condition (7) is satisfied when $k > 1$ on any of the three types of paths C_N, the representation (5) is valid when $t = 0$ as well as when t is positive.

68. Alterations of the Inversion Integral. When the singular points of $f(s)$ are not all isolated, it is often possible to reduce the inversion integral to a desirable form by introducing a new path of integration. We illustrate the procedure by finding an inverse transform that was obtained by another method in Sec. 23.

Let us find $F(t)$ when

$$(1) \qquad\qquad f(s) = \frac{1}{s} \exp{(-s^{\frac{1}{2}})},$$

where $s = re^{i\theta}$ and $s^{\frac{1}{2}}$ is the single-valued function

$$(2) \quad s^{\frac{1}{2}} = \sqrt{r}\, e^{\frac{1}{2}i\theta} = \sqrt{r}\left(\cos\frac{\theta}{2} + i\sin\frac{\theta}{2}\right) \quad (r > 0, -\pi < \theta < \pi).$$

Since the function (2) is analytic everywhere except on the branch cut $\theta = \pi$, $r \geqq 0$, $f(s)$ is analytic in the same region. In the half plane $\Re(s) \geqq \gamma$, where γ is a positive constant, $-\frac{1}{2}\pi < \theta < \frac{1}{2}\pi$ and $\cos\frac{1}{2}\theta > 1/\sqrt{2}$; therefore

$$|s^k f(s)| = r^{k-1} \exp\left(-\sqrt{r}\cos\frac{\theta}{2}\right) < r^{k-1} e^{-\sqrt{r/2}}.$$

This last function of r is continuous when $r \geqq \gamma$ and vanishes as $r \to \infty$, hence it is bounded and therefore $|f(s)|$ is $O(s^{-k})$ in the half plane for every value of the constant k, and in particular if $k > 1$. According to Theorem 5 the inversion integral along the line $x = \gamma$ therefore represents the inverse transform $F(t)$,

$$(3) \qquad F(t) = \frac{1}{2\pi i} \lim_{\beta \to \infty} \int_{\gamma - i\beta}^{\gamma + i\beta} e^{tz} \exp\left(-z^{\frac{1}{2}}\right) \frac{dz}{z} \qquad (t \geqq 0).$$

The sum of the integral in formula (3) and the integral along the path $ACDD'C'A'$, consisting of the circular arcs and line segments shown in Fig. 73, is zero, since the integrand is analytic except on the negative real axis. Thus if I_{AC} denotes the integral of $e^{zt}f(z)$ over the arc AC, etc., we can write

$$(4) \qquad -\int_{\gamma - i\beta}^{\gamma + i\beta} e^{zt}f(z)\, dz = I_{AC} + I_{CD} + I_{DD'} + I_{D'C'} + I_{C'A'}.$$

Let R and r_0 denote the radii of the large and small circular arcs; thus $R^2 = \gamma^2 + \beta^2$ so that $\beta \to \infty$ when $R \to \infty$. Along the arc AC, $z = Re^{i\theta}$, $dz = iRe^{i\theta}\, d\theta$, and $z^{\frac{1}{2}} = \sqrt{R}\, e^{i\theta/2}$. Hence the integrand of the integral is a continuous function of θ whenever $\epsilon \geqq 0$, where ϵ is the angle between DC or $D'C'$ and the negative real axis. For any fixed R, the limit of the integrals I_{AC} and $I_{A'C'}$, as $\epsilon \to 0$, therefore exists. Likewise for any fixed positive r_0 the limits of the integrals over the other parts of the path exist. Since formula (4) is true for every positive ϵ and the integral on the left is independent of ϵ, it follows that we can let each of the integrals on the right have their limiting values as $\epsilon \to 0$, and consider hereafter the path in Fig. 74. Write $J_{AC} = \lim_{\epsilon \to 0} I_{AC}$, and so on, for the integrals over the other arcs and lines.   We shall now let r_0 approach zero and R tend to infinity, so that the left-hand member of equation (4), which is incidentally independent of r_0, becomes the inversion integral or $F(t)$, except for a factor $-2\pi i$.

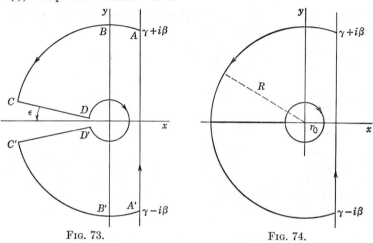

FIG. 73.   FIG. 74.

When z is on the circle $r = r_0$, $z = r_0 e^{i\theta}$, and the integral over that circle can be written

$$J_{DD'} = i \int_\pi^{-\pi} \exp\left(tr_0 e^{i\theta} - \sqrt{r_0}\, e^{\frac{1}{2}i\theta}\right) d\theta,$$

and the integrand is a continuous function of θ and r_0 when $r_0 \geqq 0$.   Therefore

$$\lim_{r_0 \to 0} J_{DD'} = i \int_\pi^{-\pi} d\theta = -2\pi i.$$

On the line CD, $z = re^{i(\pi-\epsilon)}$ and $z^{\frac{1}{2}} = \sqrt{r}\, e^{i(\pi-\epsilon)/2}$; thus as $\epsilon \to 0$, $z \to -r$ and $z^{\frac{1}{2}} \to i\sqrt{r}$.   On the limiting position of $D'C''$, however, $z = -r$ and $z^{\frac{1}{2}} = -i\sqrt{r}$.   Therefore

$$J_{CD} + J_{D'C'} = \int_R^{r_0} e^{-tr} e^{-i\sqrt{r}} \frac{dr}{r} + \int_{r_0}^R e^{-tr} e^{i\sqrt{r}} \frac{dr}{r}$$

$$= 2i \int_{r_0}^R e^{-tr} \frac{\sin\sqrt{r}}{r}\, dr,$$

and $\lim_{r_0 \to 0} (J_{CD} + J_{D'C'}) = 2i \int_0^R e^{-tr} \frac{\sin\sqrt{r}}{r}\, dr$

$$= 4i \int_0^{\sqrt{R}} e^{-t\mu^2} \frac{\sin\mu}{\mu}\, d\mu.$$

Consequently we can write, in view of formula (4),

$$(5) \quad F(t) = -\frac{1}{2\pi i} \lim_{R \to \infty} (J_{AC} + J_{C'A'}) + 1 - \frac{2}{\pi} \int_0^\infty e^{-t\mu^2} \frac{\sin \mu}{\mu} \, d\mu.$$

Now when z is on the arc AB, the real part of the exponent $tz - z^{\frac{1}{2}}$ is not greater than $t\gamma$. Hence

$$\left| \frac{1}{z} \exp (zt - z^{\frac{1}{2}}) \, dz \right| \leqq e^{t\gamma} \, d\theta$$

and, if θ_A is the angle θ at A,

$$|J_{AB}| \leqq e^{t\gamma} \int_{\theta_A}^{\pi/2} d\theta = e^{t\gamma} \left(\frac{\pi}{2} - \theta_A \right).$$

Since $\theta_A \to \pi/2$ when $R \to \infty$, it follows that J_{AB} vanishes as $R \to \infty$. Likewise $J_{B'A'}$ tends to zero as R tends to infinity.

Finally, on the arc BC the real part of the exponent $tz - z^{\frac{1}{2}}$ is less than $tR \cos \theta$ and

$$|J_{BC}| < \int_{\pi/2}^{\pi} e^{tR \cos \theta} \, d\theta = \int_0^{\pi/2} e^{-tR \sin \phi} \, d\phi,$$

where we have substituted $\phi + \pi/2$ for θ. Since $2\phi/\pi < \sin \phi$ when $0 < \phi < \pi/2$,

$$|J_{BC}| < \int_0^{\pi/2} e^{-\frac{2tR\phi}{\pi}} \, d\phi = \frac{\pi}{2tR} (1 - e^{-tR}) \qquad (t > 0),$$

and hence J_{BC} vanishes as R becomes infinite, when $t > 0$. Similarly, the limit of $J_{C'B'}$ is zero.

Therefore the integrals over the large circular arcs AC and $C'A'$ vanish as R becomes infinite, and it follows from equation (5) that

$$F(t) = 1 - \frac{2}{\pi} \int_0^\infty e^{-t\mu^2} \frac{\sin \mu}{\mu} \, d\mu \qquad (t > 0).$$

When we integrate both members of the known[1] integration formula

$$\int_0^\infty e^{-t\mu^2} \cos \alpha\mu \, d\mu = \frac{1}{2} \sqrt{\frac{\pi}{t}} \exp \left(-\frac{\alpha^2}{4t} \right) \qquad (t > 0),$$

---

[1] See, for instance, R. V. Churchill "Complex Variables and Applications," p. 133, 1948.

with respect to α, from zero to one, we find that

$$\frac{2}{\pi} \int_0^\infty e^{-t\mu^2} \frac{\sin \mu}{\mu} \, d\mu = \frac{1}{\sqrt{\pi t}} \int_0^1 e^{-\frac{\alpha^2}{4t}} \, d\alpha = \frac{2}{\sqrt{\pi}} \int_0^{\frac{1}{2\sqrt{t}}} e^{-\lambda^2} \, d\lambda.$$

Thus we can write our result in the form

(6) $$F(t) = 1 - \operatorname{erf}\left(\frac{1}{2\sqrt{t}}\right) = \operatorname{erfc}\left(\frac{1}{2\sqrt{t}}\right).$$

PROBLEMS

1. Instead of simply using partial fractions, show that Theorems 5 and 10 apply to $f(s)$ when

(a) $$f(s) = \frac{2s + 1}{s(s^2 + 1)},$$ (b) $f(s) = \frac{1}{s^2(s + 1)},$

and find $F(t)$ as a sum of residues.   *Ans.* (a) $F(t) = 1 - \cos t + 2 \sin t$.

2. Prove that $|\tanh s|$ is bounded in each of the half planes $x \geq x_0$ and $x \leq -x_0$, where $x_0 > 0$ and $s = x + iy$, and everywhere on the lines $y = \pm N\pi$ ($N = 1, 2, \ldots$). Thus show that the function

$$f(s) = \frac{\tanh s}{s^2}$$

satisfies conditions in Theorems 5 and 10 such that $F(t)$ is represented by a series of residues as follows,

$$F(t) = 1 - \frac{8}{\pi^2} \sum_{n=1}^\infty \frac{1}{(2n - 1)^2} \cos \frac{(2n - 1)\pi t}{2}.$$

3. Write $F(t)$ formally as a series of residues when

$$f(s) = \frac{2 \tanh s}{4s^2 + \pi^2}.$$

Ans. $\pi^2 F(t) = \pi t \sin \dfrac{\pi t}{2} + \cos \dfrac{\pi t}{2} - \displaystyle\sum_{n=2}^\infty \frac{1}{n(n - 1)} \cos \frac{(2n - 1)\pi t}{2}.$

4. When $f(s) = s^{-2}e^{-s}$, show that $F(t)$ is represented by the inversion integral of $f(s)$, where $\gamma > 0$, but that the residue of $e^{st}f(s)$ at the lone singular point of $f(s)$ represents $F(t)$ only when $t \geq 1$. This example illustrates how the formal process of writing the sum of residues $\rho_n(t)$ may fail to give the inverse transform.

5. Since the function $f(s) = s^{-1}e^{-s}$ is known to be the transform of

$S_1(t)$, show that the inversion integral applies to $f(s)$ to give $S_1(t)$ (Theorem 6). But show that the series of residues of $e^{st}f(s)$ does not represent $S_1(t)$ for all positive t.

6. Derive formula (15), Sec. 66, in full.

7. Establish conditions (c) in Theorem 10 pertaining to circular arcs.

8. Show that conditions (6) in Theorem 10 are satisfied when $|f(z)| < B|z|^{-k}$ for all points z on the open rectangles C_N, where the constants B and k are independent of N and where $k > 0$. If $k > 1$, show that the series representation (5), Theorem 10, is valid when $t = 0$.

9. Apply the real form of the inversion integral (Sec. 62) to the transform

$$f(s) = \frac{1 - e^{-s}}{s} \qquad (s \neq 0), \qquad\qquad f(0) = 1,$$

to find $F(t)$. Here we can take γ to be zero and use the integration formula (8), Sec. 32.

CHAPTER 7

PROBLEMS IN HEAT CONDUCTION

We shall now illustrate the use of the theory just developed in solving further boundary value problems in the conduction of heat in solids. We present examples of problems that cannot be fully treated with the more elementary theory used in solving the problems of Chap 4.

The formal solution of the problem in the next section is followed by a complete mathematical treatment of that problem. The purpose is to illustrate a means of rigorously establishing the solutions of such problems. Since the procedure is lengthy, the reader is advised to use it sparingly in his work on the sets of problems that follow. A clear understanding of the formal method of solution is of primary importance.

69. Temperatures in a Bar with Ends at Fixed Temperatures. Let $U(x,t)$ denote the temperature at any point in a bar (Fig. 75)

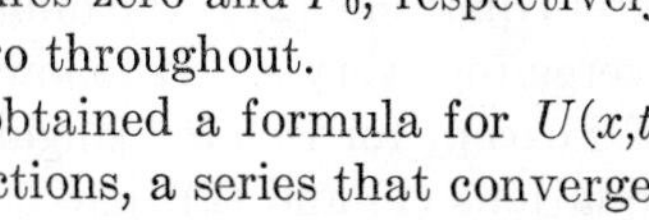

FIG. 75.

with insulated lateral surface and with its ends $x = 0$ and $x = 1$ kept at temperatures zero and F_0, respectively, when the initial temperature is zero throughout.

In Sec. 46 we obtained a formula for $U(x,t)$ in the form of a series of error functions, a series that converges rapidly when t is small. We shall now obtain another series representation of this temperature function. This series will converge rapidly for large t. Let us proceed formally to the solution here, leaving the full justification of our result to the next section.

We have taken the unit of length as the length of the bar, and we observed earlier that, by a proper choice of the unit of time,

199

we can write $k = 1$ in the heat equation, where k is the diffusivity. The boundary value problem in $U(x,t)$ is then

$$U_t(x,t) = U_{xx}(x,t) \quad (0 < x < 1, t > 0),$$
$$U(x,+0) = 0 \qquad (0 < x < 1),$$
$$U(+0,t) = 0, \quad U(1 - 0, t) = F_0 \qquad (t > 0),$$

where F_0 is a constant.

The problem in the transform of $U(x,t)$ is then

$$su(x,s) = u_{xx}(x,s) \qquad (0 < x < 1),$$
$$u(+0,s) = 0, \quad u(1 - 0, s) = \frac{F_0}{s}.$$

Since this problem in ordinary differential equations has a solution that is continuous at $x = 0$ and $x = 1$, $u(+0,s) = u(0,s)$ and $u(1 - 0, s) = u(1,s)$. The solution is

$$(1) \qquad u(x,s) = F_0 \frac{\sinh x \sqrt{s}}{s \sinh \sqrt{s}},$$

where the symbol $\sqrt{s}$ denotes some branch of the double-valued function $s^{\frac{1}{2}}$ (Sec. 56). As long as $\sqrt{s}$ represents the same branch, regardless of which one, in both numerator and denominator, the quotient of hyperbolic sines can be written

$$(2) \qquad \frac{\sinh x \sqrt{s}}{\sinh \sqrt{s}} = \frac{x \sqrt{s} + \dfrac{(x \sqrt{s})^3}{3!} + \cdots}{\sqrt{s} + \dfrac{(\sqrt{s})^3}{3!} + \cdots} = \frac{x + \dfrac{x^3 s}{3!} + \cdots}{1 + \dfrac{s}{3!} + \cdots},$$

except at those points where $\sinh \sqrt{s} = 0$, namely,

$$(3) \qquad s = 0, \quad s = -n^2\pi^2 \qquad (n = 1, 2, \ldots).$$

The final member of equations (2) is the quotient of two power series in s that converge for every s. It follows that $u(x,s)$ is an analytic function of s except for isolated singular points (3). It also follows from equations (1) and (2) that

$$(4) \qquad \lim_{s \to 0} su(x,s) = F_0 x;$$

therefore when $x \neq 0$, the function $u(x,s)$ has a simple pole at $s = 0$ with residue $F_0 x$.

Now let the branch cut of $\sqrt{s}$ be taken as the positive real axis, so that $\sqrt{s}$ is analytic on the negative real axis.   Then $u(x,s)$ has the fractional form $p(x,s)/q(s)$, where the functions

$$p(x,s) = \frac{F_0}{s}\sinh x \sqrt{s}, \qquad q(s) = \sinh \sqrt{s}$$

are analytic at $s = -n^2\pi^2$, and

$$q'(-n^2\pi^2) = \frac{1}{2\sqrt{-n^2\pi^2}} \cosh \sqrt{-n^2\pi^2} = \frac{\cos n\pi}{2n\pi i} \neq 0.$$

Hence $s = -n^2\pi^2$ are simple poles, where the residues of $e^{st}u(x,s)$ are

(5) $\qquad \dfrac{p(x,-n^2\pi^2)}{q'(-n^2\pi^2)}\, e^{-n^2\pi^2 t} = \dfrac{F_0 i \sin n\pi x}{-n^2\pi^2}\,(-1)^n 2n\pi i e^{-n^2\pi^2 t}.$

At least formally then (Sec. 66) the inverse transform of $u(x,s)$ is the sum of the residues (4) and (5) of $e^{st}u(x,s)$ at the poles (3); that is

(6) $\qquad U(x,t) = F_0\left[x + \dfrac{2}{\pi}\sum_{n=1}^{\infty}\dfrac{(-1)^n}{n}\, e^{-n^2\pi^2 t}\sin n\pi x \right].$

This formal solution can be verified by showing that the function defined by formula (6) satisfies all the conditions of our boundary value problem (see Probs. 18 and 19, Sec. 75).   But we shall now see that the theory in the preceding chapter enables us to make the verification in another way that has some advantages.

70. The Solution Established.   We have seen that the function

$$u(x,s) = F_0\,\frac{\sinh x \sqrt{s}}{s\,\sinh \sqrt{s}}$$

is analytic with respect to s in any half plane $\Re(s) \geqq \gamma$ where $\gamma > 0$.   To examine its order in this half plane, let us write

$$s = re^{i\theta}, \qquad \sqrt{s} = \sqrt{r}\, e^{i\theta/2}\left(-\frac{\pi}{2} < \theta < \frac{\pi}{2}\right);$$

then $\Re(\sqrt{s}) = \sqrt{r}\cos(\theta/2) > \sqrt{r/2} \geqq \sqrt{\gamma/2}.$ Thus

$$\left|\frac{\sinh x \sqrt{s}}{\sinh \sqrt{s}}\right| = \left| e^{(x-1)\sqrt{s}}\left(\frac{1 - e^{-2x\sqrt{s}}}{1 - e^{-2\sqrt{s}}}\right)\right|$$

$$< \frac{1 + e^{-2x\sqrt{\gamma/2}}}{1 - e^{-2\sqrt{\gamma/2}}}\, e^{-(1-x)\sqrt{r/2}} \leqq M e^{-(1-x)\sqrt{r/2}},$$

where $M = 2/(1 - e^{-2\sqrt{\gamma/2}})$. Thus if $x \neq 1$, $r^k u(x,s)$ is bounded throughout the half plane for every fixed k. In fact if $x_1 < 1$ and $0 \leq x \leq x_1$, then a constant M', independent of x in that interval, exists such that

$$|u(x,s)| < \frac{M'}{|s|^k} \qquad (\Re(s) \geq \gamma).$$

In view of this order condition, it follows from Theorem 8, Sec. 65, that the inversion integral of $u(x,s)$ along the line $\Re(s) = \gamma$ converges to the inverse transform of $u(x,s)$,

$$(1) \qquad U(x,t) = L_i^{-1}\{u(x,s)\}$$

when $0 \leq x < 1$; also that the function $U(x,t)$ is continuous with respect to $t(t \geq 0)$ and satisfies the condition

$$(2) \qquad U(x,+0) = U(x,0) = 0 \qquad (0 \leq x < 1),$$

and that

$$(3) \qquad U_t(x,t) = L_i^{-1}\{su(x,s)\} \qquad (0 \leq x < 1).$$

Condition (2) is the initial condition in our boundary value problem.

The derivatives of $u(x,s)$ with respect to x,

$$u_x(x,s) = F_0 \frac{\cosh x \sqrt{s}}{\sqrt{s} \sinh \sqrt{s}}, \qquad u_{xx}(x,s) = su(x,s),$$

are also of the order $O(s^{-k})$ for any constant k, in the half plane, uniformly with respect to $x(0 \leq x \leq x_1)$ where $x_1 < 1$. This is evident when these functions are compared with $u(x,s)$. Hence Theorem 9, Sec. 65, applies and the second derivative with respect to x of the function (1) can be written

$$U_{xx}(x,t) = L_i^{-1}\{u_{xx}(x,s)\} \qquad (0 < x < 1).$$

Since $u_{xx}(x,s) = su(x,s)$, it follows from equation (3) that the function (1) satisfies the heat equation

$$U_t(x,t) = U_{xx}(x,t) \qquad (0 < x < 1).$$

Furthermore, the inversion integral represents a continuous function of x when $0 \leq x \leq x_1$, and therefore

$$U(+0,t) = U(0,t) = L_i^{-1}\{u(0,s)\} = 0,$$

since $u(0,s) = 0$.

We have now shown that the function (1) satisfies all the conditions of our boundary value problem except the end condition

(4) $$U(1 - 0, t) = F_0 \qquad (t > 0).$$

Of course it is evident that the function (1) satisfies the condition

$$U(1,t) = L_i^{-1}\{u(1,s)\} = L_i^{-1}\left\{\frac{F_0}{s}\right\}$$

and, since F_0/s is the transform of F_0, that $U(1,t) = F_0$. But this does not assure us that our function approaches F_0 as x approaches 1, which is the condition that the temperature function should satisfy.

Let us write

$$\frac{\sinh x \sqrt{s}}{\sinh \sqrt{s}} = e^{(x-1)\sqrt{s}} \left(\frac{1 - e^{-2x\sqrt{s}}}{1 - e^{-2\sqrt{s}}}\right)$$

$$= e^{-(1-x)\sqrt{s}} \left(1 + \frac{e^{-2\sqrt{s}} - e^{-2x\sqrt{s}}}{1 - e^{-2\sqrt{s}}}\right).$$

Thus

(5) $$\frac{1}{F_0}\, u(x,s) = \frac{1}{s}\, e^{-(1-x)\sqrt{s}} + g(x,s),$$

where $$g(x,s) = \frac{1}{s}\, e^{-(1-x)\sqrt{s}} \left(\frac{e^{-2\sqrt{s}} - e^{-2x\sqrt{s}}}{1 - e^{-2\sqrt{s}}}\right).$$

The first term on the right of equation (5) is the transform of a known function (Secs. 23 and 68):

$$L\left\{\operatorname{erfc}\left(\frac{1 - x}{2\sqrt{t}}\right)\right\} = \frac{1}{s}\, e^{-(1-x)\sqrt{s}} \qquad (0 \leq x \leq 1).$$

The complementary error function here is continuous and bounded with respect to t, for each fixed x, so that it is represented by the inversion integral (Theorem 6, Sec. 64) along the line $\Re(s) = \gamma$:

(6) $$L_i^{-1}\left\{\frac{1}{s}\, e^{-(1-x)\sqrt{s}}\right\} = \operatorname{erfc}\left(\frac{1 - x}{2\sqrt{t}}\right) \qquad (0 \leq x \leq 1).$$

If we note that

$$g(x,s) = \frac{1}{s}\, e^{-(1+x)\sqrt{s}} \left(\frac{e^{-2(1-x)\sqrt{s}} - 1}{1 - e^{-2\sqrt{s}}}\right),$$

it follows, when $\mathcal{R}(s) \geq \gamma$ so that $\mathcal{R}(\sqrt{s}) > \sqrt{r/2}$, that

$$|g(x,s)| \leq \frac{1}{r} e^{-\sqrt{r/2}} \left(\frac{2}{1 - e^{-\sqrt{2\gamma}}} \right) \qquad (0 \leq x \leq 1).$$

That is, $g(x,s)$ is of the order $O(s^{-k})$ in the half plane, where k is any constant, uniformly with respect to x. Consequently the inversion integral of $g(x,s)$ represents a function $G(x,t)$ that is continuous with respect to x, and thus

$$G(1 - 0, t) = G(1,t) = L_i^{-1}\{g(1,s)\} = 0,$$

since $g(1,s) = 0$.

In view of formulas (5) and (6), therefore,

$$(7) \qquad U(x,t) = F_0 \left[\operatorname{erfc} \left(\frac{1 - x}{2 \sqrt{t}} \right) + G(x,t) \right]$$

and, when $t > 0$,

$$U(1 - 0, t) = F_0[\operatorname{erfc}(0) + G(1,t)] = F_0.$$

Our function (1) thus satisfies the end condition (4), and it is therefore completely established as a solution of our boundary value problem. Moreover we have shown that the transform of our temperature function is the function $u(x,s)$ from which we obtained $U(x,t)$. Some interesting properties of $U(x,t)$ will follow from the order properties of $u(x,s)$.

We still have to prove that the series obtained in the last section represents our solution (1).

71. The Series Form Established. We have seen that the function

$$u(x,s) = F_0 \frac{\sinh x \sqrt{s}}{s \sinh \sqrt{s}}$$

is analytic except for the poles $s = 0$ and $s = -n^2\pi^2$ and that its inversion integral converges to a function $U(x,t)$ that is a solution of our boundary value problem. The series representation of $U(x,t)$, given in Sec. 69, is valid provided the integral

$$\int_{C_n} e^{zt} u(x,z) \, dz,$$

taken along a curve C_n of a family of curves $(n = 1, 2, \ldots)$ between the poles, tends to zero as n tends to infinity (Sec. 66).

To select curves C_n so that $|u(x,z)|$ has a suitable order property whenever z is on C_n, we first note that

$$|\sinh \sqrt{z}|^2 = \sinh^2 \left(\sqrt{r} \cos \frac{\theta}{2} \right) + \sin^2 \left(\sqrt{r} \sin \frac{\theta}{2} \right).$$

Hence if $\sqrt{r} \sin \frac{1}{2}\theta = a_n$, where

(1) $$a_n = \left(n - \frac{1}{2} \right) \pi \qquad (n = 1, 2, \ldots),$$

then

(2) $$|\sinh \sqrt{z}|^2 = \sinh^2 \left(\sqrt{r} \cos \frac{\theta}{2} \right) + 1.$$

Let us therefore take C_n as the arc of the parabola

(3) $$r = \frac{a_n{}^2}{\sin^2 \theta/2} = \frac{2a_n{}^2}{1 - \cos \theta}$$

that lies to the left of the line $\xi = \gamma$, where γ is any positive

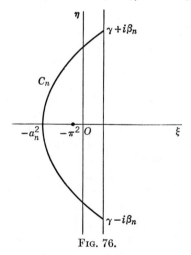

FIG. 76.

constant and $z = \xi + i\eta$ (Fig. 76). Then when z is on C_n

(4) $$\left| \frac{zu(x,z)}{F_0} \right|^2 = \frac{\sinh^2 (x \sqrt{r} \cos \theta/2) + \sin^2 (x \sqrt{r} \sin \theta/2)}{\sinh^2 (\sqrt{r} \cos \theta/2) + 1} \leqq 1,$$

because $0 \leqq x \leqq 1$ and $\sinh^2 y$ increases when $|y|$ increases. Thus $|u(x,z)|$ is $O(z^{-1})$ on C_n and, according to Theorem 10,

Sec. 67, the series of residues of $e^{zt}u(x,z)$ converges to the inversion integral for all positive values of t. The series (6), Sec. 69, therefore does represent a solution of our problem; that is, our solution can be written

$$(5) \qquad U(x,t) = F_0 \left[x + \frac{2}{\pi} \sum_{n=1}^{\infty} \frac{(-1)^n}{n} e^{-n^2\pi^2 t} \sin n\pi x \right] \qquad (t > 0).$$

We found in Sec. 70 that $U(x,0) = 0$, where $0 \leqq x < 1$. Other order conditions satisfied by $u(x,z)$ on C_n are actually adequate to show that the representation (5) is valid when $t = 0$ and consequently that

$$(6) \qquad x = -\frac{2}{\pi} \sum_{n=1}^{\infty} \frac{(-1)^n}{n} \sin n\pi x \qquad (0 \leqq x < 1).$$

For if ϵ is a small positive angle and z is on either part of any of the parabolic paths C_n on which $|\theta| < \pi - \epsilon$, it can be seen from the equation (4) that for each fixed x $(x < 1)$ a number M_ϵ independent of n exists such that $|z^k u(x,z)| < M_\epsilon$, for any constant k. This order property, together with the inequality (4) satisfied on the remaining part of C_n, is sufficient to show that the representation (5) is valid when $t = 0$ and $x < 1$. The proof, made by first selecting ϵ small and then n large, is left to the problems. It establishes the Fourier sine series representation (6) of the function x on the interval $0 \leqq x < 1$. We shall use a similar procedure in Chap. 9 to establish a generalization of Fourier series representations of arbitrary functions.

72. Properties of the Temperature Function. It was shown in Sec. 70 that for any constant k the transform $u(x,s)$ of our temperature function $U(x,t)$ is of the order of $|s|^{-k}$ in a right half plane of the variable s, uniformly for all x in any interval $0 \leqq x \leqq x_1$ where $x_1 < 1$. The derivatives of $u(x,s)$ with respect to x also satisfy that order property. As a consequence, our temperature function possesses the following properties, according to Theorems 5, 8, and 9 of the preceding chapter.

The function $U(x,t)$ is a continuous function of both x and t when $t \geqq 0$ and $0 \leqq x < 1$, and each of its derivatives with respect to x or t has this continuity property.

At any interior point of the bar, the temperature begins to change very slowly at the time $t = 0$, since

(1) $U_t(x,0) = U_{tt}(x,0) = U_{ttt}(x,0) = \cdots = 0$ $(0 \leqq x < 1)$.

The temperature at each interior point does begin to change at time $t = 0$, for we found in Sec. 46 that

(2) $U(x,t) = F_0 \displaystyle\sum_{n=0}^{\infty} \left[\operatorname{erf}\left(\frac{2n + 1 + x}{2\sqrt{t}}\right) - \operatorname{erf}\left(\frac{2n + 1 - x}{2\sqrt{t}}\right) \right].$

Since the quantity in the brackets is positive when $t > 0$ and $0 < x < 1$, this temperature formula shows that the temperature immediately after the time $t = 0$ is not zero.   In fact if $F_0 > 0$, then

(3) $U(x,t) > 0$ when $t > 0$ $(0 < x < 1)$.

The flux of heat through any section $x = x_0$ is

$$\Phi(x_0,t) = -KU_x(x_0,t),$$

where K is the thermal conductivity.   Its transform is

$$\phi(x_0,s) = -KF_0 \frac{\cosh x_0 \sqrt{s}}{\sqrt{s}\,\sinh\sqrt{s}},$$

and we can see by the usual argument that

(4) $\Phi(x_0,0) = \Phi_t(x_0,0) = \Phi_{tt}(x_0,0) = \cdots = 0$ $(0 \leqq x_0 < 1)$;

also that the flux through every section begins to change at the time $t = 0$.   In fact from formula (2) it can be seen that, if $F_0 > 0$,

(5) $\Phi(x_0,t) < 0$ when $t > 0$ $(0 \leqq x_0 \leqq 1)$.

In Sec. 70 we found that

$$U(x,t) = F_0 \left[\operatorname{erfc}\left(\frac{1 - x}{2\sqrt{t}}\right) + G(x,t) \right],$$

where the function $G(x,t)$ and each of its derivatives vanish as t approaches zero, when $0 \leqq x \leqq 1$.   Therefore the flux through the right-hand face of the bar is

$$\Phi(1,t) = -KF_0 \left[\frac{1}{\sqrt{\pi t}} + G_x(1,t) \right],$$

and

(6) $\displaystyle\lim_{t \to 0} \left[\Phi(1,t) + \frac{KF_0}{\sqrt{\pi t}} \right] = 0.$

That is, the flux of heat at that face becomes infinite like

$$-\frac{KF_0}{\sqrt{\pi t}},$$

or it is of the order of $1/\sqrt{t}$, as $t \to 0$.

This infinite flux is the result of the discontinuity in the temperature of that face at $t = 0$, a discontinuity we have introduced in our idealization of the problem of temperatures in a bar when the temperature of one face is quickly raised or lowered.

The total quantity of heat that has passed through a unit area of any section up to the time t is

$$Q(x_0,t) = \int_0^t \Phi(x_0,\tau)\, d\tau.$$

Consequently its transform is

$$q(x_0,s) = \frac{1}{s}\,\phi(x_0,s) = -KF_0 \frac{\cosh x_0 \sqrt{s}}{s \sqrt{s}\, \sinh \sqrt{s}}.$$

It follows from the order of $q(1,s)$ that

(7) $$\lim_{t\to 0} Q(1,t) = 0,$$

a condition that would not be satisfied if there were an instantaneous source of heat over the surface $x = 1$ at $t = 0$. Such a source is an idealization of an actual situation in which a large quantity of heat is generated over a surface in a very short time interval, by combustion, for instance.

73. Uniqueness of the Solution.   Our treatment of the boundary value problem is not strictly complete until we have shown that our solution is the only one possible.   The physical problem of the temperatures in a bar with prescribed initial temperature and prescribed thermal conditions at the boundary must have just one solution.   If we have completely stated the problem as one in mathematics, that problem must also have a unique solution.

The conditions we have imposed on $U(x,t)$, namely,

(1) $$U_t(x,t) = U_{xx}(x,t) \quad (0 < x < 1,\, t > 0),$$
(2) $$U(x,+0) = 0 \quad\quad\quad\quad (0 < x < 1),$$
(3) $$U(+0,t) = 0, \quad U(1-0,\,t) = F_0 \quad\quad (t > 0),$$

are not sufficient to ensure just one solution.   They do not exclude the possibility of instantaneous sources of heat at the ends of the bar at $t = 0$. The equation of conduction (1) is the statement that heat distributes itself interior to the bar after the time $t = 0$, by conduction. In the derivation of that equation, it is assumed that the functions U, U_t, U_x, and U_{xx} are continuous with respect to the two variables x and t, interior to the solid after conduction begins. We shall therefore require our solution to have those properties of continuity. Physically, the presence of heat sources interior to the bar when $t > 0$ is then prohibited.

Let the required temperature function satisfy the conditions (1), (2), and (3) and the following continuity and order conditions.

(a) $U(x,t)$ is continuous in x and t when $t \geqq 0$ and $0 \leqq x < 1$, and when $t > 0$ and $0 \leqq x \leqq 1$. Also, $|U(x,t)| < Me^{\alpha t}$ when $t > 0$ and $0 < x < 1$, where M and α are constants.

(b) The derivatives $U_x(x,t)$ and $U_t(x,t)$ are continuous functions whose absolute values are less than $Ne^{\alpha t}$, in the region $t \geqq 0$, $0 \leqq x \leqq x_1$, whenever $x_1 < 1$. The constant N may depend on x_1, but α is independent of x_1.

Of course, U_{xx} satisfies the conditions imposed on U_t since the two functions are required to be identical.

We have seen that the function

$$(4) \qquad U(x,t) = L_i^{-1}\left\{ F_0 \frac{\sinh x \sqrt{s}}{s \sinh \sqrt{s}} \right\}$$

satisfies the conditions (1), (2), and (3) and that it is continuous, together with each of its partial derivatives, when $0 \leqq x < 1$ and $t \geqq 0$. When $0 \leqq x \leqq x_1 < 1$, the transform of this function, or that of any of its derivatives, is of the order of s^{-k} in any right half plane $\mathfrak{R}(s) \geqq \gamma > 0$, uniformly with respect to x, where k is any constant. Hence the derivatives of the function (4) satisfy the conditions (b).

In Sec. 70 it was found that the function (4) can be written

$$U(x,t) = F_0 \left[\mathrm{erfc}\left(\frac{1-x}{2\sqrt{t}} \right) + G(x,t) \right].$$

The function $G(x,t)$ is continuous in x and t and less in absolute value than $Me^{\gamma t}$ when $t \geqq 0$ and $0 \leqq x \leqq 1$, whenever $\gamma > 0$. This follows from the character of $g(x,s)$. Although the error function here is not a continuous function of x and t when $x = 1$

and $t = 0$, it is bounded for all x and t and continuous with respect to x and t, when $t > 0$. Consequently the function (4) satisfies the conditions (a).

Suppose there is another function $V(x,t)$ that satisfies the conditions (1), (2), (3), and (a) and (b). Then the function

$$(5) \qquad W(x,t) = U(x,t) - V(x,t),$$

where $U(x,t)$ is the function (4), also satisfies the continuity and order conditions (a) and (b). Since both U and V satisfy the heat equation and boundary conditions, W must satisfy the homogeneous conditions

$$(6) \qquad W_t(x,t) = W_{xx}(x,t) \qquad (0 < x < 1, t > 0),$$
$$(7) \qquad W(x,0) = 0 \qquad\qquad (0 < x < 1),$$
$$(8) \qquad W(0,t) = 0, \qquad W(1,t) = 0 \qquad\qquad (t > 0).$$

In writing conditions (8) we have used the fact that $W(x,t)$ is continuous when $0 \leqq x \leqq 1$ and $t > 0$.

Since $W(x,t)$ satisfies conditions (a) and (b), its transform $w(x,s)$ exists, and the transforms of W_x and W_{xx} are $w'(x,s)$ and $w''(x,s)$, where the primes denote derivatives with respect to x. Moreover, these transforms are continuous functions of x when $0 \leqq x < 1$. Also, in view of condition (7), the transform of W_t is sw. From conditions (6) and (8) we see that, for every s in some right half plane,

$$(9) \qquad sw(x,s) = w''(x,s) \qquad (0 < x < 1),$$
$$(10) \qquad w(0,s) = 0, \qquad w(1,s) = 0.$$

The continuity of $w(x,s)$ with respect to x actually extends to the point $x = 1$. To prove it we write

$$w(x,s) = \int_0^{t_0} e^{-st} W(x,t)\, dt + \int_{t_0}^{\infty} e^{-st} W(x,t)\, dt \qquad (t_0 > 0),$$

where the second integral is a continuous function of x when $0 \leqq x \leqq 1$ that vanishes when $x = 1$. Since $W(x,t)$ satisfies conditions (a) and $\Re(s) > \alpha$, the integrand of the first integral is bounded for all positive t when $0 < x < 1$. We take t_0 small enough to make the value of the first integral arbitrarily small for all x. Then for that value of t_0 the value of the second integral becomes arbitrarily small when $1 - x$ is sufficiently small. Hence $w(1 - 0, s) = w(1,s) = 0$.

We have now shown that for each s in a right half plane, $w(x,s)$ is a continuous function of $x(0 \leq x \leq 1)$ that satisfies the linear ordinary differential equation (9) with continuous (constant) coefficients; also that $w'(x,s)$ is continuous when $0 \leq x < 1$, and $w(0,s) = 0$. In the theory of linear differential equations it is shown that, when the value $w'(0,s)$ of the derivative at $x = 0$ is also prescribed, such an equation has one and only one solution satisfying those continuity conditions. In our case that solution is

$$w(x,s) = \frac{w'(0,s)}{\sqrt{s}} \sinh x \sqrt{s} \qquad (0 \leq x \leq 1).$$

But $w(1,s) = 0$, and since $\sinh \sqrt{s} = 0$ only when $s = -n^2\pi^2$ ($n = 0, 1, 2 \ldots$) and not for all s in a right half plane, then $w'(0,s) = 0$; hence

(11) $w(x,s) = 0.$

Since $w(x,s)$ is the transform of the continuous function $W(x,t)$ of exponential order, then $W(x,t) = 0$; that is

(12) $V(x,t) = U(x,t).$

The proof that the problem consisting of the conditions (1), (2), (3), and (a) and (b) has just one solution is now complete. The conditions (a) and (b) could have been relaxed somewhat. It is necessary to do so, for instance, when there are discontinuities in either the initial temperature distribution or in the prescribed surface temperatures.

74. Arbitrary End Temperatures. Let the temperature of the end $x = 1$ of the bar be a prescribed function $F(t)$ (Fig. 58). The temperature function U then satisfies the heat equation $U_t = U_{xx}$, the initial condition $U(x,+0) = 0$, and the end conditions

$$U(+0,t) = 0, \qquad U(1 - 0, t) = F(t) \qquad (t > 0).$$

As noted in Sec. 46, the solution of the transformed problem is

(1) $$u(x,s) = f(s) \frac{\sinh x \sqrt{s}}{\sinh \sqrt{s}}.$$

Let $V(x,t)$ denote the temperature function found in the

preceding sections when $F(t) = 1$.   Then

(2) $$u(x,s) = sf(s)v(x,s)$$

since $$v(x,s) = \frac{\sinh x \sqrt{s}}{s \sinh \sqrt{s}}.$$

Now $sv(x,s)$ is the transform of $V_t(x,t)$ when $0 \leqq x < 1$.   In view of the convolution property, it follows from equation (2) that

(3) $$U(x,t) = \int_0^t F(t - \tau) V_t(x,\tau) \, d\tau.$$

It was shown that $V(x,t)$ is represented by a series:

$$V(x,t) = x + \frac{2}{\pi} \sum_{n=1}^{\infty} \frac{(-1)^n}{n} e^{-n^2\pi^2t} \sin n\pi x.$$

The series obtained by differentiating this series term by term with respect to t does not converge when $t = 0$; but it was shown that the function $V_t(x,t)$ is continuous when $t \geqq 0$ and $0 \leqq x < 1$ and that

$$V_t(x,0) = 0 \qquad\qquad (0 \leqq x < 1).$$

The differentiated series simply fails to represent $V_t(x,t)$ at $t = 0$.

To arrive at another form of the temperature function U, we assume that $F(t)$ is continuous, that $F'(t)$ is sectionally continuous, and that $F(t)$ is of exponential order.   Then

$$L\{F'(t)\} = sf(s) - F(+0),$$

and $$u(x,s) = F(+0)v(x,s) + L\{F'(t)\}v(x,s).$$

Consequently we have the formula

(4) $$U(x,t) = F(+0)V(x,t) + \int_0^t F'(t - \tau) V(x,\tau) \, d\tau.$$

The two formulas (3) and (4) give the temperature $U(x,t)$ in terms of the temperature $V(x,t)$ corresponding to a fixed surface temperature.   They are two forms of Duhamel's formula.   The above series for $V(x,t)$ can be substituted into formula (4), and it can be shown that the temperature function can be written

(5) $$U(x,t) = xF(t) + \frac{2F(+0)}{\pi} \sum_{n=1}^{\infty} \frac{(-1)^n}{n} e^{-n^2\pi^2t} \sin n\pi x$$

$$+ \frac{2}{\pi} \sum_{n=1}^{\infty} \frac{(-1)^n}{n} \sin n\pi x \int_0^t F'(t - \tau)e^{-n^2\pi^2\tau} \, d\tau.$$

Alternate forms of equations (3) and (4) can be written by substituting another variable of integration $\lambda = t - \tau$. When $F(t)$ is continuous and $F'(t)$ sectionally continuous, formula (4) can be established as a solution by using the alternate form whenever it is more convenient, together with the properties of $V(x,t)$ found in the preceding sections. If we assume also that $F(t)$ and $F'(t)$ are of exponential order, the function $U(x,t)$ given by formula (4) satisfies conditions (a) and (b) in the preceding section (cf. Sec. 14 on properties of convolution). Then the proof of uniqueness of solution (4) is that used in Sec. 73. Other forms of the solution arise when the function $V(x,t)$ in equations (3) and (4) is written as the series of error functions found in Sec. 46.

75. Special End Temperatures. When the end temperature $F(t)$ is a specific function, a convenient formula for $U(x,t)$ may be found directly from the transform $u(x,s)$.

For example, let

(1) $$F(t) = At$$

in the problem of the last section, where A is a constant. Then

$$u(x,s) = A \frac{\sinh x \sqrt{s}}{s^2 \sinh \sqrt{s}},$$

a function with a pole of the second order at $s = 0$. We noted in Sec. 69 that

$$\frac{\sinh x \sqrt{s}}{\sinh \sqrt{s}} = \frac{x + (x^3 s/3!) + (x^5 s^2/5!) + \cdots}{1 + (s/3!) + (s^2/5!) + \cdots}.$$

By carrying out the indicated division here, the first two terms are found to be $x + x(x^2 - 1)s/3!$; hence $u(x,s)$ has the following representation in a neighborhood of $s = 0$:

$$u(x,s) = A \left[\frac{x}{s^2} + \frac{x(x^2 - 1)}{3!s} + \sum_{n=0}^{\infty} a_n(x)s^n \right].$$

The residue of $e^{zt}u(x,z)$ at $z = 0$ is therefore (Sec. 66)

$$A \left[xt + \frac{x(x^2 - 1)}{3!} \right].$$

The residue of $e^{zt}u(x,z)$ at the simple pole $z = -n^2\pi^2$ is

$$2A \left. \frac{e^{zt} \sinh x \sqrt{z}}{z \sqrt{z} \cosh \sqrt{z}} \right]_{z = -n^2\pi^2} = \frac{2A(-1)^{n-1}}{\pi^3 n^3} \sin (n\pi x) e^{-n^2\pi^2 t}.$$

Consequently the formula for the temperatures can be written

$$(2) \quad U(x,t) = A \left[\frac{x^3 - x}{6} + xt + \frac{2}{\pi^3} \sum_{n=1}^{\infty} \frac{(-1)^{n-1}}{n^3} e^{-n^2\pi^2 t} \sin n\pi x \right].$$

This function can be verified completely as a solution of the boundary value problem by just the same procedure that was used in Secs. 70 and 71. But the procedure can be simplified in this case in view of the fact that $u(x,s)$ is of the order $O(s^{-2})$ in a right half plane and on the parabolas C_n, uniformly with respect to x when $0 \leqq x \leqq 1$. Consequently $U(x,t)$ is a continuous function of its two variables for all x and t $(0 \leqq x \leqq 1, t \geqq 0)$; also the series representation (2) is valid at $t = 0$. Since $U(x,0) = 0$, it follows from equation (2) that

$$x - x^3 = \frac{12}{\pi^3} \sum_{n=1}^{\infty} \frac{(-1)^{n-1}}{n^3} \sin n\pi x \quad (0 \leqq x \leqq 1),$$

which is the Fourier sine series expansion of the function $x - x^3$ on the interval $0 \leqq x \leqq 1$.

As a second example, let the face $x = 1$ of the bar be kept at a fixed temperature A from $t = 0$ to $t = t_0$ and thereafter at temperature zero:

$$(3) \qquad \begin{aligned} F(t) &= A & \text{when } 0 < t < t_0, \\ &= 0 & \text{when } t > t_0. \end{aligned}$$

Then
$$f(s) = A \frac{1 - e^{-t_0 s}}{s}$$

and
$$u(x,s) = A \frac{\sinh x \sqrt{s}}{s \sinh \sqrt{s}} (1 - e^{-t_0 s}).$$

Again let $V(x,t)$ denote the temperature function when $F(t) = 1$, obtained in the foregoing sections; also let $V(x,t) = 0$ when $t < 0$. Then

$$(4) \qquad U(x,t) = A[V(x,t) - V(x, t - t_0)].$$

The total quantity of heat conducted across any section $x = x_0$, per unit area, from time $t = 0$ on, is

$$\lim_{t \to \infty} Q(x_0,t) = -K \int_0^\infty U_x(x_0,\tau) \, d\tau.$$

The integral on the right is the transform of $U_x(x_0,t)$ when $s = 0$, provided the integral exists; that is,

$$(5) \qquad \lim_{t \to \infty} Q(x_0,t) = -K u_x(x_0,0).$$

In our second example, where $F(t)$ has the form (3),

$$u_x(x_0,s) = A \cosh x_0 \sqrt{s} \; \frac{\sqrt{s}}{\sinh \sqrt{s}} \; \frac{1 - e^{-t_0 s}}{s},$$

and the limit of this function as $s \to 0$ is $A t_0$. Therefore

$$(6) \qquad \lim_{t \to \infty} Q(x_0,t) = -K A t_0.$$

The reader can show that, for an arbitrary $F(t)$,

$$(7) \qquad \lim_{t \to \infty} Q(x_0,t) = -K \int_0^\infty F(\tau) \, d\tau$$

if the end temperature $F(t)$ is such that $L\{F(t)\}$ exists when $s \geqq 0$. That is, the total quantity of heat per unit area conducted through the bar is proportional to the integrated temperature of the face whose temperature varies.

PROBLEMS

1. Derive formula (7) above.

2. If the length of the bar is l, show that

$$\lim_{t \to \infty} Q(x_0,t) = -\frac{K}{l} \int_0^\infty F(\tau) \, d\tau$$

when the temperature $F(t)$ of the surface $x = l$ is such that $L\{F(t)\}$ exists when $s \geqq 0$.

3. Derive the formula

$$U(x,t) = 1 - \frac{4}{\pi} \sum_{n=1}^{\infty} \frac{(-1)^{n-1}}{2n-1} \cos \frac{(2n-1)\pi x}{2l} \exp\left[-\frac{(2n-1)^2 \pi^2 t}{4l^2} \right]$$

for the temperatures in a wall with its face $x = 0$ insulated and its face $x = l$ kept at temperature $U = 1$, if the initial temperature is zero (Fig. 77) and if $k = 1$.

4. Obtain solution of Prob. 3 as a series of error functions (cf. Sec. 45).

5. Establish the formula in Prob. 3 as a solution of the boundary value problem.

6. Obtain the solution of the problem in Sec. 45 in the form

$$U(x,t) = \frac{4u_0}{\pi} \sum_{n=1}^{\infty} \frac{(-1)^{n-1}}{2n-1} \cos \frac{(2n-1)\pi x}{2l} \exp \left[-\frac{(2n-1)^2\pi^2 kt}{4l^2} \right].$$

7. Let the temperature of the face $x = l$ of the wall in Prob. 3 be $F(t)$, where $F(t)$ is continuous, $F'(t)$ is sectionally continuous, and

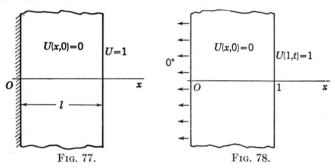

Fig. 77.   Fig. 78.

$F(0) = 0$. Derive the temperature formula

$$U(x,t) = F(t) - \frac{4}{\pi} \sum_{n=1}^{\infty} \frac{(-1)^{n-1}}{2n-1} \cos \frac{(2n-1)\pi x}{2l} G_n(x,t),$$

where

$$G_n(x,t) = \int_0^t F'(t-\tau) \exp \left[-\frac{(2n-1)^2\pi^2\tau}{4l^2} \right] d\tau.$$

8. Obtain the solution of the temperature problem

$$U_t(x,t) = U_{xx}(x,t) \qquad (0 < x < 1, t > 0),$$
$$U(x,0) = 1, \qquad U(0,t) = U(1,t) = 0,$$

in the form

$$U(x,t) = \frac{4}{\pi} \sum_{n=1}^{\infty} \frac{\sin (2n-1)\pi x}{2n-1} \exp \left[-(2n-1)^2\pi^2 t\right].$$

9. Obtain another form of the solution of Prob. 11, Sec. 48.

10. At the face $x = 0$ of a wall, surface heat transfer takes place into a medium at temperature zero according to the linear law of heat transfer, so that

$$U_x(+0,t) = hU(+0,t),$$

where h is a positive constant. Units are so selected that $k = 1$ and the wall has unit thickness. If the other conditions are those indicated in Fig. 78, set up the boundary value problem for the temperature function $U(x,t)$ and show that

$$u(x,s) = \frac{1}{s} \frac{h \sinh x \sqrt{s} + \sqrt{s} \cosh x \sqrt{s}}{h \sinh \sqrt{s} + \sqrt{s} \cosh \sqrt{s}}.$$

Derive the formula

$$U(x,t) = \frac{hx + 1}{h + 1} - 4 \sum_{n=1}^{\infty} \frac{\sin [\alpha_n(1 - x)]}{2\alpha_n - \sin 2\alpha_n} e^{-\alpha_n^2 t},$$

where $\alpha_1, \alpha_2, \ldots$ are the positive roots of the equation

$$\tan \alpha = -\frac{\alpha}{h}.$$

Show how those roots can be approximated graphically when the value of h is known, and note that α_n is only slightly greater than $(n - \frac{1}{2})\pi$ when n is large. To show that $s = 0$ and $s = -\alpha_n^2$ are the only singular points of $u(x,s)$, write $\sqrt{s} = \lambda + i\mu$ and prove that the denominator in the above expression for $u(x,s)$ cannot vanish unless $\lambda = 0$, so that s is real.

11. If heat is extracted from each unit area of the face $x = 1$ of a slab at a constant rate ϕ_0, while the face $x = 0$ is kept at the initial temperature zero, the boundary value problem can be written

$$U_t(x,t) = U_{xx}(x,t) \qquad (0 < x < 1, t > 0),$$
$$U(x,0) = U(0,t) = 0, \qquad -KU_x(1,t) = \phi_0,$$

where K is the thermal conductivity of the material. Derive the solution

$$U(x,t) = -\frac{\phi_0}{K} \left\{ x - \frac{8}{\pi^2} \sum_{n=1}^{\infty} \frac{(-1)^{n-1}}{(2n - 1)^2} \sin \frac{(2n - 1)\pi x}{2} \right.$$
$$\left. \times \exp \left[-\frac{(2n - 1)^2 \pi^2 t}{4} \right] \right\}.$$

12. Derive the solution of Prob. 11 in the form of a series involving error functions.

13. If heat is extracted from each unit area of the face $x = 1$ of the slab in Prob. 11 at the constant rate ϕ_0 from time $t = 0$ to time $t = t_0$ and if that face is insulated thereafter, show that the temperature

$V(x,t)$ can be written

$$V(x,t) \;=\; U(x,t) \;-\; U(x,t-t_0),$$

where $U(x,t)$ is the temperature function given in Prob. 11 when $t > 0$, and $U(x,t) = 0$ when $t < 0$.

14. Derive the formula

$$U(x,t) = B + (C - B)x$$

$$+ \frac{2}{\pi} \sum_{n=1}^{\infty} \frac{C(-1)^n - B}{n} \sin{(n\pi x)} \exp{(-n^2\pi^2 kt)}$$

$$+ \frac{4u_0}{\pi} \sum_{n=1}^{\infty} \frac{\sin{(2n-1)\pi x}}{2n-1} \exp{[-(2n-1)^2\pi^2 kt]},$$

for the temperatures in a bar with insulated lateral surface, if its initial temperature is u_0 and its ends $x = 0$ and $x = 1$ are kept at temperatures B and C (Fig. 79). Here u_0, B, and C are constants as is the thermal diffusivity k of the material.

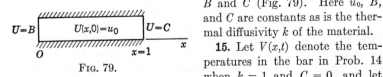

$U=B$ $U(x,0)=u_0$ $U=C$

O $x=1$ x

FIG. 79.

15. Let $V(x,t)$ denote the temperatures in the bar in Prob. 14 when $k = 1$ and $C = 0$, and let $W(x,t)$ denote the temperatures in that bar when $k = 1$ and when the condition $U(1,t) = C$ is replaced by the condition $W(1,t) = At$. Then if $U(x,t)$ is the function (2), Sec. 75, show by superposition of solutions that

$$W(x,t) \;=\; V(x,t) + U(x,t).$$

16. The face $x = 0$ of a slab is insulated. The temperature of the face $x = \pi$ is $U = t(t \geqq 0)$. If the initial temperature is zero throughout the slab and $k = 1$, derive the formula

$$U(x,t) = t - \frac{\pi^2 - x^2}{2} + \frac{2}{\pi} \sum_{n=0}^{\infty} (-1)^n \frac{\cos{(n + \frac{1}{2})x}}{(n + \frac{1}{2})^3} \exp{\left[-\left(n + \frac{1}{2}\right)^2 t\right]}.$$

Verify this as a solution of the boundary value problem.

17. Give the details of the proof, outlined at the end of Sec. 71, of the Fourier series representation (6) in that section.

18. When $t \geqq t_0 > 0$ and $0 \leqq x \leqq 1$, prove that the series (6), Sec. 69, and the series obtained by differentiating that series once or twice with respect to x or once with respect to t, are uniformly convergent with respect to x and t. The series then represent continuous functions of x and t and termwise differentiation is valid, since the terms themselves are continuous functions. As a consequence, show that the function $U(x,t)$ defined by the series satisfies the heat equation $U_t = U_{xx}$ when $0 < x < 1$ and $t > 0$, and end conditions $U(+0,t) = 0$, $U(1 - 0, t) = F_0$, when $t > 0$.

19. According to *Abel's test for uniform convergence*,[1] a series $\sum_{n=1}^{\infty} A_n T_n(t)$ converges uniformly with respect to t if the series $\sum_{n=1}^{\infty} A_n$ converges, and if functions $T_n(t)$ are bounded uniformly with respect to t and n and such that $T_{n+1}(t) \leqq T_n(t)$. Given that the Fourier series representation (6), Sec. 71, is valid, use Abel's test when $0 \leqq t \leqq t_0$ to show that the function defined by equation (6), Sec. 69, is continuous with respect to t when $t \geqq 0$ and that it satisfies the initial condition $U(x,+0) = 0$ for each fixed x such that $0 < x < 1$. This, together with the result in Prob. 18, establishes the solution (6), Sec. 69.

76. Arbitrary Initial Temperatures. Let the initial temperature distribution in a bar or slab be any prescribed function $g(x)$ of the distance from one face. When the lateral surface of the bar is insulated and the ends are kept at temperature zero (Fig.

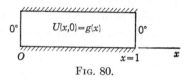

FIG. 80.

80), units can be selected so that the boundary value problem for the temperature in the bar becomes

$$U_t(x,t) = U_{xx}(x,t) \qquad (0 < x < 1, \, t > 0),$$
$$U(x,+0) = g(x) \qquad (0 < x < 1),$$
$$U(+0,t) = U(1 - 0, t) = 0 \qquad (t > 0).$$

The problem in the transform of $U(x,t)$,

(1) $\qquad u''(x,s) - su(x,s) = -g(x) \qquad (0 < x < 1),$
(2) $\qquad u(0,s) = u(1,s) = 0,$

can be solved by any one of several methods, including a Laplace transformation with respect to x, or the process of using a Green's function to be described in Chap. 9. Regardless of the method used, the solution can be written in terms of Green's function R for the problem, in the form

(3) $\qquad u(x,s) = -\int_0^1 R(x,\xi,s)g(\xi) \, d\xi,$

[1] For a proof, see R. V. Churchill "Fourier Series and Boundary Value Problems," pp. 128, 129, 1941.

where

(4) $R(x,\xi,s) = -\dfrac{\sinh\,[(1\,-\,x)\,\sqrt{s}]\,\sinh\,\xi\,\sqrt{s}}{\sqrt{s}\,\sinh\,\sqrt{s}}$ $(0 \leqq \xi \leqq x)$,

$\qquad\quad = -\dfrac{\sinh\,[(1\,-\,\xi)\,\sqrt{s}]\,\sinh\,x\,\sqrt{s}}{\sqrt{s}\,\sinh\,\sqrt{s}}$ $(x \leqq \xi \leqq 1)$.

By writing Maclaurin's series in powers of $\sqrt{s}$ for the hyperbolic sines and properly defining $R(x,\xi,0)$ we see that, regardless of which branch of $s^{\frac{1}{2}}$ is represented by $\sqrt{s}$, R is an analytic function of s except for the singular points

(5) $s = -n^2\pi^2$ $(n = 1, 2, \ldots)$.

If $g(x)$ is sectionally continuous, the order of integration with respect to ξ in equation (3) and differentiation with respect to s can be interchanged, and hence $u(x,s)$ is analytic except for the singular points (5). By taking the branch cut of $\sqrt{s}$ along the positive real axis and selecting $q(s)$ as $\sinh\,\sqrt{s}$ in the formula (7), Sec. 66, we find that the points (5) are simple poles of $u(x,s)$, where the residues of $e^{st}u(x,s)$ are

$$-\frac{e^{-n^2\pi^2 t}}{\frac{1}{2}\cos n\pi}\left[\int_0^x g(\xi)\,\sin\,n\pi(1-x)\,\sin\,n\pi\xi\,d\xi\right.$$

$$\left.+ \int_x^1 g(\xi)\,\sin\,n\pi x\,\sin\,n\pi(1-\xi)\,d\xi\right].$$

Since $\sin\,n\pi(1-x) = -\cos\,n\pi\,\sin\,n\pi x$, the residues can be written

$$2e^{-n^2\pi^2 t}\,\sin\,n\pi x\int_0^1 g(\xi)\,\sin\,n\pi\xi\,d\xi.$$

Formally, therefore, the solution of our problem is

(6) $U(x,t) = 2\displaystyle\sum_{n=1}^{\infty} e^{-n^2\pi^2 t}\,\sin\,n\pi x\int_0^1 g(\xi)\,\sin\,n\pi\xi\,d\xi.$

When $t = 0$, the series here is the Fourier sine series for the function $g(x)$ on the interval $0 < x < 1$. In fact, the boundary value problem in $U(x,t)$ here is especially well adapted to the classical method of solution by using separation of variables and Fourier series, a method we shall discuss in Chap. 9.

The solution (6) can be established by the procedure used in Secs. 70 and 71. Since some variations are needed, we outline the method here. The function R has the order of $r^{-\frac{1}{2}} \times$ exp $(-|x - \xi| \sqrt{r/2})$ in any half plane $\Re(s) \geq \gamma$, where $\gamma > 0$ and $r = |s|$. Since $g(\xi)$ is bounded, it follows from equation (3) that $u(x,s)$ is $O(r^{-1})$; but this is not sufficient to show that the inversion integral applies to u.

For the sake of brevity, we assume $g''(x)$ continuous and $g'''(x)$ sectionally continuous ($0 \leq x \leq 1$). Let R_1 denote the function $-R$ when $0 < \xi < x$ and R_2 the function $-R$ when $x < \xi < 1$; then

$$u(x,s) = \int_0^x g(\xi) R_1(x,\xi,s) \, d\xi + \int_x^1 g(\xi) R_2(x,\xi,s) \, d\xi.$$

Integrating both of these integrals by parts and simplifying, we find that

$$(7) \quad u(x,s) = \frac{g(x)}{s} - g(0)P(x,0,s) + g(1)P(x,1,s)$$

$$- \int_0^1 g'(\xi)P(x,\xi,s) \, d\xi,$$

where P is the following integral of $-R$, with respect to ξ:

$$(8) \quad P(x,\xi,s) = \frac{\sinh\left[(1 - x)\sqrt{s}\right]\cosh \xi \sqrt{s}}{s \sinh \sqrt{s}} \qquad (0 \leq \xi < x),$$

$$= -\frac{\sinh x \sqrt{s} \cosh\left[(1 - \xi)\sqrt{s}\right]}{s \sinh \sqrt{s}} \qquad (x < \xi \leq 1).$$

The integral in equation (7) is $O(r^{-\frac{3}{2}})$ in the half plane $\Re(s) \geq \gamma$. In Sec. 70 we found that the inversion integral applies to $P(x,1,s)$ or $P(x,0,s)$ and that it satisfies certain boundary conditions. According to Theorem 6, Sec. 64, $L_i^{-1}\{g(x)/s\} = g(x)$. We can conclude that the inversion integral of $u(x,s)$ exists and represents a function $U(x,t)$ that satisfies the end conditions $U(+0,t) = 0$, $U(1 - 0, t) = 0$ and the initial condition $U(x,+0) - g(x) = 0$.

From equation (7) we can show that

$$u'(x,s) = -g(0)P_x(x,0,s) + g(1)P_x(x,1,s) - \int_0^1 g'(\xi)P_x(x,\xi,s) \, d\xi$$

and, by an integration by parts here, that $u'(x,s)$ is $O(r^{-\frac{3}{2}})$ when $0 < x < 1$. That $u''(x,s)$ also has this same order follows from the fact that $u'' = su - g$ and integration by parts twice in equation (7). Thus $U_{xx} = L_i^{-1}\{u''\}$ and, since $s(u - g/s)$ is

$O(r^{-\frac{1}{2}})$, then

$$L_i^{-1}\left\{s\left(u - \frac{g}{s}\right)\right\} = [U(x,t) - g(x)]_t = U_t(x,t) = U_{xx}(x,t)$$
$$(0 < x < 1).$$

The function

(9) $U(x,t) = L_i^{-1}\{u(x,s)\}$ $(\gamma > 0)$

is therefore established as a solution of our problem.

From equations (3) and (4) it can be shown that $u(x,s)$ is $O(r^{-\frac{1}{2}})$ when s is on the parabolas

$$r = \left(n - \frac{1}{2}\right)^2 \pi^2 \csc^2 \frac{\theta}{2}.$$

Therefore the series (6) represents the solution (9) when $t > 0$.

In addition to this, we can see from equation (7) that the inversion integral of the function $u(x,s) - g(x)/s$ converges to zero when $t = 0$ and that it is represented by its series of residues when $t = 0$, provided $0 < x < 1$. It follows that

$$2 \sum_{n=1}^{\infty} \sin n\pi x \int_0^1 g(\xi) \sin n\pi\xi \, d\xi - g(x) = 0 \quad (0 < x < 1),$$

which is the Fourier series expansion mentioned above.

The results hold true if $g(x)$ or its derivatives are sectionally continuous instead of continuous. The proof is longer, since it involves the writing of each integral as the sum of integrals over intervals on which the functions are continuous.

77. Temperatures in a Cylinder. Let us derive formally the temperature function $U(r,t)$ for a solid circular cylinder of infinite length whose initial temperature is zero and whose surface is kept at unit temperature (Fig. 81). Units of time and length can be chosen so that the boundary value problem becomes

$$U_t(r,t) = U_{rr}(r,t) + \frac{1}{r} U_r(r,t) \quad (0 \leq r < 1, t > 0),$$

(1) $U(r,0) = 0$ $(0 \leq r < 1)$
$$U(1,t) = 1 \qquad\qquad\qquad (t > 0),$$

where the cylindrical coordinate r is distance from the axis of the cylinder. The function U is to be continuous interior to the cylinder, and at $r = 0$ in particular.

The transformed problem is therefore

(2)
$$su(r,s) = u_{rr}(r,s) + \frac{1}{r} u_r(r,s),$$

$$u(1,s) = \frac{1}{s}.$$

Also $u(0,s)$ must at least be finite. A solution of Bessel's equation (2) that is finite at $r = 0$ is

$$u(r,s) = CI_0(r \sqrt{s}),$$

where $I_0(x)$ is Bessel's function of the first kind corresponding to an imaginary argument:

$$I_0(x) = J_0(ix) = 1 + \frac{x^2}{2^2} + \frac{x^4}{2^2 \times 4^2} + \frac{x^6}{2^2 \times 4^2 \times 6^2} + \cdots.$$

In view of the condition $u(1,s) = 1/s$, it follows that

(3)
$$u(r,s) = \frac{1}{s} \frac{I_0(r \sqrt{s})}{I_0(\sqrt{s})}.$$

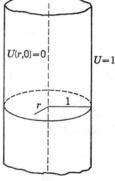

The roots of the equation $J_0(z) = 0$ are all real and form an infinite sequence. Their values are tabulated. Let $\pm \alpha_1, \pm \alpha_2,$ . . . denote their values:

$$J_0(\pm \alpha_n) = 0.$$

Then $u(r,s)$ has singularities when

$$i \sqrt{s} = \pm \alpha_n,$$

or
$$s = -\alpha_n^2.$$

FIG. 81.

Since $J_0'(\pm \alpha_n) \neq 0$, the singular points $s = -\alpha_n^2$ are simple poles of $u(x,s)$. The residue of $u(r,z)e^{zt}$ at the simple pole $z = 0$ is 1, and the residue at $z = -\alpha_n^2$ is

$$\frac{I_0(r \sqrt{z})}{z \, d/dz \, I_0(\sqrt{z})} e^{zt} \Bigg]_{z = -\alpha_n^2} = \frac{2}{i\alpha_n} \frac{J_0(\alpha_n r)}{I_0'(i\alpha_n)} e^{-\alpha_n^2 t}.$$

Since $I_0'(x) = iJ_0'(ix)$ and $J_0'(z) = -J_1(z) = J_1(-z)$, this residue can be written

$$-\frac{2}{\alpha_n} \frac{J_0(\alpha_n r)}{J_1(\alpha_n)} e^{-\alpha_n^2 t}.$$

The formula for the temperatures in the cylinder is therefore

$$(4) \qquad U(r,t) = 1 - 2 \sum_{n=1}^{\infty} \frac{J_0(\alpha_n r)}{\alpha_n J_1(\alpha_n)} e^{-\alpha_n^2 t}.$$

To write this formula in terms of standard units of length and time, centimeters and seconds, for example, let ρ denote the radial distance and τ the time in such units. If the radius of the cylinder is ρ_0 and the thermal diffusivity of the material is k, then to transform the heat equation (1) into $U_\tau = k(U_{\rho\rho} + U_\rho/\rho)$ $(0 \leqq \rho < \rho_0)$ we put

$$r = \frac{\rho}{\rho_0}, \qquad t = \frac{k\tau}{\rho_0^2},$$

where r and t are the variables used in formula (4). Also let $V(\rho,\tau) = A U(r,t)$ so that the constant surface temperature is arbitrary:

$$V(\rho_0,\tau) = A.$$

Our temperature formula then takes the form

$$(5) \qquad V(\rho,\tau) = A \left[1 - 2 \sum_{n=1}^{\infty} \frac{J_0(\alpha_n \rho/\rho_0)}{\alpha_n J_1(\alpha_n)} e^{-\alpha_n^2 k\tau/\rho_0^2} \right],$$

where $\alpha_1, \alpha_2, \ldots$ are the positive roots of the equation $J_0(\alpha) = 0$; in particular,

$$\alpha_1 = 2.405, \qquad \alpha_2 = 5.520, \qquad \alpha_3 = 8.654, \qquad \alpha_4 = 11.79.$$

PROBLEMS

1. The initial temperature of a slab is $U(x,0) = Ax$. If the faces $x = 0$ and $x = l$ are kept at temperature zero, derive the temperature formula

$$U(x,t) = \frac{2Al}{\pi} \sum_{n=1}^{\infty} \frac{(-1)^{n-1}}{n} e^{-n^2\pi^2 kt/l^2} \sin \frac{n\pi x}{l}.$$

2. Derive the following formula for the temperature function in Prob. 1:

$$U(x,t) = Ax - Al \sum_{n=0}^{\infty} \left\{ \text{erf} \left[\frac{(2n+1)l+x}{2\sqrt{kt}} \right] - \text{erf} \left[\frac{(2n+1)l-x}{2\sqrt{kt}} \right] \right\}.$$

3. If slab in Prob. 1 is 20 cm thick and is made of iron for which $k = 0.15$ cgs unit, and if the initial temperature varies uniformly through the slab from 0° to 100°C, find to the nearest degree the temperature at the center after the faces have been kept at 0°C (*a*) for 1 min, (*b*) for 100 min.   *Ans.* (*a*) 48°C; (*b*) 0°C.

4. Solve Prob. 3 if the slab is made of concrete for which $k = 0.005$ cgs unit.

5. If the faces $x = 0$ and $x = l$ of a slab are insulated (Fig. 82) and the initial temperature is $U(x,0) = g(x)$, set up the boundary value problem for the temperature $U(x,t)$ and derive the formula

$$U(x,t) = \frac{1}{l} \int_0^l g(\xi)\, d\xi$$

$$+ \frac{2}{l} \sum_{n=1}^{\infty} \cos \frac{n\pi x}{l} \int_0^l g(\xi) \cos \frac{n\pi\xi}{l}\, d\xi \exp\left(-\frac{n^2\pi^2 kt}{l^2}\right).$$

6. In Prob. 5, let the initial temperature distribution be

$$g(x) = A \qquad \text{when } 0 < x < \tfrac{1}{2}l,$$
$$= 0 \qquad \text{when } \tfrac{1}{2}l < x < l.$$

Show that

$$U(x,t) = \frac{A}{2} + \frac{2A}{\pi} \sum_{n=1}^{\infty} \frac{(-1)^{n-1}}{2n-1} \cos \frac{(2n-1)\pi x}{l} \exp\left[-\frac{(2n-1)^2\pi^2 kt}{l^2}\right].$$

7. The face $x = 0$ of a slab is kept at temperature zero while the face $x = 1$ is insulated. If the initial temperature is $U = g(x)$, derive a formula for the temperature $U(x,t)$ when $k = 1$.

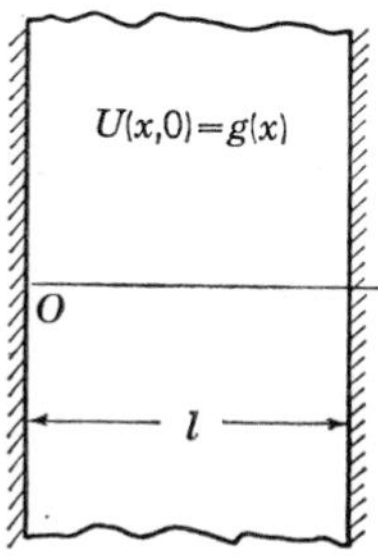

8. The initial temperature of a cylinder of infinite length is zero. If the surface $r = 1$ is kept at temperature A from $t = 0$ to $t = t_0$ and at temperature zero thereafter, and if $k = 1$, derive the following formula for the temperatures in the cylinder:

$$W(r,t) = A[U(r,t) - U(r, t - t_0)],$$

U(x,0)=g(x)

O   x

l

FIG. 82.

where $U(r,t)$ is the function defined by formula (4), Sec. 77, when $t \geq 0$ and $U(r,t) = 0$ when $t < 0$.

9. The flux of heat into a cylinder of infinite length through its surface $r = 1$ is a constant, so that $U_r(1,t) = A$. If $k = 1$ and the initial temperature is zero, derive the temperature formula

$$U(r,t) = \frac{A}{4}\left[2r^2 - 1 + 8t - 8\sum_{n=1}^{\infty} \frac{J_0(\beta_n r)}{\beta_n^2 J_0(\beta_n)}\, e^{-\beta_n^2 t}\right],$$

where β_1, β_2, . . . are the positive roots of the equation $J_1(\beta) = 0$, given that the equation has only real roots and that $J_1'(\beta_n) \neq 0$. Note that according to Bessel's equation $-J_0''(x) = J_0(x) - J_1(x)/x$, and since $-J_0''(x) = J_1'(x)$ it follows that $J_1'(\beta_n) = J_0(\beta_n)$.

78. Evaporation from a Semi-infinite Body.

The transform of the solution of the following problem has a branch cut as its singularity. The solution will be obtained in the form of a real integral by altering the path of integration for the inversion integral. Although the form of the boundary value problem is adapted to the method of separation of variables, a generalization of the Fourier cosine integral formula is needed to complete the solution by that method. The generalized formula is suggested by the solution obtained below.

Let $U(x,t)$ denote concentration of moisture in a porous semi-infinite solid $x \geqq 0$. The initial concentration is a prescribed function $f(x)$. Evaporation of the moisture takes place at the face $x = 0$ into a dry medium according to the linear law

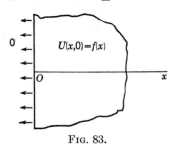

$$KU_x(0,t) = E[U(0,t) - 0].$$

FIG. 83.

Here K is the coefficient of diffusion and E is a coefficient of transfer of moisture into the adjacent medium, where the concentration is zero (Fig. 83).

If the unit of time is properly chosen with respect to K, the boundary value problem can be written

(1)
$$U_t(x,t) = U_{xx}(x,t) \qquad (x > 0, t > 0),$$
$$U(x,+0) = f(x) \qquad (x > 0)$$
(2)
$$U_x(+0,t) = hU(+0,t) \qquad (t > 0),$$

where the positive constant h is a relative coefficient of evaporation, $h = E/K$. One further condition on the function U is needed, to take the place of a condition at the right-hand boundary. We shall assume that $f(x)$ is *bounded, continuous and absolutely integrable* from zero to infinity. Then it is reasonable to assume that, for some constant M,

$$|U(x,t)| < M \qquad (x > 0, t > 0).$$

The problem in the transform of $U(x,t)$ becomes

$$u''(x,s) - su(x,s) = -f(x) \qquad (x > 0),$$
$$u'(0,s) = hu(0,s), \qquad |u(x,s)| < N,$$

where the constant N may depend on s. The solution of this problem can be written in the form

$$(3) \qquad u(x,s) = \int_0^\infty f(\xi)g(x,\xi,s) \, d\xi,$$

where

$$(4) \quad 2\sqrt{s}\, g(x,\xi,s) = \exp\left(-|x - \xi|\sqrt{s}\right)$$
$$+ \frac{\sqrt{s} - h}{\sqrt{s} + h} \exp\left[-(x + \xi)\sqrt{s}\right],$$

and where $\sqrt{s} = \sqrt{r}\, e^{\frac{1}{2}i\theta}(-\pi < \theta < \pi)$. Thus $\Re(\sqrt{s}) > 0$ and g is an analytic function of s except for the branch cut $\theta = \pi$. Also, g is of the order of $r^{-\frac{1}{2}}$ for all $\theta(-\pi \leqq \theta \leqq \pi)$, and $u(x,s)$ has that same order.

If $f'(x)$ *is also absolutely integrable*, the integral in equation (3) can be integrated by parts to show that $u - f(x)/s$ is of the order of $r^{-\frac{3}{2}}$ in a half plane $\Re(s) \geqq \gamma > 0$, when $x > 0$. Thus the inversion integral applies to u and its limit is $f(x)$ when t tends to zero. In terms of the notation used in Fig. 73, we replace the partial path $A'A$ of integration for the inversion integral by the path $A'C'D'DCA$, consisting of circles and rays, and let ϵ tend to zero.

Because $u(x,s)$ is $O(r^{-\frac{1}{2}})$ in the left half plane, the proof of part (c) of Theorem 10, Sec. 67, applies to show that the integrals over the large circular arcs vanish as the radius tends to infinity, when $\epsilon \geqq 0$ and $t > 0$. The same order property ensures the vanishing of the integral around the small circle as its radius r_0 approaches zero.

The limiting value of the integral along the ray $C'D'$ can be seen by writing $s = re^{-i\pi} = -r$, and $\sqrt{s} = \sqrt{r}\, e^{-\frac{1}{2}\pi i} = -i\sqrt{r}$. Then from equation (4)

$$(5) \quad -2i\sqrt{r}\, g(x,\xi,re^{-i\pi}) = e^{i|x-\xi|\sqrt{r}} + \frac{\sqrt{r} - ih}{\sqrt{r} + ih}\, e^{i(x+\xi)\sqrt{r}}$$
$$= e^{i|x-\xi|\sqrt{r}} + e^{-2\alpha i}e^{i(x+\xi)\sqrt{r}},$$

where $\sqrt{r} + ih = \sqrt{r + h^2}\, e^{i\alpha}$. On the ray DC, $s = re^{i\pi} = -r$

and $\sqrt{s} = \sqrt{r}\, e^{\frac{1}{2}\pi i} = i\,\sqrt{r}$, and we find that

(6) $\qquad 2i\,\sqrt{r}\, g(x,\xi,re^{i\pi}) = e^{-i|x-\xi|\sqrt{r}} + e^{2\alpha i}e^{-i(x+\xi)\sqrt{r}}.$

The inversion integral of $u(x,s)$, when $t > 0$, then becomes

(7) $\dfrac{1}{2\pi i}\left[-\displaystyle\int_{\infty}^{0} e^{-rt}u(x,re^{-i\pi})\, dr - \int_{0}^{\infty} e^{-rt}u(x,re^{i\pi})\, dr \right]$

$\qquad = \dfrac{1}{2\pi i}\displaystyle\int_{0}^{\infty} e^{-rt}\int_{0}^{\infty} f(\xi)[g(x,\xi,re^{-i\pi}) - g(x,\xi,re^{i\pi})]\, d\xi\, dr.$

The quantity inside the brackets can be written, with the aid of equations (5) and (6), as the product

$\dfrac{i}{2\,\sqrt{r}}\,[e^{i(x\sqrt{r}-\alpha)} + e^{-i(x\sqrt{r}-\alpha)}][e^{i(\xi\sqrt{r}-\alpha)} + e^{-i(\xi\sqrt{r}-\alpha)}]$

$\qquad\qquad\qquad = \dfrac{2i}{\sqrt{r}}\cos\,(x\,\sqrt{r} - \alpha)\cos\,(\xi\,\sqrt{r} - \alpha).$

When we substitute a new variable of integration β for $\sqrt{r}$, the integral (7), or our formal solution, becomes

(8) $U(x,t)$

$\qquad = \dfrac{2}{\pi}\displaystyle\int_{0}^{\infty} e^{-\beta^2 t}\cos\,[\beta x - \alpha(\beta)]\int_{0}^{\infty} f(\xi)\cos\,[\beta\xi - \alpha(\beta)]\, d\xi\, d\beta,$

where

(9) $\qquad\qquad\qquad \alpha(\beta) = \arg\,(\beta + ih).$

But this function $U(x,t)$ is the same as $L_i^{-1}\{u(x,s)\}$ when $t > 0$ and the inversion integral satisfies the initial condition; therefore it follows that $U(x,+0) = f(x)$ when $x > 0$. The inner integral in formula (8) is a bounded continuous function of β. From the uniform convergence of the outer integral (8), with respect to x and t when $t \geqq t_0 > 0$, and of the integrals arising when the integrand is differentiated with respect to x or t, we can see that the function satisfies the rest of conditions (1) and (2). Thus the function (8) is established as a solution.

Another form of the solution is given in Prob. 2, Sec. 79.

The generalized Fourier integral formula mentioned above,

(10) $f(x) = \dfrac{2}{\pi}\displaystyle\int_{0}^{\infty}\cos\,[\beta x - \alpha(\beta)]\int_{0}^{\infty} f(\xi)\cos\,[\beta\xi - \alpha(\beta)]\, d\xi\, d\beta$

$\qquad\qquad\qquad\qquad\qquad\qquad\qquad (x > 0),$

is suggested by writing $t = 0$ and $U = f(x)$ in formula (8).   The representation (10) is known to be valid when $f(x)$ and $f'(x)$ are sectionally continuous on each finite interval in the range $x \geqq 0$, provided $\int_0^\infty |f(x)|\, dx$ exists, if $f(x)$ is defined as its mean value at each point of discontinuity.[1]   When $h = 0$, then $\alpha = 0$ and the representation reduces to the Fourier cosine integral formula.   It becomes the Fourier sine integral formula when $\alpha = \frac{1}{2}\pi$ $(h \to \infty)$.

79. Duhamel's Formula in Heat Conduction.   In Sec. 74 we obtained a formula for the temperatures in a bar with variable end temperature, in terms of the temperature function when the end temperature is constant.   We now obtain a more general formula that simplifies heat conduction problems in the same way.

Let $U(x,y,z,t)$ be the temperatures in any solid, filling a region R, that is initially at temperature zero throughout.   Let the temperature at every point of some part S of the boundary be a prescribed function $F(t)$ of time, and let the

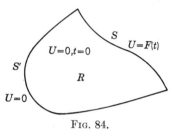

Fig. 84.

remainder S' of the boundary be kept at temperature zero (Fig. 84).

If $\Lambda(U)$ represents the linear differential form

(1) $$\Lambda(U) = \frac{1}{c}\left[\frac{\partial}{\partial x}\left(K\frac{\partial U}{\partial x}\right) + \frac{\partial}{\partial y}\left(K\frac{\partial U}{\partial y}\right) + \frac{\partial}{\partial z}\left(K\frac{\partial U}{\partial z}\right)\right],$$

the equation of conduction can be written

(2) $$U_t = \Lambda(U) \qquad [(x,y,z) \text{ in } R,\, t > 0].$$

We assume that the thermal coefficients K and c are either constants or independent of t.   The boundary value problem in U consists of equation (2) and the conditions

(3) $\qquad\qquad U(x,y,z,0) = 0 \qquad\qquad$ interior to R,
(4) $\qquad\qquad U = 0 \qquad\qquad$ on S'
$\qquad\qquad\qquad\quad = F(t) \qquad\qquad$ on S.

---

[1] This result is included in a more general one established by the author in a paper entitled Generalized Fourier Integral Formulas, *Mich. Math Jour.*, vol. 2, pp. 133–139, 1953–54.

The transform $u(x,y,z,s)$ then satisfies the conditions

(5) $\qquad\qquad\qquad su = \Lambda(u) \qquad\qquad\qquad$ in R,

(6) $\qquad\qquad\qquad u = 0 \qquad\qquad\qquad$ on S'

$\qquad\qquad\qquad\qquad = f(s) \qquad\qquad\qquad$ on S.

Let $V(x,y,z,t)$ be the temperature function U when $F(t) = 1$; that is, V satisfies the heat equation (2), the initial condition (3), and the surface conditions

(7) $\qquad\qquad\qquad V = 0 \qquad\qquad\qquad$ on S'

$\qquad\qquad\qquad\qquad = 1 \qquad\qquad\qquad$ on S.

Then the transform $v(x,y,z,s)$ satisfies the differential equation (5) and the conditions

(8) $\qquad\qquad\qquad v = 0 \qquad\qquad\qquad$ on S'

$\qquad\qquad\qquad\qquad = \dfrac{1}{s} \qquad\qquad\qquad$ on S.

Since s is a parameter in the linear homogeneous differential equation (5), the product of $sf(s)$ by the solution v is also a solution. But according to conditions (8),

$$sf(s)v = 0 \qquad\qquad \text{on } S'$$
$$= f(s) \qquad\qquad \text{on } S;$$

thus the function $sf(s)v$ also satisfies all the conditions (5) and (6), and it is therefore the same as the function u:

(9) $\qquad\qquad u(x,y,z,s) = sf(s)v(x,y,z,s).$

Since sv is the transform of V_t, it follows from equation (9) with the aid of the convolution that

(10) $\qquad U(x,y,z,t) = \displaystyle\int_0^t F(t - \tau)V_t(x,y,z,\tau)\, d\tau.$

This is the formula of Duhamel, giving the temperature U corresponding to a variable surface temperature in terms of the temperature V corresponding to a constant surface temperature.

If the function $F(t)$ is continuous $(t \geqq 0)$ and of exponential order, if $F'(t)$ is sectionally continuous, and if $F(0) = 0$, then $sf(s)$ is the transform of $F'(t)$ and it follows from equation (9) that

(11) $\qquad U(x,y,z,t) = \displaystyle\int_0^t F'(t - \tau)V(x,y,z,\tau)\, d\tau.$

When $F(0) \neq 0$, then $sf(s) = L\{F'(t)\} + F(0)$ and an additional term appears in the form (11) of Duhamel's formula. Another form is the following:

$$(12) \qquad U(x,y,z,t) = \frac{\partial}{\partial t} \int_0^t F(t - \tau) V(x,y,z,\tau) \, d\tau.$$

These forms can be verified directly under broad conditions on the function $F(t)$ as solutions of the boundary value problem in U.

The differential operator Λ could clearly be replaced by any linear differential operator in space coordinates with coefficients that are not functions of t.

PROBLEMS

1. When the initial concentration is uniform, $f(x) = u_0$, in the problem solved in Sec. 78, derive the formula

$$U(x,t) = u_0 \left[\operatorname{erf} \left(\frac{x}{2 \sqrt{t}} \right) + e^{hx} e^{h^2 t} \operatorname{erfc} \left(h \sqrt{t} + \frac{x}{2 \sqrt{t}} \right) \right]$$

for the concentration in the semi-infinite body, with the aid of the tables in Appendix 3.

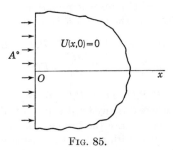

FIG. 85.

2. Use the tables in Appendix 3 to write the inverse transform of the function $g(x,\xi,s)$ in Sec. 78, and obtain formally this alternate formula for the concentration given by equation (8) in that section:

$$U(x,t) = \frac{1}{2 \sqrt{\pi t}} \int_0^\infty f(\xi) \left\{ \exp \left[-\frac{(x - \xi)^2}{4t} \right] + \exp \left[-\frac{(x + \xi)^2}{4t} \right] \right\} d\xi$$

$$- h \exp (hx + h^2 t) \int_0^\infty e^{h\xi} f(\xi) \operatorname{erfc} \left(h \sqrt{t} + \frac{x + \xi}{2 \sqrt{t}} \right) d\xi.$$

3. The face $x = 0$ of a semi-infinite solid (Fig. 85) is exposed to a medium at constant temperature A. Heat is transferred from that medium to the face of the solid according to the law that the flux of heat is $E[A - U(0,t)]$, where $U(x,t)$ is the temperature in the solid. Thus the boundary condition at the face becomes

$$U_x(0,t) = h[U(0,t) - A],$$

where $h = E/K$. If the initial temperature is zero, derive the following formula with the aid of the tables in Appendix 3:

$$U(x,t) = A \left[\text{erfc} \left(\frac{x}{2\sqrt{kt}} \right) - e^{hx}e^{h^2kt} \, \text{erfc} \left(h\sqrt{kt} + \frac{x}{2\sqrt{kt}} \right) \right].$$

Examine the variation of the temperature $U(0,t)$ of the face.

4. Let $V(x,t)$ be the temperature function for the solid in Prob. 3 when $A = 1$. Let $W(x,t)$ be the temperature of the solid when the constant A is replaced by a function $\Phi(t)$, so that the medium to which the face is exposed has a variable temperature. Derive the formula

$$W(x,t) = \int_0^t \Phi(t - \tau) V_t(x,\tau) \, d\tau.$$

5. Use the generalized convolution property found in Prob. 15, Sec. 23, to make a formal derivation of the following more general Duhamel formula. Let $\Lambda(U)$ denote the differential form (1), P the point (x,y,z), n the distance normal to the boundary surface S or S', and let $a(P)$, $b(P)$, H, F, and G represent prescribed functions. The temperature function $U(P,t)$ in the region R is to satisfy the conditions

$$U_t = \Lambda(U) + H(P,t), \qquad U(P,0) = G(P) \qquad (P \text{ in } R);$$

$$a(P)U + b(P)\frac{dU}{dn} = F(P,t) \qquad (P \text{ on } S \text{ or } S').$$

When the functions $H(P,t)$ and $F(P,t)$ are replaced by $H(P,t')$ and $F(P,t')$ respectively, where t' is any fixed value of t, $V(P,t,t')$ denotes the solution of the problem. Write the problem in the transform $v(P,s,t')$ and transform its members with respect to t', using the same parameter s, to obtain a problem in the iterated transform $\bar{v}(P,s,s)$ and thus derive this generalization of formula (12) above:

$$U(P,t) = \frac{\partial}{\partial t} \int_0^t V(P, t - \tau, \tau) \, d\tau.$$

Note that if $a(P) = F(P,t) = 0$ when P is on S', then the surface S' is insulated. Thus the generalized formula could be applied to Prob. 7, Sec. 75.

6. The temperature of the face of a semi-infinite solid $x \geq 0$ varies in the following manner:

$$U(0,t) = A \sin \omega t.$$

Taking the initial temperature as zero, for convenience, show that, when t is large, the temperature at each point is approximately

$$U(x,t) = A \sin\left(\omega t - x\sqrt{\frac{\omega}{2k}}\right) \exp\left(-x\sqrt{\frac{\omega}{2k}}\right),$$

a simple periodic function of time. Note that the closed contour corresponding to the one shown in Fig. 73 will enclose two simple poles $s = \pm i\omega$ of $u(x,s)$ in this case. Also note that the above formula could be obtained without the use of the transform by assuming that $U(x,t)$ has the form

$$f(x) \sin \omega t + g(x) \cos \omega t$$

and solving for $f(x)$ and $g(x)$.

7. The diffusivity k of the earth's soil in a certain locality is 0.005 cgs unit. The temperature of the surface of the soil has an annual variation from -8 to $22°C$. Assuming the variation is approximately sinusoidal (Prob. 6), show that the freezing temperature will penetrate to a depth of approximately 170 cm (considerably less, because of the latent heat of freezing).

8. In Prob. 7 find the approximate depth at which the variation of temperature with time is six months out of phase with the variation of the surface temperature. Show that the amplitude of the variation at that depth is less than $1°C$. *Ans.* $x = 705$ cm $= 23$ ft, approximately.

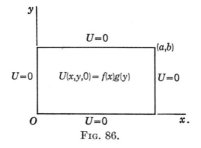

Fig. 86.

9. Let the functions $V(x,t)$ and $W(y,t)$ satisfy the heat equations $V_t = kV_{xx}$ and $W_t = kW_{yy}$, respectively. Prove by direct substitution that the *product of* those *temperature functions,*

$$U(x,y,t) = V(x,t)W(y,t),$$

satisfies the heat equation

$$U_t = k(U_{xx} + U_{yy}).$$

If in addition $V(0,t) = V(a,t) = 0$ and $W(0,t) = W(b,t) = 0$, and if $V(x,0) = f(x)$ and $W(y,0) = g(y)$, then show that $U(x,y,t)$ represents the temperatures in a rectangular plate (Fig. 86) with insulated faces, if the edges are at temperature zero and the initial temperature is

$$U(x,y,0) = f(x)g(y).$$

10. Use the product of solutions (Prob. 9) to obtain the following formula for the temperatures in an infinite prism with a square cross section, if the initial temperature is A and the surface temperature is zero, taking the unit of length as the side of the square, and $k = 1$:

$$V(x,y,t) = A U(x,t) U(y,t),$$

where U is the temperature function found in Prob. 8 of Sec. 75.

11. With the aid of Prob. 9, derive the formula

$$U(x,y,t) = \frac{4}{\pi} \operatorname{erf}\left(\frac{x}{2\sqrt{t}}\right) \sum_{n=1}^{\infty} \frac{\sin(2n-1)y}{2n-1} e^{-(2n-1)^2\pi^2 t}$$

for the temperatures in the semi-infinite slab $x \geq 0$, $0 \leq y \leq 1$ with

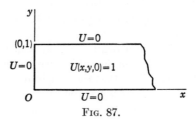

FIG. 87.

its boundary at temperature zero, if $U(x,y,0) = 1$ (Fig. 87), where $k = 1$.

12. Generalize the method of Prob. 9 to the case of three dimensions, and give an illustration of its use in finding the temperatures in a cube.

CHAPTER 8

PROBLEMS IN MECHANICAL VIBRATIONS

This chapter contains further illustrations of the uses of those properties of the Laplace transformation that involve complex variables. The problems taken as illustrations deal with vibrations and resonance in continuous mechanical systems—systems in which the mass and elastic characteristics are distributed over the system. Consequently these problems are boundary value problems in partial differential equations, of the type treated in Chap. 4. It is the intention here to present fairly simple physical problems in their mathematical form, although the mathematical problems may have more important physical interpretations. Some electrical analogues of mechanical vibrations, involving transmission lines, are included among the exercises.

80. A Bar with a Constant Force on One End. In Sec. 41 we derived a formula for the longitudinal displacements in an elastic bar in the form of a prism, when one end of the bar is fixed and a constant force F_0 per unit area acts parallel to the bar on the other end (Fig. 88). Let all

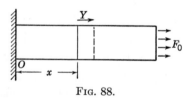

FIG. 88.

parts of the bar be initially at rest and unstrained. The displacements $Y(x,t)$ then satisfy the conditions in the boundary value problem

$$Y_{tt}(x,t) = a^2 Y_{xx}(x,t) \qquad (0 < x < c,\ t > 0),$$
$$Y(x,0) = Y_t(x,0) = 0,$$
$$Y(0,t) = 0, \qquad EY_x(c,t) = F_0,$$

where $a^2 = E/\rho$, E is Young's modulus of elasticity, and ρ is the mass per unit volume of the material.

Let us obtain another formula for $Y(x,t)$ here.

235

From the above problem, we found that the transform of $Y(x,t)$ is

$$y(x,s) = \frac{aF_0}{E} \frac{\sinh(sx/a)}{s^2 \cosh(sc/a)}.$$

We can write

$$\frac{1}{s} \sinh \frac{sx}{a} = \frac{x}{a} + \frac{s^2 x^3}{3!a^3} + \frac{s^4 x^5}{5!a^5} + \cdots,$$

a function that is analytic at $s = 0$. The function $y(x,s)$ therefore has a simple pole at $s = 0$. The residue at that pole is

$$\frac{aF_0}{E} \frac{x}{a} = \frac{F_0}{E} x.$$

The remaining singularities of $y(x,s)$ are the zeros of the function $\cosh(sc/a)$; that is, $s = s_n$, where

$$s_n = \frac{a}{c} (2n - 1) \frac{\pi}{2} i \quad (n = 0, \pm1, \pm2, \ldots).$$

Since the derivative of the analytic function $\cosh(sc/a)$ does not vanish at the points $s = s_n$, those points are all simple poles of $y(x,s)$. The residue of $e^{st}y(x,s)$ at s_n is, according to formula (7), Sec. 66,

$$\rho_n = \frac{aF_0}{E} \frac{\sinh \dfrac{s_n x}{a}}{s_n^2 \dfrac{c}{a} \sinh \dfrac{s_n c}{a}} e^{s_n t} = -\frac{F_0 c}{E\pi^2} \frac{\sin \dfrac{(2n-1)\pi x}{2c}}{\left(n - \dfrac{1}{2}\right)^2 \sin\left(n - \dfrac{1}{2}\right)\pi} e^{s_n t}$$

$$= \frac{4cF_0(-1)^n}{\pi^2 E(2n-1)^2} \sin \frac{(2n-1)\pi x}{2c} \exp\left[\frac{(2n-1)\pi at}{2c} i\right].$$

The poles s_n consist of a set of points on the positive imaginary axis and their complex conjugates. Let us add the residues ρ_1 and ρ_0, corresponding to the poles $\pm \pi ai/(2c)$:

$$\rho_1 + \rho_0 = -\frac{4cF_0}{\pi^2 E} \sin \frac{\pi x}{2c} \left[\exp\left(\frac{\pi at i}{2c}\right) + \exp\left(-\frac{\pi at i}{2c}\right)\right]$$

$$= -\frac{8cF_0}{\pi^2 E} \sin \frac{\pi x}{2c} \cos \frac{\pi at}{2c}.$$

Adding the residues corresponding to any pole and its conjugate we find, in just the same way,

$$\rho_n + \rho_{-(n-1)} = \frac{8cF_0}{\pi^2 E} \frac{(-1)^n}{(2n-1)^2} \sin \frac{(2n-1)\pi x}{2c} \cos \frac{(2n-1)\pi at}{2c}.$$

Formally, then, the inverse transform of $y(x,s)$ is

(1) $Y(x,t)$

$$= \frac{F_0}{E}\left[x + \frac{8c}{\pi^2} \sum_{n=1}^{\infty} \frac{(-1)^n}{(2n-1)^2} \sin \frac{(2n-1)\pi x}{2c} \cos \frac{(2n-1)\pi at}{2c}\right].$$

Every term in this series is a periodic function of t with the period

(2) $$T_0 = \frac{4c}{a} = 4c \sqrt{\frac{\rho}{E}}.$$

Hence every point of the bar vibrates with this period.

81. Another Form of the Solution. Since $Y(x,0) = 0$, our formula (1) of the foregoing section indicates that

$$x = -\frac{8c}{\pi^2} \sum_{n=1}^{\infty} \frac{(-1)^n}{(2n-1)^2} \sin \frac{(2n-1)\pi x}{2c} \qquad (0 < x < c).$$

Moreover the values of the terms of this series remain the same after x is replaced by $2c - x$, and the terms are antiperiodic with

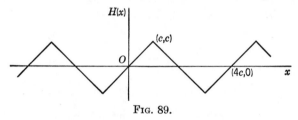

FIG. 89.

respect to x with the period $2c$. Hence if the range of the variable x is unlimited, this series should represent the triangular wave function $H(x)$ shown in Fig. 89 and defined as follows:

(1) $$\begin{aligned} H(x) &= x & \text{when } 0 < x < c \\ &= 2c - x & \text{when } c < x < 2c, \\ &= -H(-x); \\ H(x + 4c) &= H(x) & \text{for all } x. \end{aligned}$$

Incidentally, this function can be described easily in terms of the function $H(2c,x)$ of Sec. 19. Thus, for all real x, we should have

(2) $$H(x) = \frac{8c}{\pi^2} \sum_{n=1}^{\infty} \frac{(-1)^{n-1}}{(2n-1)^2} \sin \frac{(2n-1)\pi x}{2c}.$$

The series here is actually the Fourier series representation of the periodic function $H(x)$, and therefore formula (2) is valid.

In our formula for the displacement $Y(x,t)$, let $m = 2n - 1$ and write

$$2 \sin \frac{m\pi x}{2c} \cos \frac{m\pi at}{2c} = \sin \frac{m\pi(x + at)}{2c} + \sin \frac{m\pi(x - at)}{2c}.$$

Then

$$Y(x,t) = \frac{F_0}{E} \left\{ x - \frac{4c}{\pi^2} \sum_{n=1}^{\infty} \frac{(-1)^{n-1}}{m^2} \left[\sin \frac{m\pi(x + at)}{2c} \right. \right.$$
$$\left. \left. + \sin \frac{m\pi(x - at)}{2c} \right] \right\},$$

and, in view of formula (2) above, our formula can be written

$$(3) \qquad Y(x,t) = \frac{F_0}{E} \left[x - \frac{1}{2} H(x + at) - \frac{1}{2} H(x - at) \right].$$

This formula is simple enough that it can easily be verified as the solution of our problem. In showing that it satisfies the end condition $EY_x(c,t) = F_0$, it is necessary to observe that the derivative of the function $H(x)$ is the following square wave function:

$$H'(x) = 1 \qquad \text{when } -c < x < c,$$
$$= -1 \qquad \text{when } c < x < 3c;$$
$$H'(x + 4c) = H'(x) \qquad \text{for all } x.$$

Incidentally we have obtained the following useful inverse transformation here:

$$(4) \quad L^{-1} \left\{ \frac{2a \sinh (sx/a)}{s^2 \cosh (sc/a)} \right\} = 2x - H(x + at) - H(x - at),$$

a formula that can be verified by transforming the periodic function of t on the right.

Formula (3) is well adapted to graphical descriptions of the variation of $Y(x,t)$ with either x or t. The graph of $H(x + at)$ for a fixed t, for example, is obtained by translating the graph of $H(x)$ to the left through a distance at.

The displacement of the end $x = c$ is

$$Y(c,t) = \frac{F_0}{E} \left[c - \frac{1}{2} H(at + c) + \frac{1}{2} H(at - c) \right].$$

But $H(x + 2c) = -H(x)$ and hence $H(at + c) = -H(at - c)$; therefore

$$(5) \qquad Y(c,t) = \frac{F_0}{E}[c + H(at - c)].$$

This function is shown graphically in Fig. 45.

The reader can examine the force at the fixed end $x = 0$ and show that it assumes the values $2F_0$ and zero periodically.

82. Resonance in the Bar with a Fixed End. Let a simple periodic force per unit area,

$$F(t) = A \sin \omega t,$$

act at the end $x = c$ of the bar. If the end $x = 0$ is fixed and the initial displacement and velocity are zero, we need to change only the end condition at $x = c$ in the problem of Sec. 80 to read

$$EY_x(c,t) = A \sin \omega t.$$

The transform of the displacement now becomes

$$y(x,s) = \frac{B}{s^2 + \omega^2}\frac{\sinh(sx/a)}{s \cosh(sc/a)},$$

where $B = aA\omega/E$.

Now $y(x,s)$ is an analytic function of s except at the points $s = \pm i\omega$ and $s = s_n$, where

$$s_n = \frac{(2n - 1)\pi a}{2c} i \quad (n = 0, \pm 1, \pm 2, \ldots).$$

If $i\omega$ is not equal to any one of the numbers s_n, that is, if

$$\omega \neq \frac{(2n - 1)\pi a}{2c} \qquad (n = 1, 2, \ldots),$$

the singularities are all simple poles. They fall along the imaginary axis and are distributed symmetrically with respect to the origin. In view of formula (14), Sec. 66, the function $Y(x,t)$ can be written formally as a series of the type

$$(1) \quad Y(x,t) = a_0(x) \cos[\omega t + \theta_0(x)] + \sum_{n=1}^{\infty} a_n(x) \cos[\omega_n t + \theta_n(x)],$$

where

$$(2) \qquad \omega_n = \frac{(2n - 1)\pi a}{2c} \qquad (n = 1, 2, \ldots).$$

In Sec. 84 we shall write this series in detail and prove that it represents the solution of our problem. The form (1) of the series, however, shows that the motion of each point of the bar is the superposition of two periodic motions, one with frequency ω and the other with frequency $\omega_1 = \frac{1}{2}\pi a/c$.

But if the frequency ω of the external force coincides with one of the frequencies given by formula (2), say $\omega = \omega_r$, then the function

$$q(s) = (s^2 + \omega_r{}^2) \cosh \frac{sc}{a}$$

in the denominator of the expression for $y(x,s)$ is such that $q(s)$ and $q'(s)$ both vanish when $s = \pm i\omega_r$ while $q''(\pm i\omega_r) \neq 0$. Consequently (Sec. 55) the points $s = \pm i\omega_r$ are poles of the second order, of the function $y(x,s)$. Corresponding to those two poles $Y(x,t)$ contains an unstable component of the type

$$(3) \qquad\qquad a_r(x)t \cos [\omega_r t + \theta_r(x)] \qquad\qquad [a_r(x) \neq 0],$$

as seen from the term (15), Sec. 66. The remaining component is periodic with frequency ω_1.

This type of vibration is called resonance, for the idealized case involving no damping. The external force is in resonance with the bar when its frequency ω coincides with one of the resonance frequencies ω_r, where

$$(4) \qquad\qquad \omega_r = \frac{(2r - 1)\pi a}{2c} \qquad\qquad (r = 1, 2, \ldots).$$

We shall see that the set of resonance frequencies depends upon the manner in which the bar is supported, as well as upon the physical properties of the bar. For example, if the end $x = 0$ is free, the resonance frequencies are not the same as the frequencies (4).

For any prescribed force $F(t)$ at the end $x = c$, the transform of $Y(x,t)$ is

$$y(x,s) = \frac{a}{E} f(s) \frac{\sinh (sx/a)}{s \cosh (sc/a)}.$$

Consequently, if the function $F(t)$ contains a term of the type $A_1 \sin \omega_1 t$ or $B_1 \cos \omega_1 t$, then $y(x,s)$ will contain a term with the product $(s^2 + \omega_1{}^2) \cosh (sc/a)$ in the denominator, and $Y(x,t)$ will contain a resonance term (3) in which $r = 1$. Similarly, if the force has a simple periodic component with the frequency ω_r, resonance will occur.   Thus to cause resonance it is not necessary that $F(t)$ be limited to the simple form $F(t) = A \sin \omega_r t$.

In fact, whenever $F(t)$ is any periodic function with frequency ω_1, resonance will occur.   This can be seen either from the Fourier series representation of $F(t)$ or from the form in Sec. 19 of the transform of a periodic function.   The frequency ω_1 may be replaced by any other frequency ω_r given by equation (4).

83. Resonance When Damping Is Present.   In actual mechanical systems, some damping of vibrations is always present, at least in the form of internal resistance to the motion.   Let us consider a case in which the damping force is proportional to the velocity.

We shift to another physical interpretation of the problem considered up to this point, namely, that of the transverse

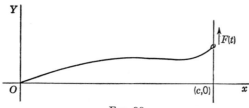

FIG. 90.

displacements $Y(x,t)$ in a string stretched from the origin and looped around a smooth support $x = c$ (Fig. 90).   In view of the damping, the equation of motion can be written

$$Y_{tt}(x,t) = a^2 Y_{xx}(x,t) - 2bY_t(x,t) \quad (0 < x < c, \, t > 0),$$

where a^2 is the tension divided by the mass per unit length and b is a damping coefficient $(b > 0)$.

If the applied vertical force on the loop is proportional to $\sin \omega t$ and the string is initially at rest along the x axis, the boundary conditions are

$$Y(x,0) = Y_t(x,0) = 0, \qquad Y(0,t) = 0, \qquad Y_x(c,t) = A \sin \omega t.$$

The transformed problem

$$a^2 y_{xx}(x,s) - (s^2 + 2bs)y(x,s) = 0,$$

$$y(0,s) = 0, \qquad y_x(c,s) = \frac{A\omega}{s^2 + \omega^2}$$

has the solution

$$y(x,s) = \frac{A\omega}{s^2 + \omega^2} \frac{\sinh px}{p \cosh pc},$$

where p is any branch of the function $a^{-1}(s^2 + 2bs)^{\frac{1}{2}}$:

$$p = \frac{\sqrt{s^2 + 2bs}}{a}.$$

The function $y(x,s)$ has singularities at $s = \pm i\omega$ and at the zeros of the function $\cosh pc$, which are the roots of the quadratic equation

$$s^2 + 2bs = -\frac{(2n-1)^2\pi^2a^2}{4c^2}.$$

When $2b < \pi a/c$, these roots can be written

(1) $$s = -b \pm i\beta_n$$

where $$\beta_n = \left[\frac{(2n-1)^2\pi^2a^2}{4c^2} - b^2\right]^{\frac{1}{2}}.$$

Since their real parts are $-b$, these roots cannot coincide with $\pm i\omega$. Regardless of the value of ω, the singularities of $y(x,s)$ are all simple poles.

Corresponding to the poles $s = \pm i\omega$, $Y(x,t)$ will have a term of the type

(2) $$Y_1(x,t) = M_\omega(x) \cos [\omega t + \epsilon_\omega(x)],$$

and corresponding to the poles (1) it will have a series of terms of the type

(3) $$Y_2(x,t) = e^{-bt} \sum_{n=1}^{\infty} \alpha_n(x) \sin [\beta_n t + \epsilon_n(x)].$$

That is, $Y(x,t)$ is composed of two components:

(4) $$Y(x,t) = Y_1(x,t) + Y_2(x,t).$$

The component $Y_1(x,t)$ is called the forced vibration. The component $Y_2(x,t)$ is the transient vibration, one that is negligible for large t. In fact, by transforming the problem in the case of an arbitrary initial displacement and velocity, an examination of $y(x,s)$ will show that the component $Y_2(x,t)$ disappears under the proper choice of those initial conditions.

The resonance frequencies are now those frequencies for which the amplitude $|M_\omega(x)|$ of $Y_1(x,t)$ is greatest. According to formula (14), Sec. 66, $|M_\omega(x)|$ is twice the absolute value of the residue of $y(x,s)$ at the pole $s = i\omega$.

Thus resonance with damping consists of a sustained periodic motion with maximum amplitude. The amplitude may be great enough to cause the mechanical system to fail.

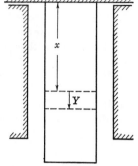

FIG. 91.

PROBLEMS

1. An elastic bar is clamped along its length c so as to prevent longitudinal displacements and then hung from its end $x = 0$. At the instant $t = 0$, the clamp is removed and the bar vibrates longitudinally due to its own weight (Fig. 91). Thus

$$Y_{tt}(x,t) = a^2 Y_{xx}(x,t) + g \qquad (0 < x < c, t > 0),$$
$$Y_x(c,t) = 0,$$

where g is the acceleration of gravity. Complete the boundary value problem, and derive the formula

$$Y(x,t) = \frac{gx}{2a^2}(2c - x)$$

$$- \frac{16gc^2}{\pi^3 a^2} \sum_1^\infty \frac{1}{(2n-1)^3} \sin \frac{(2n-1)\pi x}{2c} \cos \frac{(2n-1)\pi at}{2c}.$$

2. Derive the following formula for the angular displacements in the spinning shaft of Prob. 10, Sec. 41, whose ends $x = \pm c$ are clamped at the instant $t = 0$:

$$\Theta(x,t) = \frac{8c\omega}{\pi^2 a} \sum_{n=1}^\infty \frac{(-1)^{n-1}}{(2n-1)^2} \cos \frac{(2n-1)\pi x}{2c} \sin \frac{(2n-1)\pi at}{2c}.$$

3. Derive another formula for the displacements in the bar of Prob. 5, Sec. 41.

4. A simple periodic force acts on all points of a bar with the end $x = 0$ fixed and the end $x = c$ free. If the initial displacement and velocity are zero, the displacements satisfy the conditions

$$Y_{tt}(x,t) = a^2 Y_{xx}(x,t) + B \sin \omega t,$$
$$Y(x,0) = Y_t(x,0) = Y(0,t) = Y_x(c,t) = 0,$$

where ω is the frequency of the applied force. Show that the frequencies at which resonance will occur are

$$\omega = \frac{(2n - 1)\pi a}{2c} \qquad (n = 1, 2, \ldots).$$

5. The end $x = 0$ of a bar is fixed and the end $x = c$ is forced to move in the manner $Y(c,t) = A \sin \omega t$. Initially the bar is at rest and unstrained. Show that the resonance frequencies are

$$\omega = \frac{n\pi a}{c} \qquad (n = 1, 2, \ldots).$$

6. If the end $x = 0$ of the bar in Prob. 5 is free, rather than fixed, show that the resonance frequencies are

$$\omega = \frac{(2n - 1)\pi a}{2c} \qquad (n = 1, 2, \ldots).$$

7. A simple periodic transverse force acts on all points of a stretched string of length c with fixed ends, so that the equation of motion has the same form as the equation in Prob. 4. Initially, the string is at rest and not displaced. Show that resonance takes place only when

$$\omega = \frac{(2n - 1)\pi a}{c} \qquad (n = 1, 2, \ldots).$$

8. The supports of the ends of a stretched string vibrate in a transverse direction so that

$$Y(0,t) = A \sin \alpha t, \qquad Y(c,t) = B \sin \beta t.$$

The string is initially at rest on the x axis. In general, show that resonance takes place if either α or β has one of the values $n\pi a/c$. But if $\beta = \alpha$, show that the resonance frequencies are $2n\pi a/c$ when $B = -A$, and $(2n - 1)\pi a/c$ when $B = A$, where $n = 1, 2, \ldots$.

9. Let $I(x,t)$ denote the current and $V(x,t)$ the voltage at distance x from one end of a transmission line, at time t. Following the notation used in the telegraph equation (11), Sec. 37, and indicated in Fig. 92, let $R, L, S,$ and K represent resistance, inductance, leakage conductance, and capacitance to ground, respectively, per unit length of line. Then the functions $I(x,t)$ and $V(x,t)$ satisfy the system of partial differential equations

(a) $\qquad -V_x = RI + LI_t, \qquad -I_x = SV + KV_t,$

called the *transmission line equations*. By differentiating the members of equations (a) and eliminating one of the functions and its derivatives, show that either I or V satisfies the telegraph equation. Note that equations (a) are better adapted to initial and end conditions that involve values of both I and V, however, than is the telegraph equation (see Probs. 10 to 12).

10. Suppose that $R = S = 0$ in the transmission line shown in Fig. 92, and that the current and voltage are zero initially. If one end is kept grounded, $V(0,t) = 0$, and the current at the end $x = c$ is proportional to t, find the transform $v(x,s)$ of $V(x,t)$ using the transmission line equations (a), Prob. 9. Thus show that $V(x,t)$ is an electrical analogue of the displacements $Y(x,t)$ in the bar in Sec. 80, where a^2 corresponds to $(KL)^{-1}$.

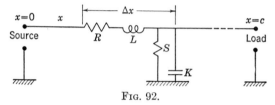

FIG. 92.

11. In the transmission line shown in Fig. 92, $R = S = 0$ and $I(x,0) = V(x,0) = 0$. If $V(0,t) = A \sin \omega t$ and the end $x = c$ is grounded, find the values of ω for which the voltage and current become unstable, using the transmission line equations (a), Prob. 9.

$$Ans. \ \omega = n\pi c^{-1}(KL)^{-\frac{1}{2}} \qquad (n = 1, 2, \dots).$$

12. Solve Prob. 11 when the condition that the end $x = c$ is grounded is replaced by the condition that the circuit is open at that end.

$$Ans. \ \omega = (n - \tfrac{1}{2})\pi c^{-1}(KL)^{-\frac{1}{2}} \qquad (n = 1, 2, \dots).$$

84. Verification of Solutions. When the formal solution of a problem can be written in terms of a finite number of simple functions, it is of course generally desirable to use that form to verify the result as the solution of the boundary value problem. This was illustrated in Sec. 81. But if a verification is required when the result is expressed only as an infinite series or an infinite integral, the procedure illustrated below may be useful. This procedure is based on the properties of the transform. It was illustrated for problems in heat conduction in Chap. 7.

Consider again the problem of the displacements in a bar with the end $x = 0$ fixed and with a force $A \sin \omega t$ per unit area on the end $x = c$. In Sec. 82, we found that the transform of the displacement is

$$y(x,s) = \frac{B}{s^2 + \omega^2} \frac{\sinh (sx/a)}{s \cosh (sc/a)}.$$

When $\Re(s) \geqq \gamma$, where $\gamma > 0$,

$$\left| \frac{\sinh \dfrac{sx}{a}}{\cosh \dfrac{sc}{a}} \right| = \left| e^{-\frac{(c-x)s}{a}} \frac{1 - e^{-\frac{2sx}{a}}}{1 + e^{-\frac{2sc}{a}}} \right| < \frac{2}{1 - e^{-\frac{2\gamma c}{a}}}.$$

Consequently, for some constant M independent of x

$$|y(x,s)| < \frac{M}{|s|^3},$$

for all s in the half plane $\Re(s) \geqq \gamma$. Since $y(x,s)$ is an analytic function of s in that half plane, it follows from Sec. 65 that the inversion integral $L_i^{-1}\{y(x,s)\}$ converges to a continuous function $Y(x,t)$ of x and t and that $Y(x,0) = Y(0,t) = 0$. Also

$$Y_t(x,t) = L_i^{-1}\{sy(x,s)\}, \qquad Y_x(x,t) = L_i^{-1}\{y_x(x,s)\}.$$

These functions are continuous. Moreover $Y_t(x,0) = 0$ and

$$Y_x(c,t) = L_i^{-1}\{y_x(c,s)\} = L_i^{-1}\left\{ \frac{B}{a(s^2 + \omega^2)} \right\} = \frac{B}{\omega a} \sin \omega t.$$

Hence the inversion integral is a function $Y(x,t)$ that satisfies all boundary conditions in the problem.

To show that it satisfies the differential equation, we first write

$$\frac{1}{s^2 + \omega^2} = \frac{1}{s^2} - \frac{\omega^2}{s^2(s^2 + \omega^2)},$$

so that the transform of $Y_t(x,t)$ can be written

$$sy(x,s) = u(x,s) + v(x,s)$$

where

$$u(x,s) = B \frac{\sinh (sx/a)}{s^2 \cosh (sc/a)}, \qquad v(x,s) = \frac{-B\omega^2}{s^2(s^2 + \omega^2)} \frac{\sinh (sx/a)}{\cosh (sc/a)}.$$

Now $v(x,s)$ is of the order of s^{-4} in the right half plane, and therefore $L_i^{-1}\{sv\} = V_t(x,t)$, where $V(x,t)$ represents the inversion integral of $v(x,s)$.

The function $u(x,s)$ is of the weaker order $O(s^{-2})$. But we found in Sec. 81 that it is the transform of the function

$$U(x,t) = \frac{B}{2a}[2x - H(x + at) - H(x - at)],$$

which is continuous, periodic in t, and has zero for its initial value. Also, $U_t(x,t)$ is sectionally continuous with respect to t, so that $su(x,s)$ is the transform of $U_t(x,t)$. According to Theorem 6 of Sec. 64 then $L_i^{-1}\{su\} = U_t(x,t)$. Consequently

$$L_i^{-1}\{s^2y\} = U_t(x,t) + V_t(x,t) = \frac{\partial}{\partial t} Y_t = Y_{tt}(x,t),$$

where $Y(x,t)$ is the inversion integral of $y(x,s)$.

Since the differentiation of $y(x,s)$ with respect to x introduces a factor s as the essential change, we can see in the same way that

$$L_i^{-1}\{y_{xx}(x,s)\} = Y_{xx}(x,t).$$

Then

$$Y_{tt}(x,t) - a^2Y_{xx}(x,t) = L_i^{-1}\{s^2y(x,s) - a^2y_{xx}(x,s)\} = 0,$$

because $y(x,s)$ satisfies the transformed equation. The inversion integral is therefore established as a solution of the boundary value problem. Note that if $y(x,s)$ had been of the order $O(s^{-4})$ the separation of sy into the components u and v would not have been necessary.

Next we shall show that the series consisting of the sum of the residues of the function $e^{st}y(x,s)$ converges to the inversion integral, so that we can conclude that this series represents the solution. We do this by showing that $y(x,s)$ satisfies the conditions of Theorem 10, Sec. 67.

The poles of $y(x,s)$ are the points

$$s = \pm\omega i, \pm \frac{\pi a}{2c} i, \pm \frac{3\pi a}{2c} i, \pm \frac{5\pi a}{2c} i, \ldots.$$

Let $s = \xi + i\eta$. Then in Fig. 72 the lines $\eta = \pm\beta_N$ will pass between the poles when N is sufficiently large if we take

$$\beta_N = \frac{N\pi a}{c} \qquad (N = 1, 2, \ldots).$$

Since $$y(x,s) = \frac{B}{s(s^2 + \omega^2)} e^{(c-x)s/a} \frac{e^{(2sx/a)} - 1}{e^{(2sc/a)} + 1},$$

it is easy to see that $|y(x,s)|$ is bounded in the half plane $\xi \leq -\gamma$ uniformly with respect to x. Therefore $|y(x, -\beta_N + i\eta)|$ is bounded.

When $s = \xi \pm i\beta_N$, it follows from identities (7), Sec. 52, that

$$\left| \frac{\sinh (sx/a)}{\cosh (sc/a)} \right|^2 = \frac{\sinh^2 (\xi x/a) + \sin^2 (\beta_N x/a)}{\sinh^2 (\xi c/a) + 1} \leq 1.$$

Therefore $|y(x,s)| \leq |B/(s^3 + \omega^2 s)|$ when $s = \xi \pm i\beta_N$, and the conditions of Theorem 10, Sec. 67, are satisfied. In fact, since $y(x,s)$ is of the order $O(s^{-3})$ on the rectangular path, the series of residues converges to the inversion integral whenever $t \geq 0$.

The series form of the solution is now rigorously established for any value of the frequency ω. When ω does not coincide with any of the resonance frequencies, the explicit form of our solution becomes

$$Y(x,t) = \frac{B}{\omega^2} \frac{\sin (\omega x/a)}{\cos (\omega c/a)} \sin \omega t$$

$$+ \frac{2B}{c} \sum_{n=1}^{\infty} \frac{(-1)^{n-1}}{m_n} \frac{\sin m_n x}{\omega^2 - m_n^2 a^2} \sin m_n at,$$

where $m_n = (n - \tfrac{1}{2})\pi/c$. This is found by computing the residues in the usual manner.

The solution found has continuous derivatives of the first order. Its derivatives of the second order are sectionally continuous functions of either x or t, and the function and its derivatives are of exponential order for large t. By following the method in Sec. 73, it can be seen that there is no other solution of this type. In this case the procedure is quite simple as a result of the favorable continuity conditions.

85. Free Vibrations of a String. A string, stretched between the origin and the point $(c,0)$, is given a prescribed initial displacement $Y = g(x)$ and released from rest in that position. To find the transverse displacements $Y(x,t)$, we must solve the problem,

$$Y_{tt}(x,t) = a^2 Y_{xx}(x,t) \quad (0 < x < c, t > 0),$$
$$Y(x,0) = g(x), \quad Y_t(x,0) = Y(0,t) = Y(c,t) = 0.$$

The transformed problem,

$$a^2 y_{xx}(x,s) - s^2 y(x,s) = -sg(x),$$
$$y(0,s) = y(c,s) = 0,$$

can be solved easily by transforming with respect to x. Its solution can be written

$$y(x,s) = \frac{\phi(x,s)}{a \sinh (sc/a)}$$

when $s \neq 0$, where

$$\phi(x,s) = \sinh \frac{(c - x)s}{a} \int_0^x g(\xi) \sinh \frac{\xi s}{a} d\xi$$

$$+ \sinh \frac{xs}{a} \int_x^c g(\xi) \sinh \frac{(c - \xi)s}{a} d\xi.$$

When $s = 0$, the solution is $y(x,s) = 0$.

The function $g(x)$ must naturally be continuous and vanish at $x = 0$ and $x = c$. If its derivative is at least sectionally continuous, the function $\phi(x,s)$ is analytic for all finite s, and, except for $s = 0$, the zeros of $\sinh sc/a$ are simple poles of $y(x,s)$. These poles are $s = \pm s_n$ where

$$s_n = \frac{n\pi a}{c} i \qquad\qquad (n = 1, 2, \ldots).$$

Since

$$\phi(x,s_n) = \cos n\pi \sin \frac{n\pi x}{c} \int_0^c g(\xi) \sin \frac{n\pi\xi}{c} d\xi = \frac{c}{2} b_n \cos n\pi \sin \frac{n\pi x}{c},$$

where

(1) $$b_n = \frac{2}{c} \int_0^c g(\xi) \sin \frac{n\pi\xi}{c} d\xi,$$

the sum of the residues of $e^{ts}y(x,s)$ at $s = \pm s_n$ is

$$\frac{1}{2} \sum_{n=1}^{\infty} b_n \sin \frac{n\pi x}{c} \left[\exp\left(\frac{in\pi at}{c}\right) + \exp\left(-\frac{in\pi at}{c}\right) \right].$$

The formal solution of the problem is therefore

(2) $$Y(x,t) = \sum_{n=1}^{\infty} b_n \sin \frac{n\pi x}{c} \cos \frac{n\pi at}{c},$$

where the coefficients b_n are given by formula (1).

When $t = 0$, the series here becomes the Fourier sine series for the function $g(x)$ on the interval $0 \leq x \leq c$. By writing

$$Y(x,t) = \frac{1}{2} \left[\sum_{n=1}^{\infty} b_n \sin \frac{n\pi(x + at)}{c} + \sum_{n=1}^{\infty} b_n \sin \frac{n\pi(x - at)}{c} \right],$$

an examination of the series indicates that

(3) $Y(x,t) = \frac{1}{2}[G(x + at) + G(x - at)]$,

where $G(x)$ is the periodic function defined as follows for all real x:

$$G(x) = -G(-x) = g(x) \quad \text{when } 0 \leq x \leq c,$$
$$G(x + 2c) = G(x) \quad \text{for all } x.$$

The result in the form (3) is easily verified as the solution of the boundary value problem. It is also a convenient form to use in studying the motion of the string.

86. Resonance in a Bar with a Mass Attached. The end $x = 0$ of a bar is fixed. To the end $x = c$, a rigid mass is attached (Fig. 93). A longitudinal periodic force $B \sin \omega t$ acts on this

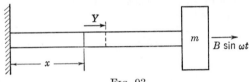

FIG. 93.

mass. Let us find the resonance frequencies. The elastic displacements in the mass itself are assumed to be negligible, and the bar is assumed to be too heavy to be considered simply as a coil spring without mass.

Let A be the area of the cross section of the bar and $Y(x,t)$ the longitudinal displacement in the bar. The force exerted by the bar on the mass m is then $-EAY_x(c,t)$, so that the end conditions are

$$Y(0,t) = 0, \quad mY_{tt}(c,t) = -EAY_x(c,t) + B \sin \omega t.$$

If the initial displacement and velocity are zero, the remaining conditions in the problem are

$$Y_{tt}(x,t) = a^2 Y_{xx}(x,t) \quad (0 < x < c, t > 0),$$
$$Y(x,0) = Y_t(x,0) = 0.$$

This is also the problem of the torsional vibrations in a shaft with one end fixed and with a flywheel, on which a periodic torque acts, attached to the other end. Note that one end condition here involves a derivative of the second order. An interpretation of the problem in terms of torsional vibrations in a propeller shaft is given in the problems at the end of the chapter.

The transformed problem is

$$s^2 y(x,s) = a^2 y_{xx}(x,s),$$

$$y(0,s) = 0, \qquad EA y_x(c,s) + m s^2 y(c,s) = \frac{B\omega}{s^2 + \omega^2}.$$

The solution of this problem can be written

$$y(x,s) = \frac{\alpha \sinh (sx/a)}{s(s^2 + \omega^2)[s \sinh (sc/a) + \beta \cosh (sc/a)]},$$

where $\qquad \alpha = \dfrac{B\omega}{m}, \qquad \beta = \dfrac{AE}{am}.$

The last factor in the denominator vanishes when s is any root of the equation

$$\tanh \frac{sc}{a} = -\frac{\beta}{s}.$$

It can be shown that the roots of this equation are pure imaginary numbers. They can be written $s = \pm ia\lambda_n/c$ where λ_n are the positive roots of

(1) $$\tan \lambda = \frac{k}{\lambda},$$

and where $k = \beta c/a$. The roots of equation (1) are easily approximated graphically.

If the factor $s^2 + \omega^2$ also vanishes when s has one of the values $ia\lambda_n/c$, then $y(x,s)$ will have poles $s = \pm ia\lambda_n/c$ of the second order and $Y(x,t)$ will contain a term of the resonance type. Hence resonance occurs when the frequency of the external force has any one of the values

(2) $$\omega = \frac{a\lambda_n}{c} \qquad\qquad (n = 1, 2, \ldots),$$

where the numbers λ_n are the positive roots of equation (1). The frequencies (2) are the required resonance frequencies.

The series form of $Y(x,t)$ can, of course, be written in the usual way by computing the residues of $e^{st} y(x,s)$ at the poles.

87. Transverse Vibrations of Beams. Let $Y(x,t)$ denote the transverse displacement of a point at distance x from one end of a bar or beam, at time t. As in the case of static displacements discussed in Sec. 31, the instantaneous bending moment transmitted through a cross section is $EI Y_{xx}(x,t)$, where I is the moment of inertia of the cross section with respect to its neutral axis. The shearing force at a cross section is $EI \partial^3 Y / \partial x^3$. When the cross section is uniform and no external force acts along the beam, the displacement function $Y(x,t)$ satisfies the equation

$$(1) \qquad \frac{\partial^2 Y}{\partial t^2} + a^2 \frac{\partial^4 Y}{\partial x^4} = 0 \qquad\qquad \left(a^2 = \frac{EI}{A\rho} \right)$$

under certain idealizing assumptions, where $A\rho$ is the mass of the beam per unit length.

Let the end $x = 0$ be hinged, so that no bending moment is transmitted across the section at $x = 0$ and the displacement is zero there. Let the end $x = c$ be hinged on a support which

FIG. 94.

moves parallel to the Y axis in a simple harmonic manner (Fig. 94). If the beam is initially at rest along the x axis, the boundary conditions that accompany equation (1) are then

$$Y(x,0) = Y_t(x,0) = 0,$$
$$Y(0,t) = Y_{xx}(0,t) = 0,$$
$$Y(c,t) = A \sin \omega t, \qquad Y_{xx}(c,t) = 0.$$

Let us find the frequencies ω at which resonance will occur.

The problem in the transform $y(x,s)$ is

$$(2) \qquad a^2 \frac{d^4 y}{dx^4} + s^2 y = 0,$$

$$y(0,s) = y_{xx}(0,s) = y_{xx}(c,s) = 0, \qquad y(c,s) = \frac{A\omega}{s^2 + \omega^2}.$$

It will be convenient to write

$$(3) \qquad\qquad s = iaq^2.$$

Then $s^2 = -a^2 q^4$, and the general solution of equation (2) can be written

$$(4) \quad y(x,s) = C_1 \sin qx + C_2 \cos qx + C_3 \sinh qx + C_4 \cosh qx,$$

where the C's can be functions of the parameter s. When these constants are determined so that the boundary conditions on $y(x,s)$ are satisfied, the solution (4) becomes

$$(5) \qquad y(x,s) = \frac{A\omega}{s^2 + \omega^2} \frac{\sin qx \sinh qc + \sinh qx \sin qc}{2 \sin qc \sinh qc}.$$

The Maclaurin series representations of the sine and hyperbolic sine functions show that the final fraction in equation (5) is an analytic function of q^2, and therefore of s, except at points where the denominator vanishes. The point $s = 0$ is a removable singular point. The denominator vanishes when $qc = \pm n\pi$ and $qc = \pm in\pi$; that is, whenever $q^2c^2 = \pm n^2\pi^2$. In view of equations (3) and (5) then, the singular points of $y(x,s)$ are

$$(6) \qquad s = \pm i\omega, \qquad s = \pm i\frac{n^2\pi^2 a}{c^2} \quad (n = 1, 2, \ldots).$$

If the value of ω is distinct from all the numbers

$$(7) \qquad \omega_n = \frac{n^2\pi^2 a}{c^2} \qquad (n = 1, 2, \ldots),$$

the derivative of the entire denominator in the expression (5) for $y(x,s)$ does not vanish at any of the points (6) and those points are therefore simple poles of $y(x,s)$. In this case the formula for the displacements has the form

$$Y(x,t) = a_0(x) \cos [\omega t + \theta_0(x)] + \sum_{n=1}^{\infty} a_n(x) \cos [\omega_n t + \theta_n(x)].$$

If the value of ω coincides with one of the numbers ω_n given by formula (7), then $y(x,s)$ has poles of the second order at the points $s = \pm i\omega_n$, and a term of resonance type appears in $Y(x,t)$. Hence the resonance frequencies are the frequencies (7).

In case the hinge at $x = c$ is kept fixed and a simple harmonic bending moment acts on that end of the beam, the conditions at $x = c$ have the form

$$Y(c,t) = 0, \qquad Y_{xx}(c,t) = B \sin \omega t.$$

The reader can show that the expression for $y(x,s)$ then has the same denominator as it does in equation (5). The resonance frequencies are again those given by formula (7). Other cases are included in the problems at the end of the chapter.

88. Duhamel's Formula for Vibration Problems. As in the case of problems in heat conduction (Sec. 79), the convolution property of the transform displays a relation between the solutions of problems in vibrations with variable boundary conditions

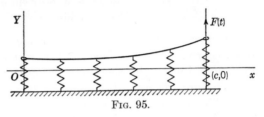

FIG. 95.

and corresponding problems with fixed conditions. Consider, for example the transverse displacements $Y(x,t)$ in a string. If both damping and an elastic support are present (Fig. 95), the equation of motion has the form

(1) $$Y_{tt}(x,t) = a^2 Y_{xx}(x,t) - bY_t(x,t) - hY(x,t).$$

To permit the end $x = 0$ to be elastically supported or kept fixed or to slide freely along the Y axis, we can write the condition

(2) $$\lambda_1(Y) = 0 \qquad\qquad \text{at } x = 0,$$

where $\lambda_1(Y) = h_1 Y - k_1 Y_x$. If a prescribed force $F(t)$ acts on the end $x = c$, a fairly general boundary condition is

(3) $$\lambda_2(Y) = F(t) \qquad\qquad \text{at } x = c,$$

where $\lambda_2(Y) = h_2 Y + k_2 Y_x$. Then if

(4) $$Y(x,0) = Y_t(x,0) = 0,$$

the transform $y(x,s)$ satisfies the conditions

(5) $$(s^2 + bs + h)y(x,s) = a^2 y_{xx}(x,s),$$
(6) $$\lambda_1[y(0,s)] = 0, \qquad \lambda_2[y(c,s)] = f(s).$$

Let $Z(x,t)$ represent the displacement $Y(x,t)$ in the special case in which $F(t) = 1$.

Then $z(x,s)$ satisfies equation (5) and the boundary conditions

$$\lambda_1[z(0,s)] = 0, \qquad \lambda_2[z(c,s)] = \frac{1}{s}.$$

It follows that the product $sf(s)z(x,s)$ satisfies the conditions (5) and (6), and therefore

(7) $$y(x,s) = sf(s)z(x,s).$$

In view of the convolution property then,

$$(8) \qquad Y(x,t) = \frac{\partial}{\partial t} \int_0^t F(t - \tau) Z(x,\tau) \, d\tau,$$

or

$$(9) \qquad Y(x,t) = \int_0^t F(t - \tau) Z_t(x,\tau) \, d\tau.$$

These are two forms of Duhamel's formula for the resolution of the problem in $Y(x,t)$ with a variable end condition into one with a fixed end condition.

The derivation of these formulas can be extended easily to other problems. In the case of transverse vibrations of bars, for instance, the derivative of the fourth order with respect to x replaces $Y_{xx}(x,t)$, and additional boundary conditions are involved. In the case of transverse displacements in a membrane, the Laplacian of Y replaces Y_{xx} in our problem. In these cases, the steps in the derivation of Duhamel's formula are the same as in the case treated above.

PROBLEMS

1. The end $x = 0$ of a bar is elastically supported (Fig. 96), so that the longitudinal force exerted on that end is proportional to the longitudinal displacement; that is,

$$Y_x(0,t) = hY(0,t).$$

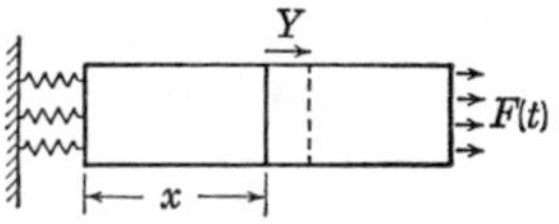

FIG. 96.

If the force on the end $x = c$ is $F(t) = A \sin \omega t$, derive the following formula for the resonance frequencies:

$$\omega = \frac{a\alpha_n}{c} \qquad (n = 1, 2, \ldots),$$

where the numbers α_n are the positive roots of the equation $\tan \alpha = hc/\alpha$.

2. The end $x = 0$ of a bar is fixed. If the bar is initially stretched so that its longitudinal displacements are $Y(x,0) = Ax$ and released from that position at $t = 0$ with no initial velocity, and if the end $x = 1$ is free, derive a formula for the longitudinal displacements $Y(x,t)$.

$$\textit{Ans.} \ Y(x,t) = \frac{2A}{\pi^2} \sum_{n=1}^{\infty} \frac{(-1)^{n+1}}{m^2} \sin m\pi x \cos m\pi a t \quad (m = n - \tfrac{1}{2}).$$

3. A string is stretched from the origin to the point $(c,0)$ and given

an initial velocity $Y_t(x,0) = g(x)$ but no initial displacement. Derive
the formula

$$Y(x,t) = \frac{2}{\pi a} \sum_{n=1}^{\infty} \frac{1}{n} \sin \frac{n\pi x}{c} \sin \frac{n\pi a t}{c} \int_0^c g(\xi) \sin \frac{n\pi \xi}{c} \, d\xi.$$

4. Derive a formula for the longitudinal displacements in the bar of
Sec. 80 when the constant force F_0 is replaced by the force

$$F(t) = At^2,$$

and make a complete verification of your solution.

$$Ans. \frac{E}{A} Y(x,t) = xt^2 + \frac{x^3}{3a^2} - \frac{c^2 x}{a^2} - \frac{4c^3}{\pi^4 a^2} \sum_{n=1}^{\infty} \frac{(-1)^n}{m^4} \sin \frac{m\pi x}{c} \cos \frac{m\pi a t}{c}$$
$$(m = n - \tfrac{1}{2}).$$

5. One end of a beam is built into a rigid support (Fig. 97); thus if
$Y(x,t)$ denotes transverse displacements,

$$Y(0,t) = Y_x(0,t) = 0.$$

The pin-support of the other end $x = c$ vibrates, so that

$$Y(c,t) = B \sin \omega t, \qquad Y_{xx}(c,t) = 0.$$

Initially the beam is at rest along the x axis. If a^2 is the coefficient in
equation (1), Sec. 87, show that resonance occurs in the vibration of this
beam if $\omega = a\alpha_n{}^2/c^2$, where α_n is any positive root of the equation $\tan \alpha = \tanh \alpha$. Show how the roots α_n can be approximated graphically.

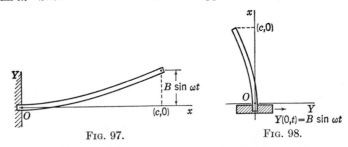

FIG. 97.   FIG. 98.

6. One end of a bar of length c is free. The other end is built into a
support that undergoes a transverse vibration $Y = B \sin \omega t$ (Fig. 98).
The bar is initially at rest with no displacements. Show that resonance
takes place in the transverse vibrations of the bar when $\omega = a\alpha_n{}^2/c^2$,
where α_n is any positive root of the equation $\cos \alpha = - \operatorname{sech} \alpha$ and a^2
is the coefficient in equation (1), Sec. 87. Also show how the roots α_n
can be approximated graphically.

7. Both ends of a beam of length c are built into rigid supports. The beam is initially at rest with no displacements. A simple periodic force per unit length acts along the entire span, in a direction perpendicular to the beam, so that the transverse displacements $Y(x,t)$ satisfy the equation

$$\frac{\partial^2 Y}{\partial t^2} + a^2 \frac{\partial^4 Y}{\partial x^4} = B \sin \omega t \qquad \left(a^2 = \frac{EI}{A\rho}\right).$$

Show that resonance occurs when $\omega = 4a\alpha_n{}^2/c^2$, where α_n is any positive root of the equation $\tan \alpha = -\tanh \alpha$.

8. A membrane, stretched across a fixed circular frame $r = c$, is initially at rest in its position of equilibrium. If a simple periodic force per unit area in a direction perpendicular to the membrane acts at all points, the transverse displacements $Z(r,t)$ satisfy an equation of the type

$$Z_{tt} = b^2 \left(Z_{rr} + \frac{1}{r} Z_r\right) + A \sin \omega t.$$

Show that the resonance frequencies are $\omega = b\alpha_n/c$, where α_n is any positive root of the equation $J_0(\alpha) = 0$.

9. The end $x = 0$ of the propeller shaft for a ship is connected rigidly to a massive flywheel that turns with uniform angular velocity ω. The end $x = c$ supports a propeller whose moment of inertia with respect to the axis of the shaft is I. In addition to the steady-state torque transmitted between shaft and propeller, the action in the water induces a perturbation in the nature of a torque proportional to $\sin 4\omega t$ exerted on the propeller. Let $\Theta(x,t)$ denote the corresponding perturbation in the angular displacements of the circular cross sections of the shaft. Thus $\Theta(x,t) = 0$ when the shaft operates under steady-state conditions with angular velocity ω. If I_p is the polar moment of inertia of the cross section of the shaft, of radius r_0 $(I_p = \frac{1}{2}r_0{}^4)$, and if E_s is the modulus of elasticity in shear for the material in the shaft, show that

$$I\Theta_{tt}(c,t) = -E_s I_p \Theta_x(c,t) + B \sin 4\omega t,$$

and that the boundary value problem in $\Theta(x,t)$ is an analogue of the problem in Sec. 86, where a^2 now represents E_s/ρ and ρ is mass of the material per unit volume. Show that torsional resonance takes place when $\omega = a\lambda_n/(4c)$, where λ_n is any positive root of the equation $\tan \lambda = k/\lambda$ and where $k = c\rho I_p/I$.

10. The propeller shaft in Prob. 9 is 150 ft long with a diameter of 10 in., and made of steel. The moment of inertia I of the propeller equals that of a steel disk 4 in. thick and 4 ft in diameter. The steel weighs 0.28 lb/cu in. $(g\rho = 0.28)$, and $E_s = 12 \times 10^6$ lb/sq in. Show that the lowest flywheel speed at which torsional resonance takes place is approximately 135 revolutions per minute.

CHAPTER 9

STURM-LIOUVILLE SYSTEMS

89. Self-adjoint Differential Equations. We begin with a few definitions and results from the theory of linear ordinary differential equations.

The *adjoint* of a linear differential form

$$(1) \qquad \alpha_2(x)y''(x) + \alpha_1(x)y'(x) + \alpha_0(x)y(x),$$

of the second order, is the related form

$$(2) \qquad [\alpha_2(x)y(x)]'' - [\alpha_1(x)y(x)]' + \alpha_0(x)y(x).$$

It is useful in the construction of integrating factors.[1] The reader can verify that the differential form

$$(3) \qquad [r(x)y'(x)]' - Q(x)y(x)$$

is the same as its adjoint, and that this *self-adjoint* form for each of two functions $y(x)$ and $z(x)$ satisfies the identity

$$(4) \qquad [(ry')' - Qy]z - [(rz')' - Qz]y = \frac{d}{dx}[(zy' - yz')r].$$

When both members of the differential equation

$$(5) \qquad y''(x) + \beta_1(x)y'(x) + \beta_0(x)y(x) = f(x)$$

are multiplied by an integrating factor

$$(6) \qquad r(x) = \exp \int \beta_1(x)\,dx,$$

the *equation* assumes its *self-adjoint* form

$$(7) \qquad [r(x)y'(x)]' - Q(x)y(x) = F(x),$$

where $Q(x) = -r(x)\beta_0(x)$ and $F(x) = r(x)f(x)$.

---

[1] See, for instance, E. D. Rainville, "Intermediate Differential Equations," p. 9, 1943, or E. L. Ince, "Ordinary Differential Equations," p. 123, 1927.

Adjoints of differential forms of order higher than two are defined in a manner that corresponds to the definition (2). But linear differential equations of higher order do not always have self-adjoint forms.

An existence theorem for solutions of the homogeneous form of equation (5), in which the coefficient $\beta_0(x)$ may involve a parameter λ in a linear manner, will now be cited. The theorem can be proved by a method of successive approximations.[1] Let $A(x)$, $B(x)$, and $C(x)$ be continuous functions at a point $x = x_0$ and in some interval I containing that point. Let λ denote a complex-valued parameter and y_0 and y_1 two prescribed constants independent of λ. Then the initial-value problem

$$\text{(8)} \qquad \begin{aligned} y'' + A(x)y' + [B(x) + \lambda C(x)]y &= 0, \\ y(x_0,\lambda) = y_0, \qquad y'(x_0,\lambda) &= y_1, \end{aligned}$$

in the complex-valued function $y(x,\lambda)$, has one and only one solution $y = u(x,\lambda)$ for each value of λ, where $u(x,\lambda)$ and $u'(x,\lambda)$ are continuous functions of their two variables for all λ when x is in the interval I. For each fixed x in I, $u(x,\lambda)$ and $u'(x,\lambda)$ are entire functions of the complex parameter λ.

When $C(x) \equiv 0$, the theorem reduces to one cited in Sec. 73. In Sec. 91 we shall show that further restrictions are needed to ensure a unique solution of a two-point boundary value problem in ordinary differential equations. This fact is illustrated by the simple boundary value problem

$$\text{(9)} \qquad y'' + \lambda y = 0, \qquad y(0,\lambda) = 0, \qquad y(1,\lambda) = 0,$$

which clearly has a solution $y(x,\lambda) \equiv 0$. But when the parameter λ has any one of the values $n^2\pi^2$ $(n = 1, 2, \ldots)$, problem (9) has the additional solutions

$$\text{(10)} \qquad y = k \sin n\pi x,$$

where the constant k is arbitrary. Also, note that the problem

$$\text{(11)} \qquad y''(x) + \pi^2 y(x) = 0, \qquad y(0) = 0, \qquad y(1) = 1,$$

has no continuous solution, since the function $k \sin \pi x$ that sat-

---

[1] See, for instance, E. C. Titchmarsh, "Eigenfunction Expansions," p. 6, 1946, or E. A. Coddington and N. Levinson, "Theory of Ordinary Differential Equations," pp. 36–37, 1955.

isfies the first two conditions fails to satisfy the condition $y(1) = 1$ for any value of the constant k.

90. Green's Functions. Let $r(x)$, $Q(x)$, and $F(x)$ denote prescribed continuous functions, where $r > 0$, r' is continuous, on an interval $a \leqq x \leqq b$. In the boundary value problem

(1) $[r(x)y'(x)]' - Q(x)y(x) = F(x), \quad y(a) = y(b) = 0,$

the unknown function $y(x)$ can be interpreted as the static transverse displacements in a stretched string attached to an elastic foundation. The elastic support may have variable properties so that it contributes a transverse force $-Q(x)y(x)$ per unit length as well as a variable tension $r(x)$ in the string. An external transverse force $-F(x)$, per unit length, acts along the string. The ends are fixed at the points $(a,0)$ and $(b,0)$ (cf. Secs. 37 and

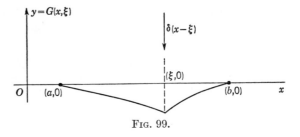

FIG. 99.

88). We make the interpretation to assist us in writing the solution of problem (1), at first formally, in terms of solutions of simpler problems.

Let $F(x)$ be replaced formally by the unit impulse symbol $\delta(x - \xi)$, where $a < \xi < b$. This corresponds to the application of a negative unit transverse force at the point $x = \xi$ (Fig. 99). When the string has that concentrated load, we write $G(x,\xi)$ for the displacements $y(x)$. Since the vertical force from left to right is $-r(x)y'(x)$, we note that the value of $-ry'$ must jump by the amount -1 at $x = \xi$; that is,

(2) $G_x(\xi + 0, \xi) - G_x(\xi - 0, \xi) = \dfrac{1}{r(\xi)}.$

The displacement function $G(x,\xi)$ itself should be continuous in the square region $a \leqq x \leqq b$, $a \leqq \xi \leqq b$, and its derivative $G_x(x,\xi)$ should be continuous there except for the jump prescribed by equation (2) at the diagonal $x = \xi$. Since $\delta(x - \xi)$ is zero except when $x = \xi$,

$$(3) \qquad [r(x)G_x(x,\xi)]_x - Q(x)G(x,\xi) = 0 \qquad (x \neq \xi);$$

therefore, in view of the conditions imposed on $r(x)$ and $Q(x)$, the function $G_{xx}(x,\xi)$ is continuous except at the diagonal $x = \xi$. Also, $G(x,\xi)$ satisfies the boundary conditions

$$(4) \qquad\qquad G(a,\xi) = G(b,\xi) = 0.$$

A function that satisfies conditions (2) to (4) and the continuity conditions stated above is called *Green's function* for problem (1).

The impulse symbol has the formal properties $\delta(-x) = \delta(x)$ and

$$F(x) = \int_a^b F(\xi)\, \delta(\xi - x)\, d\xi = \int_a^b F(\xi)\, \delta(x - \xi)\, d\xi;$$

that is, $F(x)$ is a superposition of impulses. If all members of the equations

$$(rG_x)_x - QG = \delta(x - \xi), \qquad G(a,\xi) = G(b,\xi) = 0,$$

are multiplied by $F(\xi)$ and integrated with respect to ξ from $\xi = a$ to $\xi = b$, the result is the three statements in problem (1) when we write

$$(5) \quad y(x) = \int_a^b F(\xi)G(x,\xi)\, d\xi.$$

Thus the solution of problem (1) is written as a superposition of solutions of that problem when the load is concentrated.

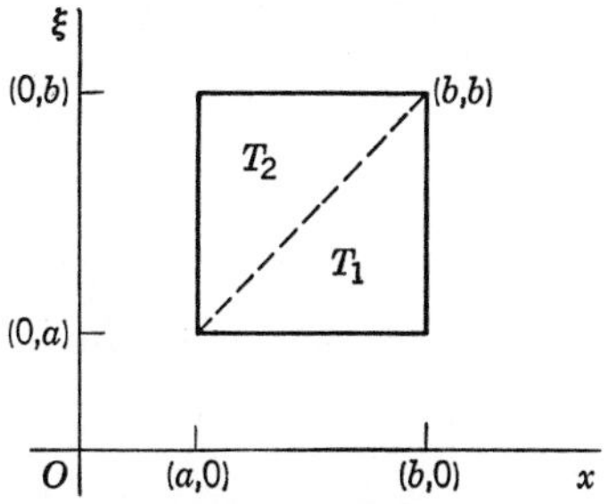

In order to verify the formal

FIG. 100.

solution (5) we first note that $y(a) = y(b) = 0$ because $G(x,\xi)$ satisfies the boundary condition (4). When we write

$$y(x) = \int_a^x F(\xi)G(x,\xi)\, d\xi + \int_x^b F(\xi)G(x,\xi)\, d\xi,$$

the integrand of each integral and its first two partial derivatives with respect to x are continuous functions of (x,ξ) in the triangular regions T_1 and T_2, respectively, in Fig. 100. Differentiation by the Leibnitz formula (Sec. 12) is therefore valid. We find that

$$y'(x) = \int_a^x F(\xi)G_x(x,\xi) \, d\xi + \int_x^b F(\xi)G_x(x,\xi) \, d\xi$$

since G is continuous, and that

(6) $$(ry')' = \int_a^b F(\xi)[r(x)G_x(x,\xi)]_x \, d\xi + F(x)r(x)J(x),$$

where $J(x) = G_x(x, \, x - 0) - G_x(x, \, x + 0)$. Thus $J(x)$ is the jump in the value of $G_x(x,\xi)$ as the point (x,ξ) moves across the diagonal from triangle T_1 into triangle T_2 (Fig. 100). According to equation (2), $J(x) = 1/r(x)$. In view of equation (3), equation (6) can now be written

$$(ry')' = Q(x) \int_a^b F(\xi)G(x,\xi) \, d\xi + F(x) = Qy + F;$$

that is, $y(x)$ satisfies differential equation (1).

The solution (5) of problem (1) is now established if Green's function G exists. In fact, the condition on $F(x)$ can be relaxed to permit that function to be sectionally continuous. The functions $y(x)$ defined by equation (5) and $y'(x)$ are continuous. The procedure here applies, with little change, when the boundary conditions are of the type $A_1y(a) + A_2y'(a) = 0$, or when the interval is semi-infinite ($x \geqq a$).

91. Construction of Green's Function. Let $u(x)$ denote the unique solution of the initial-value problem

(1) $$[r(x)u'(x)]' - Q(x)u(x) = 0, \qquad u(a) = 0, \qquad u'(a) = 1,$$

where r, r' and Q are continuous and $r > 0$ ($a \leqq x \leqq b$), and let $v(x)$ be the solution of the initial-value problem

(2) $$[r(x)v'(x)]' - Q(x)v(x) = 0, \qquad v(b) = 0, \qquad v'(b) = 1.$$

If (x,ξ) is any point of the square $a \leqq x \leqq b$, $a \leqq \xi \leqq b$, the function

(3) $$\begin{aligned} G(x,\xi) &= A(\xi)u(x) & (x \leqq \xi), \\ &= B(\xi)v(x) & (x \geqq \xi), \end{aligned}$$

satisfies the boundary conditions $G(a,\xi) = G(b,\xi) = 0$. It is continuous at $x = \xi$ and its derivative G_x has the jump prescribed by equation (2), Sec. 90, if A and B are continuous functions that satisfy the simultaneous equations

(4) $$B(\xi)v(\xi) - A(\xi)u(\xi) = 0, \qquad B(\xi)v'(\xi) - A(\xi)u'(\xi) = \frac{1}{r(\xi)}.$$

The determinant $u(\xi)v'(\xi) - v(\xi)u'(\xi)$ of this system satisfies the identity (4), Sec. 89; that is,

$$\frac{d}{d\xi}\left[(uv' - vu')r\right] = \left[(rv')' - Qv\right]u - \left[(ru')' - Qu\right]v.$$

The right-hand member vanishes, in view of differential equations (1) and (2). Hence $(uv' - u'v)r$ is constant and, since $v(b) = 0$ and $v'(b) = 1$,

(5) $$r(\xi)[u(\xi)v'(\xi) - v(\xi)u'(\xi)] = r(b)u(b).$$

If $u(b) \neq 0$, the solution of the system (4) is

$$A(\xi) = \frac{v(\xi)}{r(b)u(b)}, \qquad B(\xi) = \frac{u(\xi)}{r(b)u(b)},$$

and formula (3) for Green's function becomes

(6) $$G(x,\xi) = \frac{u(x)v(\xi)}{r(b)u(b)} \qquad \text{when } x \leqq \xi,$$

$$= \frac{u(\xi)v(x)}{r(b)u(b)} \qquad \text{when } x \geqq \xi.$$

Note that the function is symmetric in its arguments:

(7) $$G(x,\xi) = G(\xi,x).$$

If $u(b) = 0$ then, since $u(a) = 0$ and $u'(a) = 1$, the function $w = u(x)$ is not identically zero and it satisfies the homogeneous problem

(8) $$(rw')' - Qw = 0, \qquad w(a) = w(b) = 0.$$

The proof of the following theorem is now complete.

Theorem 1. *If the homogeneous problem (8) has no solution other than $w(x) \equiv 0$, Green's function $G(x,\xi)$ exists for the problem*

(9) $$[r(x)y'(x)]' - Q(x)y(x) = F(x), \qquad y(a) = y(b) = 0,$$

where r, r', and Q are continuous, F is sectionally continuous, and $r > 0$, when $a \leqq x \leqq b$. Green's function is described in terms of the solutions of the initial-value problems (1) and (2) by formula (6); it is symmetric in x and ξ. The continuous solution of problem (9), with continuous derivative, is

(10) $$y(x) = \int_a^b F(\xi)G(x,\xi)\, d\xi.$$

Although the initial-value problems (1) and (2), whose solutions provide the solution of the boundary value problem (9), are simpler than the boundary value problem, they can be solved explicitly only for limited types of coefficients $r(x)$ and $Q(x)$.

Suppose that a second function $z(x)$, in addition to the function $y(x)$ given by formula (10), satisfies all conditions in problem (9). Then the function $w = y - z$ satisfies the homogeneous problem (8) and $w(x) \equiv 0$. Thus $z(x) = y(x)$, and we have proved the following theorem on uniqueness.

Theorem 2. *Under the conditions stated in Theorem 1 the solution* (10) *of the boundary value problem* (9) *is the only one that is continuous together with its derivative* $y'(x)$.

It is of interest to note that if the homogeneous problem (8) has a solution $w = z(x)$ that is not identically zero and if $y(x)$ satisfies all conditions of problem (9) then, in view of identity (4), Sec. 89,

$$F(x)z(x) = \frac{d}{dx}\left[(zy' - yz')r\right].$$

Hence

(11) $$\int_a^b F(x)z(x)\,dx = (zy' - yz')r \Big]_a^b = 0;$$

that is, $F(x)$ *must be orthogonal to* $z(x)$ *on the interval* (a,b) *if problem* (9) *is to have a solution.*

92. Eigenvalue Problems. The homogeneous boundary value problem

(1)
$$[r(x)y'(x,\lambda)]' - [q(x) + \lambda p(x)]y(x,\lambda) = 0 \quad (a < x < b)$$
$$A_1 y(a,\lambda) + A_2 y'(a,\lambda) = 0, \qquad B_1 y(b,\lambda) + B_2 y'(b,\lambda) = 0,$$

involving a parameter λ in the manner indicated, is called a *Sturm-Liouville problem* or *system.*[1] The constants A_1, A_2, B_1, and B_2 are real and independent of λ. The functions p, q, r, and r' are real-valued and continuous, and $p > 0$ and $r > 0$, over the entire interval $a \leqq x \leqq b$.

Problem (1) has the trivial solution $y = 0$, for every value of λ. But for certain values λ_n of λ, called *eigenvalues* or *charac-*

---

[1] The first extensive development of the theory of such systems was published by J. C. F. Sturm and J. Liouville in the first three volumes of *Journal de mathématique*, 1836–1838.

teristic numbers, the problem has a nontrivial solution

$$y(x,\lambda_n) = y_n(x),$$

an *eigenfunction* or *characteristic function*. Note that $y = y_m(x)$ and $y = y_n(x)$ are solutions of different problems obtained by writing λ_m and λ_n, respectively, for λ in problem (1). Also note that if $y_n(x)$ is an eigenfunction then $Cy_n(x)$ is also one, where C is any constant other than zero.

The Sturm-Liouville problem is a particular type of eigenvalue problem. Such problems arise in the process of solving boundary value problems in partial differential equations by the classical method of separation of variables, a method we shall illustrate in this chapter.[1]

For any two eigenfunctions $y_m(x)$ and $y_n(x)$ of problem (1),

$$(ry_m')' = (q + \lambda_m p)y_m, \qquad (ry_n')' = (q + \lambda_n p)y_n.$$

When we eliminate $q(x)$ between these equations we find that

$$(\lambda_m - \lambda_n)py_m y_n = (ry_m')'y_n - (ry_n')'y_m;$$

the right-hand member is the derivative of $ry_m' y_n - ry_n' y_m$, owing to the self-adjoint forms involved. Thus

$$(\lambda_m - \lambda_n) \int_a^b p(x)y_m(x)y_n(x)\, dx = (y_m' y_n - y_n' y_m)r \Big]_a^b$$

and this last member can be written as

$$(2) \qquad r(a) \begin{vmatrix} y_m(a) & y_m'(a) \\ y_n(a) & y_n'(a) \end{vmatrix} - r(b) \begin{vmatrix} y_m(b) & y_m'(b) \\ y_n(b) & y_n'(b) \end{vmatrix}.$$

Each eigenfunction satisfies the boundary conditions in problem (1). From the first of those conditions it follows that

$$A_1 y_m(a) + A_2 y_m'(a) = 0, \qquad A_1 y_n(a) + A_2 y_n'(a) = 0.$$

Since A_1 and A_2 are not both zero, the determinant of this pair of equations in A_1 and A_2, the first determinant in expression (2), must vanish. From the second boundary condition in problem (1) we find that the second determinant in expression (2) vanishes, and therefore

$$(3) \qquad (\lambda_m - \lambda_n) \int_a^b p(x)y_m(x)y_n(x)\, dx = 0.$$

[1] Also see R. V. Churchill "Fourier Series and Boundary Value Problems."

If $\lambda_m \neq \lambda_n$, it follows that the two eigenfunctions are orthogonal on the interval (a,b) with weight function $p(x)$:

$$(4) \qquad \int_a^b p(x)y_m(x)y_n(x)\,dx = 0 \qquad (\lambda_m \neq \lambda_n).$$

If λ is a complex eigenvalue ($\lambda = \alpha + i\beta$), the eigenfunction $y(x,\lambda)$ may be complex-valued. When we take complex conjugates of all terms in problem (1), we see that

$$(r\bar{y}')' - (q + \bar{\lambda}p)\bar{y} = 0,$$
$$A_1\bar{y}(a,\lambda) + A_2\bar{y}'(a,\lambda) = 0, \qquad B_1\bar{y}(b,\lambda) + B_2\bar{y}'(b,\lambda) = 0.$$

Thus $\bar{y}(x,\lambda)$ is an eigenfunction corresponding to the eigenvalue $\bar{\lambda} = \alpha - i\beta$ and, according to equation (3),

$$(\lambda - \bar{\lambda}) \int_a^b p(x)y(x,\lambda)\bar{y}(x,\lambda)\,dx = 0.$$

If $y(x,\lambda)$ is continuous, the integral has a positive value, because $p(x) > 0$ and $y\bar{y} = |y|^2$ and $y(x,\lambda)$ is not identically zero. Therefore $\lambda - \bar{\lambda} = 0$; that is, $\beta = 0$ and λ is real.

Each eigenfunction is therefore a solution of system (1) whose coefficients are all real; thus it can be taken as a real-valued function. Assuming the existence of continuous eigenfunctions we have established the following results.

Theorem 3. *The characteristic numbers λ_n of the Sturm-Liouville problem (1) are all real and the characteristic functions $y_n(x)$ satisfy the orthogonality property (4).*

The positive number $\|y_n\|$, where

$$(5) \qquad \|y_n\|^2 = \int_a^b p(x)[y_n(x)]^2\,dx,$$

is called the *norm* of the function $y_n(x)$, with weight function $p(x)$. The normalized eigenfunctions

$$(6) \qquad \phi_n(x) = \frac{y_n(x)}{\|y_n\|} \qquad (n = 1, 2, \ldots)$$

are *orthonormal* on the interval (a,b); that is,

$$(7) \qquad \int_a^b p(x)\phi_m(x)\phi_n(x)\,dx = \begin{cases} 0 & \text{if } m \neq n \\ 1 & \text{if } m = n. \end{cases}$$

In analogy to the representation of an arbitrary vector in terms of an orthogonal set of unit reference vectors, suppose that an arbitrary function $f(x)$ can be represented by a series of the orthonormal functions $\phi_n(x)$,

$$(8) \qquad f(x) = \sum_{i=1}^{\infty} c_i \phi_i(x) \qquad (a < x < b).$$

The coefficient c_n can be determined formally by multiplying all terms by $p(x)\phi_n(x)$, integrating and applying formula (7); thus

$$(9) \qquad c_n = \int_a^b f(x)p(x)\phi_n(x)\,dx \qquad (n = 1, 2, \ldots).$$

The numbers c_n are the *Fourier constants* for $f(x)$ corresponding to the set of orthonormal functions, and the series (8) is the *generalized Fourier series* for $f(x)$.

Our theorems on the representation of the inversion integral as a series of residues are useful in establishing the following principal theorem. The procedure exhibits additional devices for determining properties of solutions of differential equations when the equations are too general to solve.

Theorem 4. *Let p, q, r, r', and $(pr)''$ be continuous real-valued functions of x, where $p(x) > 0$ and $r(x) > 0$, when $a \leqq x \leqq b$, and let the real constants A_1, A_2, B_1, and B_2 be independent of λ. Then the Sturm-Liouville system (1) has an infinite set of characteristic numbers λ_n $(n = 1, 2, \ldots)$, all real, and not more than a finite number of them are positive. It has corresponding real-valued orthonormal characteristic functions $\phi_n(x)$, where $\phi_n(x)$ and $\phi_n'(x)$ are continuous and $|\phi_n(x)|$ and $|\lambda_n^{-\frac{1}{2}}\phi_n'(x)|$ are bounded uniformly with respect to x and n (n large). Any sectionally continuous function $f(x)$ with sectionally continuous derivatives $f'(x)$ and $f''(x)$ is represented by its generalized Fourier series (8), with coefficients (9), at each point $x(a < x < b)$ where $f(x)$ is continuous.*

The theorem is true when the condition on $f''(x)$ is removed. In our proof it is convenient to require $f''(x)$ to be sectionally continuous.

Let p, q, and r satisfy the conditions stated in Theorem 4. Then when y and x are replaced by the new variables

$$(10) \qquad X = (pr)^{\frac{1}{4}}y, \qquad t = \frac{1}{C}\int_a^x \left[\frac{p(\xi)}{r(\xi)}\right]^{\frac{1}{2}} d\xi$$

and when $\mu = C^2\lambda$, where

$$C = \int_a^b \left[\frac{p(\xi)}{r(\xi)}\right]^{\frac{1}{2}} d\xi,$$

the Sturm-Liouville problem (1) takes the reduced form

$$X''(t,\mu) - [\mu + q_1(t)]X(t,\mu) = 0 \quad (0 < t < 1),$$

(11)

$$\alpha_1 X(0,\mu) + \alpha_2 X'(0,\mu) = 0, \quad \beta_1 X(1,\mu) + \beta_2 X'(1,\mu) = 0,$$

where $q_1(t)$ is continuous and the α's and β's are constants, all independent of μ. Also, the reduced system transforms back to system (1) under the above substitutions. This reduced system, the special case of problem (1) in which $p(x) = r(x) = 1$, can be used in establishing Theorem 4. Its characteristic functions are orthogonal on the interval $(0,1)$ with weight function $p = 1$.

PROBLEMS

1. Use Green's function to write the solution of (1) and (2) in Sec. 76 in the form (3) and (4) of that section.

2. Use Green's function to solve the boundary value problem for $y(x,s)$ in Sec. 85.

3. Let $w = u(x)$ and $w = v(x)$ be the solutions of the equation $w'' - Q(x)w = 0$ that satisfy the initial conditions

$$u(0) = \sin \alpha, \quad u'(0) = -\cos \alpha;$$
$$v(c) = \sin \beta, \quad v'(c) = -\cos \beta,$$

where α and β are prescribed constants. For the boundary value problem

$$y''(x) - Q(x)y(x) = F(x) \quad (0 < x < c),$$
$$y(0) \cos \alpha + y'(0) \sin \alpha = 0, \quad y(c) \cos \beta + y'(c) \sin \beta = 0,$$

derive the formula

$$G(x,\xi) = bu(x)v(\xi) \qquad (x \leqq \xi),$$
$$= bu(\xi)v(x) \qquad (x \geqq \xi),$$

for Green's function, where $b^{-1} = v(0) \cos \alpha + v'(0) \sin \alpha$, and verify the solution

$$y(x) = \int_0^c F(\xi)G(x,\xi) \, d\xi.$$

4. Use the results found in Prob. 3 to write the solution of the problem

$$y''(x) + k^2 y(x) = F(x), \quad y'(0) = 0, \quad y'(c) = 0,$$

where k^2 is a positive constant and $kc \neq \pm n\pi$, in the form

$$y(x)k \sin kc =$$
$$\int_0^x F(\xi) \cos k\xi \, d\xi \cos k(c - x) + \int_x^c F(\xi) \cos k(c - \xi) \, d\xi \cos kx.$$

5. Let $z(x,s)$ denote the transform of the longitudinal displacements $Z(x,t)$ in the bar in Sec. 82 when the initial displacement is arbitrary, $Z(x,0) = f(x)$, rather than zero.   Then

$$z'' - \frac{s^2}{a^2} z = - \frac{s}{a^2} f(x), \qquad z(0,s) = 0, \qquad z'(c,s) = \frac{A}{E} \frac{\omega}{s^2 + \omega^2}.$$

Show that the function $w = z(x,s) - y(x,s)$, where $y(x,s)$ is the transform written in that section, is the solution of a special case of the boundary value problem solved in Prob. 3.   Thus find the function $z(x,s)$ and show that resonance frequencies are not affected by an initial displacement $f(x)$.

6. Interpret the symmetry property $G(x,x_0) = G(x_0,x)$ for Green's function in terms of displacements in the string discussed in Sec. 90, and concentrated loads at x or x_0.

7. If h is a real constant, show that the eigenvalues of the Sturm-Liouville system

$$y''(x) - (h + \lambda)y(x) = 0, \qquad y(0) = y(1) = 0,$$

are the numbers $\lambda = -h - n^2\pi^2$ $(n = 1, 2, \ldots)$ and that the normalized eigenfunctions are $\phi_n(x) = \sqrt{2} \sin n\pi x$.   According to Theorem 4 any function $f(x)$ that satisfies the conditions stated there is represented by its Fourier sine series on the interval $(0,1)$:

$$f(x) = 2 \sum_{n=1}^{\infty} \sin n\pi x \int_0^1 f(\xi) \sin n\pi \xi \, d\xi \qquad (0 < x < 1).$$

Find the coefficients in the series when $f(x) = 1$.

8. Find all λ_n and $\phi_n(x)$ for the Sturm-Liouville problem

$$y''(x) - \lambda y(x) = 0, \qquad y'(0) = y'(c) = 0,$$

and obtain the Fourier cosine series expansion of $f(x)$,

$$f(x) = \frac{1}{c} \int_0^c f(\xi) \, d\xi + \frac{2}{c} \sum_{n=1}^{\infty} \cos \frac{n\pi x}{c} \int_0^c f(\xi) \cos \frac{n\pi \xi}{c} \, d\xi \qquad (0 < x < c),$$

as a special case of Theorem 4.   Note that when $\lambda = 0$ the general solution of the Sturm-Liouville equation is $y = Ax + B$, where A and B are arbitrary constants.

9. Find the characteristic numbers and functions of the systems

(a) $y''(x) - \lambda y(x) = 0,$ $y(0) = y'(c) = 0,$
(b) $y''(x) - \lambda y(x) = 0,$ $y(0) = 0,$ $y(1) + hy'(1) = 0,$

where h is a positive constant.   Note the orthogonality of the characteristic functions as given by Theorem 3.

Ans. $\lambda_n = -\alpha_n{}^2$, $y_n(x) = \sin \alpha_n x$, where in (a), $\alpha_n = (n - \frac{1}{2})\pi c^{-1}$, and in (b), $\alpha_n > 0$ and $\tan \alpha_n = -h\alpha_n$.

10. For the fourth-order eigenvalue problem

$$\frac{d^4y}{dx^4} - \lambda y = 0, \qquad y(0) = y'(0) = y(c) = y'(c) = 0,$$

prove that the eigenfunctions $y_n(x)$ and eigenvalues λ_n satisfy equation (3), Sec. 92, where $p(x) = 1$, $a = 0$, and $b = c$; hence that the eigenfunctions are orthogonal on the interval $(0,c)$ and that all eigenvalues are real.

93. The Reduced Eigenvalue Problem. We now begin a proof of Theorem 4, using the reduced form (11), Sec. 92, of the Sturm-Liouville problem. If we take the important special case in which $\alpha_2 = \beta_2 = 0$, simply as a matter of shortening the analysis, the problem can be written

(1) $\quad X''(x,\lambda) - [\lambda + q(x)]X(x,\lambda) = 0, \qquad X(0,\lambda) = X(1,\lambda) = 0.$

To serve as a guide to the analysis, we introduce a boundary value problem in partial differential equations whose solution is associated with problem (1). Let $Y(x,t)$ denote transverse displacements in a string stretched between points $(0,0)$ and $(1,0)$ when the string is attached along its span to an elastic medium that may be nonuniform. If the string starts from rest with a prescribed initial displacement $Y = f(x)$, and if the unit of time is properly chosen, then

(2)
$$Y_{tt}(x,t) = Y_{xx}(x,t) - q(x)Y(x,t) \qquad (0 < x < 1, t > 0),$$

$$Y(0,t) = Y(1,t) = Y_t(x,0) = 0, \qquad Y(x,0) = f(x).$$

The differential equation and all but one of the boundary conditions are homogeneous. Hence the method of separation of variables may apply to problem (2). First, to find all functions not identically zero of type $X(x)T(t)$ that satisfy all homogeneous conditions, we can write

$$XT'' = X''T - qXT, \qquad X(0) = X(1) = T'(0) = 0.$$

Consequently $\quad \dfrac{T''(t)}{T(t)} = \dfrac{X''(x) - q(x)X(x)}{X(x)} = \lambda,$

where the parameter λ is independent of x and t, because T''/T is independent of x and equal to a function that is independent of t. The function X therefore satisfies all conditions in problem (1). Thus λ must be an eigenvalue λ_n of that Sturm-Liouville problem and, except for an arbitrary constant factor, $X(x)$ must be the corresponding orthonormal eigenfunction $\phi_n(x)$. The function $T(t)$ then satisfies the system $T'' = \lambda_n T$, $T'(0) = 0$. The functions XT can therefore be written

$$
(3) \qquad X(x)T(t) = c_n\phi_n(x) \cos t \sqrt{-\lambda_n} \quad (n = 1, 2, \ldots),
$$

where the constants c_n are arbitrary.

A sum of functions (3) also satisfies all homogeneous conditions in problem (2). (Note that the sum itself is not a product of a function of x alone by a function of t alone.) Formally, the series

$$
(4) \qquad Y(x,t) = \sum_{n=1}^{\infty} c_n\phi_n(x) \cos t \sqrt{-\lambda_n}
$$

satisfies all conditions in the problem, including the condition $Y(x,0) = f(x)$, if the numbers c_n are the Fourier constants of $f(x)$ corresponding to the orthonormal functions $\phi_n(x)$, so that

$$
(5) \qquad f(x) = \sum_{n=1}^{\infty} c_n\phi_n(x) \qquad (0 < x < 1),
$$

where

$$
(6) \qquad c_n = \int_0^1 f(x)\phi_n(x)\, dx \qquad (n = 1, 2, \ldots).
$$

Thus the Sturm-Liouville expansion (5) is needed to complete the formal solution of problem (2) by the method of separation of variables.

94. The Transform $y(x,s)$. Formally, the Laplace transform $y(x,s)$ of the function $Y(x,t)$ in problem (2), Sec. 93, satisfies the boundary value problem

$$
(1) \quad y''(x,s) - [s^2 + q(x)]y(x,s) = -sf(x), \quad y(0,s) = y(1,s) = 0.
$$

We now make a careful study of the solution of this problem.

To construct Green's function $G(x,\xi,s)$ for problem (1), we introduce the solutions $u(x,s)$ and $v(x,s)$ of the initial-value problems

$$
(2) \quad u'' - (s^2 + q)u = 0, \quad u(0,s) = 0, \quad u'(0,s) = 1,
$$
$$
(3) \quad v'' - (s^2 + q)v = 0, \quad v(1,s) = 0, \quad v'(1,s) = 1,
$$

as in Sec. 91.   Then for all s except those for which $u(1,s) = 0$,

(4)
$$G = \frac{u(x,s)v(\xi,s)}{u(1,s)} \qquad (x \leqq \xi)$$

$$= \frac{u(\xi,s)v(x,s)}{u(1,s)} \qquad (x \geqq \xi).$$

Therefore

(5)
$$y(x,s) = -s \int_0^1 f(\xi)G(x,\xi,s)\,d\xi = -s\,\frac{h(x,s)}{u(1,s)}$$

where

(6) $h(x,s) = v(x,s) \displaystyle\int_0^x f(\xi)u(\xi,s)\,d\xi + u(x,s) \int_x^1 f(\xi)v(\xi,s)\,d\xi.$

For each fixed x, $h(x,s)$ is an entire function of the complex parameter s.   This can be seen from the properties of continuity and analyticity of u and v and their derivatives, cited in Sec. 89, provided that $f(x)$ is sectionally continuous.

Consequently $y(x,s)$ is an analytic function of s except at the zeros of the entire function $u(1,s)$, which are necessarily isolated. But when $u(1,s) = 0$, we see from problem (2) that $u(x,s)$ is a solution of our Sturm-Liouville problem (1), Sec. 93, where $\lambda = s^2$; thus $s = \pm\sqrt{\lambda_n}$, where $\sqrt{\lambda_n}$ represents one of the square roots of the real eigenvalue λ_n.   We write $s_n = \sqrt{\lambda_n}$.   Except for a constant factor, $u(x,\pm s_n)$ equals the orthonormal eigenfunction $\phi_n(x)$ and, since $u'(0,s) = 1$ for all s,

(7)
$$u(x,\pm s_n) = \frac{\phi_n(x)}{\phi_n'(0)} \qquad (s_n = \sqrt{\lambda_n}).$$

The function ϕ_n is not identically zero and it satisfies the conditions

(8) $\phi_n''(x) - [s_n{}^2 + q(x)]\phi_n(x) = 0, \qquad \phi_n(0) = \phi_n(1) = 0;$

therefore $\phi_n'(0) \neq 0$, and $\phi_n'(1) \neq 0$.

According to equation (5), Sec. 91,

$$u(x,s)v'(x,s) - u'(x,s)v(x,s) = u(1,s).$$

When $s = \pm s_n$, we see that $v(0,\pm s_n) = 0$ and, in view of conditions (3), that

(9)
$$v(x,\pm s_n) = \frac{\phi_n(x)}{\phi_n'(1)}.$$

When $s_n \neq 0$, it follows from formula (5) that the singular points $\pm s_n$ of $y(x,s)$ are simple poles if $du(1,s)/ds$ does not vanish at these points; that is, if $u_s(1, \pm s_n) \neq 0$. Upon eliminating $q(x)$ between equations (2) and (8) we find that

$$(s^2 - s_n{}^2)u\phi_n = u''\phi_n - u\phi_n'' = (u'\phi_n - u\phi_n')',$$

and therefore

$$(10) \qquad (s^2 - s_n{}^2) \int_0^1 u(x,s)\phi_n(x)\ dx = -\phi_n'(1)u(1,s).$$

It follows that

$$(11) \quad u_s(1,s_n) = -\frac{2s_n}{\phi_n'(1)} \int_0^1 u(x,s_n)\phi_n(x)\ dx = -\frac{2s_n}{\phi_n'(0)\phi_n'(1)},$$

and s_n can be replaced throughout this formula by $-s_n$. Hence $\pm s_n$ are simple poles.

From equations (6), (7), and (9) we find that, for every s_n,

$$h(x, \pm s_n) = \frac{\phi_n(x)}{\phi_n'(0)\phi_n'(1)} \int_0^1 f(\xi)\phi_n(\xi)\ d\xi = \frac{c_n\phi_n(x)}{\phi_n'(0)\phi_n'(1)},$$

where c_n's are the Fourier constants for $f(x)$. When $s_n \neq 0$, the function $y(x,s)$ has the same residue at each of the two poles $\pm s_n$, namely

$$-\frac{s_n h(x,s_n)}{u_s(1,s_n)} = \frac{1}{2}\,c_n\phi_n(x),$$

or the sum of the residues at s_n and $-s_n$ is

$$(12) \qquad \rho_n(x) = c_n\phi_n(x).$$

When $s_n = 0$, we write $s^{-1}u(1,s) = w(s)$. According to equation (10), $w(0) = 0$ and dw/ds at $s = 0$ has the value w_1, where

$$w_1 = -\frac{1}{\phi_n'(0)\phi_n'(1)} \neq 0.$$

Then the residue $-h(x,s_n)/w_1$ of $y(x,s)$ at the simple pole $s_n = 0$ has the value $\rho_n(x)$ given by formula (12).

The inverse transform of $y(x,s)$ should reduce to $f(x)$ when $t = 0$. The residues (12) of $y(x,s)$ are the terms in the generalized Fourier series (5), Sec. 93. We shall show that the series converges to $f(x)$.

95. Existence of the Eigenvalues.   The initial-value problem
(2), Sec. 94, can be written in the form

(1) $u''(x,s) - s^2 u(x,s) = q(x)u(x,s),$ $u(0,s) = 0,$ $u'(0,s) = 1.$

We can replace it by an integral equation by proceeding as if the
term qu were a prescribed function.

Let $g(x,\xi,s)$ be Green's function for the problem

$$z'' - s^2 z = F(x), \qquad z(0) = z(1) = 0;$$

then $g(x,\xi,s) = g(\xi,x,s)$ and

$$g(x,\xi,s) = - \frac{\sinh sx \, \sinh s(1 - \xi)}{s \sinh s} \qquad (x \leqq \xi).$$

When u satisfies the differential equation and the first initial condition in problem (1), we can now write

$$u(x,s) = \int_0^1 q(\xi)u(\xi,s)g(x,\xi,s)\, d\xi + C \sinh sx,$$

where the number C is determined with the aid of the condition
$u'(0,s) = 1.$ We find that

$$sC = 1 + \frac{1}{\sinh s}\int_0^1 q(\xi)u(\xi,s)\sinh s(1 - \xi)\, d\xi$$

and after simplifications are made, that

(2) $su(x,s) = \sinh sx + \int_0^x q(\xi)u(\xi,s)\sinh s(x - \xi)\, d\xi.$

The reader can verify that when u satisfies this integral equation
it is the solution of problem (1).

Likewise the solution v of initial-value problem (3), Sec. 94,
satisfies the integral equation

(3) $sv(x,s) = -\sinh s(1 - x) + \int_x^1 q(\xi)v(\xi,s)\sinh s(\xi - x)\, d\xi.$

We write $r = |s|$, $s = \nu + i\eta$ and $\sigma = |\nu|$.   For every s,

$$e^{-\sigma x}|\sinh sx| \leqq 1 \quad [\sigma = |\Re(s)|, 0 \leqq x \leqq 1].$$

For a fixed s, let $M(s)$ denote the maximum value of the contin-
uous function $r|u(x,s)|e^{-\sigma x}$ on the interval $0 \leqq x \leqq 1$.   The func-
tion assumes its maximum value at some point x_0 in the interval,

$$M(s) = r|u(x_0,s)|e^{-\sigma x_0},$$

where x_0 depends on s. From equation (2) we now find that

$$M(s) \leq 1 + \int_0^{x_0} |q(\xi)u(\xi,s) \sinh s(x_0 - \xi)|e^{-\sigma x_0}\,d\xi \quad (r > 0),$$

and when we write the integrand here in the form

$$\frac{1}{r}\,|q(\xi)|\,[r|u(\xi,s)|e^{-\sigma\xi}]\,e^{-\sigma(x_0-\xi)}|\sinh s(x_0 - \xi)|$$

we see that

$$M(s) \leq 1 + \frac{q_0}{r}\,M(s), \quad \text{where } q_0 = \int_0^1 |q(\xi)|\,d\xi.$$

Therefore

$$(4) \qquad\qquad M(s) \leq \left(1 - \frac{q_0}{r}\right)^{-1} < 2 \quad \text{whenever } r > 2q_0.$$

A similar argument applies to v; thus

$$(5) \qquad r|u(x,s)|e^{-\sigma x} < 2, \qquad r|v(x,s)|e^{-\sigma(1-x)} < 2, \qquad (r > 2q_0).$$

From equation (2) it now follows that

$$(6) \qquad\qquad su(x,s) = \sinh sx + \frac{e^{\sigma x}}{s}\,R_1(x,s),$$

$$(7) \qquad\qquad u'(x,s) = \cosh sx + \frac{e^{\sigma x}}{s}\,R_2(x,s),$$

where R_1 and R_2 are continuous functions whose absolute values are less than $2q_0$ when $r > 2q_0$. In particular,

$$(8) \qquad\qquad su(1,s)e^{-\sigma} = e^{-\sigma} \sinh s + \frac{1}{s}\,R_1(1,s).$$

We found that $u(1,s)$ cannot vanish unless s has real or pure imaginary values, $s = \pm\sqrt{\lambda_n}$. If s is real and not zero, $s = \pm\sigma$, then $e^{-\sigma} \sinh s$ approaches $\pm\frac{1}{2}$ as σ tends to infinity, and it follows from equation (8) that a number γ exists such that $u(1,s) \neq 0$ when $\sigma > \gamma$. All real zeros of the entire function $u(1,s)$ therefore lie on a finite interval of the real axis; hence they are finite in number.

When s is pure imaginary, $\sigma = 0$, $s = i\eta$ and

$$\eta u(1,i\eta) = \sin \eta - \frac{1}{\eta}\,R_1(1,i\eta);$$

also $u(x,i\eta)$ is real because all coefficients in the initial-value problem (2), Sec. 94, are real when $s = i\eta$. Hence the function

$\eta^{-1}R_1(1,i\eta)$ is real and continuous and tends to zero as $\eta \to \pm \infty$. Its graph intersects that of $\sin \eta$ at an infinite set of points $\eta = \pm\eta_j$ $(j = 1, 2, \ldots)$, where η_j is arbitrarily close to a multiple of π when η_j is sufficiently large.

An infinite set of characteristic numbers

(9) $\lambda_1, \lambda_2, \ldots, \lambda_m; \lambda_{m+1}, \ldots$

$$(\lambda_n \geqq 0 \text{ if } n \leqq m, \lambda_n < 0 \text{ if } n > m),$$

or simple poles $\pm s_n = \pm \sqrt{\lambda_n}$ of $y(x,s)$, therefore exists. When $n > m$, then $s_n = i\eta_n$, where η_n is real and, according to equations (6) and (7),

(10) $$u(x,s_n) = \frac{1}{\eta_n} \sin \eta_n x - \frac{1}{\eta_n^2} R_1(x,i\eta_n),$$

(11) $$u'(x,s_n) = \cos \eta_n x - \frac{i}{\eta_n} R_2(x,i\eta_n).$$

With the aid of the last two equations we find that the norm $\|\eta_n u(x,s_n)\|$ tends to $2^{-\frac{1}{2}}$ as $n \to \infty$, and that a constant K, independent of n, exists such that the normalized eigenfunctions $\phi_n(x)$ satisfy conditions

(12) $$|\phi_n(x)| < K, \qquad |\lambda_n^{-\frac{1}{2}}\phi_n'(x)| < K \qquad (\lambda_n \neq 0).$$

Our principal results are stated as follows.

Theorem 5. *The reduced Sturm-Liouville problem* (1), *Sec. 93, has an infinite set* (9) *of eigenvalues* λ_n. *All eigenvalues are real, and no more than a finite number of them are positive. The value of* $\sqrt{-\lambda_n}$ *is arbitrarily close to a multiple of* π *when* n *is sufficiently large. The corresponding orthonormal eigenfunctions* $\phi_n(x)$ *and their derivatives satisfy the uniform boundedness properties* (12).

96. The Generalized Fourier Series. We prepare to apply the inversion integral and its representation as a series of residues by finding order properties of $G(x,\xi,s)$ and $y(x,s)$ in the complex plane of the variable s.

When $x \leqq \xi$,

$$G(x,\xi,s) = \frac{u(x,s)v(\xi,s)}{u(1,s)} = \frac{[se^{-\sigma x}u(x,s)][se^{-\sigma(1-\xi)}v(\xi,s)]}{s^2 e^{-\sigma}u(1,s)e^{\sigma(\xi-x)}}.$$

In view of conditions (5) and equation (8), Sec. 95, then

(1) $$|G(x,\xi,s)| < \frac{4}{r|e^{-\sigma}\sinh s + s^{-1}R_1(1,s)|} \qquad (r > 2q_0).$$

This condition is also valid when $x \geqq \xi$, because of the symmetry of Green's function. The denominator vanishes only at points $\pm s_n$ lying along the imaginary axis or along a segment $\sigma < \gamma$ of the real axis, because $\pm s_n$ are the zeros of $u(1,s)$. If all points s_n lie on the imaginary axis, let γ denote any positive number. For all points s in each bounded subregion of either of the two half planes $\sigma > \gamma$, the denominator in condition (1) is greater than some positive constant, since that denominator is a continuous nonvanishing function of s there. But at every point s in either of the two half planes $\sigma > \gamma$

$$e^{-\sigma}|\sinh s| > \tfrac{1}{2}(1 - e^{-2\gamma}) > 0$$

and consequently the denominator is also bounded away from zero when r is large. Therefore G is $O(r^{-1})$ in the half planes. For points s on lines $\eta = \pm (n - \tfrac{1}{2})\pi$, where $s = \pm\sigma + i\eta$,

$$e^{-\sigma}|\sinh s| = e^{-\sigma} \cosh \sigma = \frac{1 + e^{-2\sigma}}{2} > \frac{1}{2}.$$

It follows from condition (1) that G is $O(r^{-1})$ on those lines. Hence for all s in a right half plane $\Re(s) > \gamma$ as well as at all points s on the open rectangular paths C_n used in Theorem 10, Sec. 67, in which $\beta_n = (n - \tfrac{1}{2})\pi$, a constant M_0 independent of x and ξ exists such that

$$(2) \qquad\qquad |G(x,\xi,s)| < \frac{M_0}{r} \qquad [\Re(s) > \gamma \text{ or } s \text{ on } C_n].$$

The function

$$(3) \qquad\qquad y(x,s) = -s \int_0^1 f(\xi)G(x,\xi,s) \, d\xi$$

is therefore bounded in the half plane and on C_n.

To save some steps we now assume that $f(x)$ is continuous with sectionally continuous derivatives $f'(x)$ and $f''(x)$, when $0 \leqq x \leqq 1$, and that $f(0) = f(1) = 0$. Relaxation of these conditions can be left to the problems.

Since for a fixed x Green's function satisfies the homogeneous differential equation of which $u(\xi,s)$ and $v(\xi,s)$ are solutions, we can make the substitution

$$G(x,\xi,s) = \frac{1}{s^2} G_{\xi\xi}(x,\xi,s) - \frac{1}{s^2} q(\xi)G(x,\xi,s) \qquad (\xi \neq x)$$

into equation (3). After integrating two of the integrals so obtained, namely

$$\int_0^x f(\xi)G_{\xi\xi}(x,\xi,s)\, d\xi, \qquad \int_x^1 f(\xi)G_{\xi\xi}(x,\xi,s)\, d\xi,$$

by parts and simplifying we find that

$$sy(x,s) - f(x) = \int_0^1 f(\xi)q(\xi)G(x,\xi,s)\, d\xi + \int_0^1 f'(\xi)G_\xi(x,\xi,s)\, d\xi.$$

Let $f'(x)$ have jumps b_i at points x_i ($i = 1, 2, \ldots , N$). Then, when the last integral is integrated by parts, the last equation can be written

$$(4) \quad y(x,s) - \frac{f(x)}{s}$$

$$= \int_0^1 [f(\xi)q(\xi) - f''(\xi)]\frac{G(x,\xi,s)}{s}\, d\xi - \sum_{i=1}^N b_i \frac{G(x,x_i,s)}{s}.$$

From condition (2) and equation (4) we can see that a constant M_1, independent of x, exists such that

$$(5) \qquad \left| y(x,s) - \frac{f(x)}{s} \right| < \frac{M_1}{r^2} \quad [\Re(s) > \gamma \text{ or } s \text{ on } C_n].$$

According to the findings in Chap. 6 the inversion integral of the function $y - s^{-1}f$ therefore has the value zero when $t = 0$, and this value is represented by the series of residues of the function; thus, in view of formula (12), Sec. 94,

$$(6) \qquad \sum_{n=1}^\infty c_n\phi_n(x) - f(x) = 0 \qquad (0 \leq x \leq 1).$$

Because of the uniformity of the order property (5), with respect to x, the convergence of the series (6) is uniform. The following representation theorem is now proved.

   Theorem 6. *If $f(x)$ is continuous and $f'(x)$ and $f''(x)$ are sectionally continuous, when $0 \leq x \leq 1$, and if $f(0) = f(1) = 0$, then the generalized Fourier series*

$$(7) \qquad \sum_{n=1}^\infty \phi_n(x) \int_0^1 f(\xi)\phi_n(\xi)\, d\xi,$$

where $\phi_n(x)$ represents all normalized eigenfunctions of the reduced

Sturm-Liouville problem (1), Sec. 93, *converges uniformly to* $f(x)$ *when* $0 \leq x \leq 1$.

With the aid of the formula established in Prob. 3, Sec. 92, the proof of the theorem can be modified to accommodate the more general boundary conditions

$$X(0,\lambda) \cos \alpha + X'(0,\lambda) \sin \alpha = 0,$$
$$X(1,\lambda) \cos \beta + X'(1,\lambda) \sin \beta = 0,$$

of the Sturm-Liouville problem, where α and β are real constants independent of λ. Then after the conditions on $f(x)$ are relaxed to permit $f(x)$ to be sectionally continuous and to have arbitrary limits at the end points of the interval $0 \leq x \leq 1$, our more general Theorem 4 can be obtained by means of substitutions (10), Sec. 92.

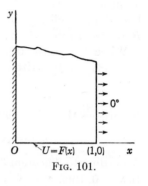

FIG. 101.

97. Steady Temperatures in a Wall. Let $U(x,y)$ be the steady-state temperatures in a semi-infinite wall bounded by the planes $x = 0$, $x = 1$, and $y = 0$ (Fig. 101). Let the face $x = 0$ be insulated, and let surface heat transfer take place at the face $x = 1$, while the face $y = 0$ is kept at temperature $F(x)$, so that the boundary value problem becomes

(1) $$U_{xx}(x,y) + U_{yy}(x,y) = 0 \quad (0 < x < 1,\ y > 0),$$
(2) $$U_x(0,y) = 0, \qquad U_x(1,y) = -hU(1,y) \qquad (y > 0),$$
(3) $$U(x,0) = F(x), \qquad \lim_{y \to \infty} U(x,y) = 0 \quad (0 < x < 1),$$

where the constant h is positive and the function $F(x)$ is prescribed.

Although the variable y has a semi-infinite range, the problem is not well adapted to solution by using the Laplace transformation for reasons indicated in Sec. 49. The method of separation of variables does apply.

To find all functions of type $X(x)Y(y)$, other than zero itself, that satisfy all homogeneous conditions in the problem we first note that, from condition (1),

$$X''(x)Y(y) + X(x)Y''(y) = 0.$$

Therefore $$\frac{X''(x)}{X(x)} = -\frac{Y''(y)}{Y(y)} = \lambda,$$

where the parameter λ is independent of x and y (cf. Sec. 93). Then all the homogeneous conditions are satisfied if $X(x)$ is a solution of the Sturm-Liouville problem

(4) $X''(x) - \lambda X(x) = 0$, $X'(0) = 0$, $hX(1) + X'(1) = 0$,

and if $Y(y)$ satisfies the conditions

(5) $Y''(y) + \lambda Y(y) = 0$, $\lim\limits_{y \to \infty} Y(y) = 0$.

When $\lambda = 0$, the general solution of the differential equation in problem (4) is $X(x) = Ax + B$, and this satisfies the two boundary conditions in the problem only if the constants A and B are both zero. Consequently zero is not an eigenvalue.

When $\lambda \neq 0$, the function that satisfies the first two of conditions (4) can be written

$$X(x) = C \cosh x \sqrt{\lambda}.$$

It satisfies the third condition if

(6) $h \cosh \sqrt{\lambda} + \sqrt{\lambda} \sinh \sqrt{\lambda} = 0$.

According to Theorem 3, all eigenvalues of problem (4) are real. If $\lambda > 0$, then $\cosh \sqrt{\lambda} > 0$ and equation (6) can be written

$$\tanh \sqrt{\lambda} = -\frac{h}{\sqrt{\lambda}}.$$

Since the graphs of the functions $\tanh \mu$ and $-h/\mu$ do not intersect, the equation has no solution. All eigenvalues of problem (4) are therefore negative.

We write $\lambda = -\alpha^2$. Then equation (6) becomes

(7) $\tan \alpha = \dfrac{h}{\alpha}$,

an equation that has an infinite set of roots $\pm\alpha_n$ ($n = 1, 2, \ldots$) that can be approximated graphically. In fact the number α_n is only slightly greater than $n\pi$ when n is large.

The complete set of eigenvalues of problem (4) is therefore

$$\lambda_n = -\alpha_n^2 \qquad (n = 1, 2, \ldots),$$

where the numbers α_n are the positive roots of equation (7), and the corresponding eigenfunctions are

$$X_n(x) = \cos \alpha_n x.$$

Let β_n denote the norm $\|X_n(x)\|$. Then

$$\beta_n{}^2 = \int_0^1 \cos^2 \alpha_n x \, dx = \frac{1}{2}\left(1 + \frac{\sin \alpha_n \cos \alpha_n}{\alpha_n}\right)$$

and, since α_n is a root of equation (7), we find that

$$(8) \qquad \beta_n = 2^{-\frac{1}{2}}\left(1 + \frac{h}{h^2 + \alpha_n{}^2}\right)^{\frac{1}{2}}.$$

The orthonormal eigenfunctions of problem (4) are therefore

$$(9) \qquad \phi_n(x) = \frac{1}{\beta_n}\cos \alpha_n x \qquad (n = 1, 2, \ldots).$$

When $\lambda = -\alpha_n{}^2$, the solution of problem (5) is

$$Y(y) = c_n \exp(-\alpha_n y),$$

where the constant c_n is arbitrary, and therefore

$$X(x)Y(y) = c_n \frac{\cos \alpha_n x}{\beta_n} \exp(-\alpha_n y) \quad (n = 1, 2, \ldots).$$

The sum of any number of these functions also satisfies all homogeneous conditions in problem (1) to (3); but unless $F(x)$ is a linear combination of the functions $\cos \alpha_n x$, no finite sum will satisfy the remaining condition

$$(10) \qquad U(x,0) = F(x) \qquad (0 < x < 1).$$

The function represented by the infinite series

$$\sum_{n=1}^{\infty} \frac{c_n}{\beta_n} \cos \alpha_n x \exp(-\alpha_n y)$$

formally satisfies the homogeneous conditions. According to Theorem 4, this function reduces to $F(x)$ when $y = 0$, provided $F(x)$ and its first two derivatives are sectionally continuous, if the numbers c_n are the Fourier constants for $F(x)$ with respect to $\phi_n(x)$; that is, if

$$(11) \qquad c_n = \int_0^1 F(x)\phi_n(x) \, dx = \frac{1}{\beta_n}\int_0^1 F(x) \cos \alpha_n x \, dx.$$

Note that the series used to represent $F(x)$ here,

$$(12) \qquad F(x) = \sum_{n=1}^{\infty} \frac{c_n}{\beta_n} \cos \alpha_n x \qquad (0 < x < 1),$$

is a generalized Fourier series, not the Fourier cosine series for the interval $0 < x < 1$.

The formal solution of our problem is therefore

$$(13) \qquad U(x,y) = \sum_{n=1}^{\infty} \frac{c_n}{\beta_n} \exp\,(-\alpha_n y) \cos \alpha_n x,$$

where the constants β_n and c_n are given by formulas (8) and (11).

98. Verification of the Solution. We assume that the prescribed temperature function $F(x)$ in the foregoing section is sectionally continuous, together with $F'(x)$ and $F''(x)$. The generalized Fourier series (12) then converges to $F(x)$.

We order the numbers α_n so that $\alpha_{n+1} > \alpha_n$. Then the functions $\exp\,(-\alpha_n y)$ are bounded uniformly with respect to n and y and monotone nonincreasing with respect to n:

$$0 < \exp\,(-\alpha_n y) \leqq 1, \qquad \exp\,(-\alpha_{n+1} y) \leqq \exp\,(-\alpha_n y) \quad (y \geqq 0).$$

According to Abel's test (Prob. 19, Sec. 75), therefore, the series

$$(1) \qquad \sum_{n=1}^{\infty} \frac{c_n}{\beta_n} \cos \alpha_n x \exp\,(-\alpha_n y) \quad (0 < x < 1, y \geqq 0)$$

converges uniformly with respect to y when $y \geqq 0$. Since its terms are continuous functions of y, the series represents a continuous function of y when $y \geqq 0$. The formal solution (13), Sec. 97, therefore satisfies the condition

$$U(x,+0) = U(x,0) = F(x) \qquad (0 < x < 1).$$

Let y_0 be any positive number. When $y \geqq y_0$, the absolute values of the terms in the series (1) are all less than a constant times $\exp\,(-\alpha_n y_0)$. Consequently the series is uniformly convergent with respect to x and y when $y \geqq y_0$ and $0 \leqq x \leqq 1$. Similarly, the series obtained by differentiating that series term by term are uniformly convergent. The series can therefore be differentiated term by term when $y > 0$. Since the terms of the series (1) satisfy the partial differential equation $U_{xx} + U_{yy} = 0$, it follows that the function represented by the series satisfies that equation when $y > 0$. In view of the uniform convergence, the function represented by the series, together with its derivatives, is a continuous function of x and y ($0 \leqq x \leqq 1$, $y > 0$). It follows readily that the remaining boundary conditions in the problem are satisfied.

Thus formula (13), Sec. 97, is established as a solution of the boundary value problem of that section.

PROBLEMS

1. If $h = 0$ in the problem of Sec. 97, show that $\lambda = 0$ is a characteristic number and that the solution is

$$U(x,y) = \int_0^1 F(\xi)\, d\xi + 2 \sum_{n=1}^{\infty} e^{-n\pi y} \cos n\pi x \int_0^1 F(\xi) \cos n\pi\xi\, d\xi.$$

Use the method of separation of variables to solve the following boundary value problems.

2. The problem in $Y(x,t)$, Sec. 85.

3. Prob. 2, Sec. 88.

4. Prob. 3, Sec. 88.

5. The problem in $U(x,t)$, Sec. 76.

6. In the region $0 \leqq x \leqq 1$, $y \geqq 0$, a function $U(x,y)$ satisfies

$$U_{xx} + U_{yy} = 0, \qquad U_x(0,y) = 0, \qquad U(1,y) = 0, \qquad U(x,0) = F(x);$$

also $U(x,y)$ is bounded. Give a physical interpretation of this problem, and derive the formula

$$U(x,y) = 2 \sum_{n=1}^{\infty} e^{-my} \cos mx \int_0^1 F(\xi) \cos m\xi\, d\xi,$$

where $m = (n - \tfrac{1}{2})\pi$.

7. Let $U(x,y)$ be the steady-state temperatures in a thin plate in the shape of a semi-infinite strip. Let surface heat transfer take place at the faces into a medium at temperature zero so that

$$U_{xx} + U_{yy} - bU = 0 \qquad (0 < x < 1, y > 0).$$

If $U(x,y)$ is bounded and satisfies the conditions

$$U(0,y) = 0, \qquad U_x(1,y) = -hU(1,y), \qquad U(x,0) = 1 \qquad (0 < x < 1)$$

derive the formula

$$U(x,y) = 2h \sum_{n=1}^{\infty} \frac{A_n}{\alpha_n} \exp\left[-y(b + \alpha_n^2)^{\frac{1}{2}}\right] \sin \alpha_n x \qquad (b > 0,\ h > 0),$$

where $A_n = (1 - \cos \alpha_n)/(h + \cos^2 \alpha_n)$ and α_1, α_2, . . . are the positive roots of the equation $\tan \alpha = -\alpha/h$.

8. Let $U(x,y)$ be the steady-state temperatures in an infinite prism bounded by the planes $x = 0$, $y = 0$, $x = 1$, and $y = 1$. If $U = 1$ on

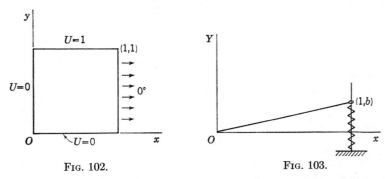

Fig. 102.   Fig. 103.

the face $y = 1$ and if $U_x = -hU$ at $x = 1$, where $h > 0$, and $U = 0$ on the other two faces (Fig. 102), derive the formula

$$U(x,y) = 2h \sum_{n=1}^{\infty} \frac{A_n}{\alpha_n} \frac{\sinh \alpha_n y}{\sinh \alpha_n} \sin \alpha_n x,$$

where the numbers A_n and α_n are those described in Prob. 7.

9. Solve the problem

$$U_{xx}(x,t) = (t + 1)U_t(x,t),$$
$$U(0,t) = 0, \qquad U_x(1,t) = 0, \qquad U(x,0) = F(x),$$

where $0 \leqq x \leqq 1$, $t \geqq 0$. When $F(x) = 1(0 < x < 1)$, show that the solution becomes

$$U(x,t) = 2 \sum_{n=1}^{\infty} \frac{1}{m} (t + 1)^{-m^2} \sin mx,$$

where $m = (n - \frac{1}{2})\pi$.

10. The end $x = 1$ of a stretched string is elastically supported (Fig. 103) so that the transverse displacement $Y(x,t)$ satisfies the condition $Y_x(1,t) = -hY(1,t)$. Let

$$Y(0,t) = 0, \qquad Y(x,0) = bx, \qquad Y_t(x,0) = 0.$$

Show that the solution of the equation $Y_{tt}(x,t) = Y_{xx}(x,t)$ is then

$$Y(x,t) = 2bh(h + 1) \sum_{n=1}^{\infty} \frac{\sin \alpha_n \sin \alpha_n x}{\alpha_n{}^2(h + \cos^2 \alpha_n)} \cos \alpha_n t,$$

where $\alpha_1, \alpha_2, \ldots$ are the positive roots of the equation $\tan \alpha = -\alpha/h$.

11. The longitudinal displacements $Y(x,t)$ in a certain nonuniform bar satisfy the conditions

$$\frac{\partial}{\partial x} \left(e^x \frac{\partial Y}{\partial x} \right) = e^{-x} \frac{\partial^2 Y}{\partial t^2} \qquad (0 < x < 1, t > 0),$$

$$Y(0,t) = Y(1,t) = Y_t(x,0) = 0, \qquad Y(x,0) = F(x) \quad (0 < x < 1).$$

Derive the formula

$$Y(x,t) = \sum_{n=1}^{\infty} c_n \phi_n(x) \cos \beta_n t,$$

where $\beta_n = n\pi e/(e - 1)$ and

$$\phi_n(x) = \sqrt{\beta_2/\pi} \sin [\beta_n(1 - e^{-x})], \qquad c_n = \int_0^1 F(x)e^{-x}\phi_n(x) \, dx.$$

12. The electrostatic potential $V(r,z)$ in the space bounded by the cylinders $r = a$ and $r = b$ above the plane $z = 0$ satisfies Laplace's equation $(rV_r)_r + rV_{zz} = 0$ and the boundary conditions

$$V(a,z) = V(b,z) = 0 \qquad\qquad (z > 0),$$
$$V(r,0) = F(r) \qquad\qquad (a < r < b);$$

also $V(r,z)$ is bounded. Derive the formula

$$V(r,z) = \sum_{n=1}^{\infty} A_n \exp (-\alpha_n z)\psi(\alpha_n r),$$

where $\psi(\alpha r) = J_0(\alpha r)Y_0(\alpha a) - J_0(\alpha a)Y_0(\alpha r)$. J_0 and Y_0 are Bessel functions of the first and second kind, linearly independent solutions of Bessel's equation. The numbers α_n are the roots of the equation $\psi(b\alpha) = 0$, and

$$A_n = \frac{\displaystyle\int_a^b rF(r)\psi(\alpha_n r) \, dr}{\displaystyle\int_a^b r[\psi(\alpha_n r)]^2 \, dr}.$$

13. If $\phi_n(x)$ and $\theta_n(x)$ are two different normalized eigenfunctions of the Sturm-Liouville problem (1), Sec. 93, corresponding to the same eigenvalue λ_n, show that

$$\theta_n(x)\phi_n'(x) - \phi_n(x)\theta_n'(x) = 0$$

and prove that $\theta_n(x) = -\phi_n(x)$. Recall that eigenfunctions are continuous, together with their derivatives of the first order, and not identically zero.

14. By writing problem (1), Sec. 93, in the form

$$X'' - qX = \lambda X, \qquad X(0,\lambda) = X(1,\lambda) = 0,$$

show that if zero is not an eigenvalue, then each eigenfunction $X(x,\lambda_n)$ is a solution of the homogeneous integral equation

$$X(x,\lambda) = \lambda \int_0^1 X(\xi,\lambda)G(x,\xi,0)\, d\xi$$

when $\lambda = \lambda_n$, where G is Green's function (4), Sec. 94.

15. Corresponding to equations (6) and (7) in Sec. 95, show that

$$sv(x,s) = -\sinh s(1-x) + s^{-1}e^{\sigma(1-x)}R_3(x,s),$$
$$v'(x,s) = \cosh s(1-x) - s^{-1}e^{\sigma(1-x)}R_4(x,s),$$

where $|R_3|$ and $|R_4|$ are bounded uniformly with respect to x when $|s| > 2q_0$.

16. If c is independent of s and $0 \leqq c < 1$, (a) show by elementary methods that the function

$$\psi(c,s) = \frac{1}{s}\frac{\sinh cs}{\sinh s}$$

is the transform of a step function $\Psi(t,c)$ such that $\Psi(c,t) = 0$ when $0 < t < 1 - c$, and hence that $L_i^{-1}(\psi) = 0$ when $t = 0$. (b) Prove that when $t = 0$ the inversion integral of the function $\psi(c,s)$ is represented by the series of residues of the function.

17. When $f(x)$ is the step function

$$f(x) = a \qquad\qquad (0 < x < x_0)$$
$$ = b \qquad\qquad (x_0 < x < 1),$$

write formula (3), Sec. 96, in terms of u, v, a, and b and use the differential equations satisfied by $u(\xi,s)$ and $v(\xi,s)$ to show that, when $x < x_0$,

$$y(x,s) - \frac{a}{s} = \frac{P_1(x,s)}{su(1,s)} + P_2(x,s)$$

where P_1 and P_2 are the functions

$$P_1(x,s) = av(x,s) - bu(x,s) + (b-a)u(x,s)v'(x_0,s),$$
$$P_2(x,s) = \int_0^1 f(\xi)q(\xi)\frac{G(x,\xi,s)}{s}\, d\xi,$$

where $|P_2(x,s)|$ satisfies the order property (5), Sec. 96. Note the formulas in Prob. 15 and show that the terms in $P_1/(su)$ that have weaker order are functions $\psi(c,s)$ considered in Prob. 16.   Hence show that the generalized Fourier series for $f(x)$ converges to $f(x)$ when $0 < x < x_0$.   The result is also valid when $x_0 < x < 1$.   *Remark:* In isolating terms of weaker order it is useful to note that when

$$p = \frac{\sinh cs}{\sinh s + e^\sigma s^{-1} R_1}, \qquad \text{then} \qquad p = \frac{\sinh cs}{\sinh s} - \frac{e^\sigma R_1}{s \sinh s} p.$$

18. Use the result in Prob. 17 to indicate how the conditions in Theorem 6 can be relaxed to permit $f(x)$ to be any sectionally continuous function such that $f'(x)$ and $f''(x)$ are also sectionally continuous.

CHAPTER 10

FOURIER TRANSFORMS

As indicated in Sec. 1, other linear integral transformations besides the Laplace transformation have operational properties under which they convert differential forms into algebraic forms involving boundary values. Among those additional transformations are the various Fourier transformations. Brief presentations of the operational mathematics of Fourier transformations and their generalizations will now be given.

99. Finite Fourier Sine Transforms. Let $F(x)$ denote a function that is sectionally continuous over some finite interval of the variable x. By a proper choice of the origin and the unit of length, the end points of the interval become $x = 0$ and $x = \pi$. The Fourier sine transformation of $F(x)$ on that interval is the operation

$$\int_0^\pi F(x) \sin nx \, dx \qquad (n = 1, 2, \ldots),$$

denoted here by $S_n\{F(x)\}$. This operation produces a function $f_s(n)$ called the *finite sine transform* of $F(x)$; that is,

(1) $\quad S_n\{F(x)\} = \int_0^\pi F(x) \sin nx \, dx = f_s(n) \qquad (n = 1, 2, \ldots).$

The transformation sets up a correspondence between functions $F(x)$ on the interval $0 < x < \pi$ and sequences of numbers $f_s(n)$ $(n = 1, 2, \ldots)$. For example, the function $F(x) = 1$ has the transform

$$f_s(n) = \int_0^\pi \sin nx \, dx = \frac{1 - (-1)^n}{n} \qquad (n = 1, 2, \ldots).$$

For the function $F(x) = x (0 < x < \pi)$, we have

$$S_n\{x\} = \int_0^\pi x \sin nx \, dx = \pi \frac{(-1)^{n+1}}{n} \qquad (n = 1, 2, \ldots).$$

288

Let the derivative $F'(x)$ also be a sectionally continuous function, and let $F(x)$ be defined at each point x_0 of discontinuity as its mean value,

$$(2) \qquad F(x_0) = \tfrac{1}{2}[F(x_0 + 0) + F(x_0 - 0)] \quad (0 < x_0 < \pi).$$

Then, according to the classical theory of Fourier series, or as a special case of the generalized Fourier series representation, presented in Chap. 9, the Fourier sine series for the function $F(x)$ on the interval $(0,\pi)$ converges to the function:

$$F(x) = \frac{2}{\pi} \sum_{n=1}^{\infty} \sin nx \int_0^{\pi} F(\xi) \sin n\xi \, d\xi \quad (0 < x < \pi).$$

In view of the definition (1) of the sine transform, we see that

$$(3) \qquad F(x) = \frac{2}{\pi} \sum_{n=1}^{\infty} f_s(n) \sin nx \qquad (0 < x < \pi).$$

This is an *inversion formula* for the transformation, giving the function in terms of the transform; that is, it is an explicit formula for $S_n^{-1}\{f_s(n)\}$, the function whose transform is $f_s(n)$.

In the class of sectionally continuous functions with sectionally continuous derivatives of the first order considered here, we can see from formula (3) that there is only one function with a given transform; that is, the inverse transformation is unique. The transformation $S_n\{F\}$ and its inverse are clearly linear transformations.

As a special case of the vanishing of Dirichlet integrals noted in equations (5), Sec. 61, we see that whenever $F(x)$ is sectionally continuous then

$$(4) \qquad \lim_{n \to \infty} f_s(n) = 0.$$

The Fourier sine transform $S_{n\pi/c}\{F(x)\}$ of a function on an interval $0 < x < c$ can be written in terms of the transform on our standard interval by means of the substitution $r = \pi x/c$,

$$\int_0^c F(x) \sin \frac{n\pi x}{c} \, dx = \frac{c}{\pi} \int_0^{\pi} F\left(\frac{cr}{\pi}\right) \sin nr \, dr = \frac{c}{\pi} S_n \left\{ F\left(\frac{cx}{\pi}\right) \right\}.$$

The function $F(x) = x$ $(0 < x < c)$, for example, has the sine transform

$$S_{n\pi/c}\{x\} = \frac{c}{\pi} S_n \left\{\frac{cx}{\pi}\right\} = \frac{c^2}{\pi} \frac{(-1)^{n+1}}{n} \quad (n = 1, 2, \ldots).$$

100. Operational Properties of $S_n\{F\}$. If $F(x)$ and $F'(x)$ are continuous and $F''(x)$ is sectionally continuous, then

$$\int_0^\pi F''(x) \sin nx \, dx = F'(x) \sin nx \Big]_0^\pi - n \int_0^\pi F'(x) \cos nx \, dx$$
$$= -n \cos nx F(x) \Big]_0^\pi - n^2 \int_0^\pi F(x) \sin nx \, dx.$$

Thus we have the basic operational property

(1) $\quad S_n\{F''(x)\} = -n^2 S_n\{F(x)\} + n[F(0) - (-1)^n F(\pi)].$

Theorem 1. *The finite Fourier sine transformation resolves the differential form $F''(x)$ into a linear algebraic form in the transform $f_s(n)$ and the boundary values $F(0)$ and $F(\pi)$ in the manner*

(2) $\quad S_n\{F''(x)\} = -n^2 f_s(n) + n[F(0) - (-1)^n F(\pi)],$

whenever $F(x)$ and $F'(x)$ are continuous and $F''(x)$ is sectionally continuous, on the interval $0 \leqq x \leqq \pi$.

When $F''(x)$ satisfies the conditions imposed on $F(x)$ in the theorem, we can replace $F(x)$ by $F''(x)$ in the formula (1):

$$S_n\{F^{(4)}(x)\} = -n^2 S_n\{F''(x)\} + n[F''(0) - (-1)^n F''(\pi)].$$

The iterated differential form $(F'')''$ therefore transforms according to the formula

(3) $\quad S_n\{F^{(4)}(x)\} = n^4 f_s(n) - n^3[F(0) - (-1)^n F(\pi)]$
$$+ n[F''(0) - (-1)^n F''(\pi)].$$

Note that the values of F and F'' at both end points are involved here. Formulas for the transforms of other derivatives $F^{(2m)}(x)$ of even order can be found in like manner.

Property (1) has incidental applications to the construction of tables of transforms. When $F(x) = x^2$, for example, then $F''(x) = 2$ and

$$S_n\{2\} = -n^2 S_n\{x^2\} - n(-1)^n \pi^2.$$

Since $S_n\{2\} = 2S_n\{1\} = 2[1 - (-1)^n]/n$, it follows that

$$S_n\{x^2\} = \frac{\pi^2}{n} (-1)^{n-1} - \frac{2}{n^3} [1 - (-1)^n].$$

For all real values of x, let $F_1(x)$ denote the *odd periodic extension*, with period 2π, of $F(x)$; that is,

(4)
$$F_1(x) = F(x) \qquad (0 < x < \pi),$$
$$F_1(-x) = -F_1(x),$$
$$F_1(x + 2\pi) = F_1(x) \qquad (-\infty < x < \infty).$$

Further operational properties of the finite Fourier sine transformation can now be stated as follows.

Theorem 2. *If $f_s(n)$ is the sine transform of a sectionally continuous function $F(x)$ $(0 \leq x \leq \pi)$, then*

(5) $$S_n^{-1}\left\{\frac{f_s(n)}{n^2}\right\} = \frac{x}{\pi}\int_0^\pi \int_0^t F(r)\,dr\,dt - \int_0^x \int_0^t F(r)\,dr\,dt$$

$$= \frac{x}{\pi}\int_0^\pi (\pi - r)F(r)\,dr - \int_0^x (x - r)F(r)\,dr;$$

(6) $$f_s(n)\cos nk = S_n\{\tfrac{1}{2}[F_1(x - k) + F_1(x + k)]\},$$

where F_1 is the extension (4) *of F and k is a constant; also*

(7) $$f_s(n)(-1)^{n+1} = S_n\{F(\pi - x)\}.$$

Property (5) is easily verified by showing that either of the integral forms given there represents a function $Y(x)$ which satisfies the conditions in Theorem 1, and that $Y''(x) = -F(x)$ and $Y(0) = Y(\pi) = 0$. Hence $S_n\{-F\} = -n^2 S_n\{Y\}$. It is derived by writing $f_s/n^2 = y_s$ or $-n^2 y_s(n) = -f_s(n)$, and determining $Y(x)$, in view of property (2), as the solution of the problem

(8) $$Y''(x) = -F(x), \qquad Y(0) = Y(\pi) = 0.$$

To derive property (6) we write

$$f_s(n)\cos nk = \int_0^\pi F_1(x)\sin nx \cos nk\,dx.$$

Since the integrand is an even function of x, the integral here is one half the integral from $-\pi$ to π; thus the integral can be written

$$\tfrac{1}{4}\int_{-\pi}^\pi F_1(x)[\sin n(x - k) + \sin n(x + k)]\,dx$$

$$= \tfrac{1}{4}\int_{-\pi-k}^{\pi-k} F_1(\xi + k)\sin n\xi\,d\xi + \tfrac{1}{4}\int_{-\pi+k}^{\pi+k} F_1(\xi - k)\sin n\xi\,d\xi.$$

The integrands here are periodic functions of ξ with period 2π, so that the limits of both integrals can be replaced by the limits $-\pi$ to π. Moreover

$$\int_{-\pi}^{0} F_1(\xi + k) \sin n\xi \, d\xi = -\int_{0}^{\pi} F_1(-\lambda + k) \sin n\lambda \, d\lambda,$$

and $F_1(-\lambda + k) = -F_1(\lambda - k)$. Making a corresponding change in the last integral of the preceding equation, we obtain the formula

$$f_s(n) \cos nk = \tfrac{1}{2} \int_{0}^{\pi} [F_1(x - k) + F_1(x + k)] \sin nx \, dx,$$

which is a statement of property (6).

Now $F_1(x + \pi) = F_1(x - \pi) = -F_1(\pi - x)$ and, when $0 < x < \pi$, $F_1(\pi - x) = F(\pi - x)$. Thus when $k = \pi$, property (6) becomes

$$f_s(n) \cos n\pi = S_n\{-F(\pi - x)\},$$

which reduces to property (7). As an illustration of this property we note that, since the transform of x is $\pi n^{-1}(-1)^{n+1}$, then

$$S_n\{\pi - x\} = \frac{\pi}{n} \qquad (n = 1, 2, \ldots).$$

PROBLEMS

1. With the aid of Theorem 1, obtain the following transformations, in which c is any real constant and k is a constant that is not an integer:

(a) $S_n\{e^{cx}\} = \dfrac{n}{n^2 + c^2} [1 - (-1)^n e^{\pi c}];$

(b) $S_n\{\sin kx\} = \dfrac{n(-1)^{n+1}}{n^2 - k^2} \sin k\pi;$

(c) $S_n\{\cos kx\} = \dfrac{n}{n^2 - k^2} [1 - (-1)^n \cos k\pi];$

(d) $S_n\{x^3\} = \pi(-1)^n \left(\dfrac{6}{n^3} - \dfrac{\pi^2}{n}\right).$

2. When $F(x) = \sin mx$, where m is a positive integer, show that $f_s(n) = 0$ if $n \neq m$ and that $f_s(m) = \pi/2$.

3. Give the details in the derivation of property (5), Sec. 100.

4. With the aid of property (5), Sec. 100, show that

(a) $S_n^{-1} \left\{\dfrac{1 - (-1)^n}{n^3}\right\} = \dfrac{x}{2} (\pi - x);$

(b) $S_n^{-1} \left\{\dfrac{1}{n^3} (-1)^{n+1}\right\} = \dfrac{x(\pi^2 - x^2)}{6\pi}.$

5. If $F(\pi - x) = F(x)$ whenever $0 < x < \pi$, show that $f_s(n) = 0$ when $n = 2, 4, \ldots$. Also show that the converse is true, provided that $F(x)$ is represented by the inversion formula (3), Sec. 99.

6. If $F(x)$ and $F'(x)$ are continuous except that $F'(x)$ has a jump b at $x = c$, where $0 < c < \pi$, and if $F''(x)$ is sectionally continuous, show that

$$S_n\{F''(x)\} = -n^2 f_s(n) + n[F(0) - (-1)^n F(\pi)] - b \sin nc.$$

7. Show that Green's function $G(x,\xi)$ for the elementary boundary value problem (8), Sec. 100, can be written

$$G(x,\xi) = \frac{x(\xi - \pi)}{\pi} \qquad (x \leqq \xi),$$

$$= \frac{\xi(x - \pi)}{\pi} \qquad (x \geqq \xi).$$

Apply the formula in Prob. 6 to $G(x,c)$ to show that

$$S_n\{G(x,c)\} = -\frac{\sin nc}{n^2} \qquad (0 < c < \pi).$$

8. Differentiate the members of the final equation in Prob. 7, with respect to c, to show that

$$S_n^{-1}\left\{-\frac{\cos nc}{n}\right\} = G_c(x,c) = \begin{cases} \pi^{-1}x & (0 < x < c) \\ \pi^{-1}(x - \pi) & (c < x < \pi). \end{cases}$$

9. Show that, when $|r| < 1$,

$$\log (1 + re^{i\theta}) = -\sum_{n=1}^{\infty} \frac{1}{n}(-r)^n e^{in\theta}.$$

Also, if $R^2 = (1 + r \cos \theta)^2 + r^2 \sin^2 \theta$ and $\tan \Theta = r \sin \theta/(1 + r \cos \theta)$, then

$$\log (1 + re^{i\theta}) = \log (Re^{i\Theta}) = \log R + i\Theta.$$

Thus by equating imaginary parts of the members of the first equation, show that

$$\arctan \frac{r \sin \theta}{1 + r \cos \theta} = -\sum_{n=1}^{\infty} \frac{1}{n}(-r)^n \sin n\theta.$$

From the uniform convergence of the series with respect to θ, when $|r| < 1$, prove that

$$S_n\left\{\arctan \frac{k \sin x}{1 + k \cos x}\right\} = \frac{\pi}{2} \frac{(-1)^{n+1}}{n} k^n \qquad (|k| < 1).$$

When $k = \pm 1$, this formula reduces to known transformations.

10. From the transform found in Prob. 9, observe that

$$S_n \left\{ \arctan \frac{k \sin x}{1 - k \cos x} \right\} = \frac{\pi}{2} \frac{k^n}{n} \qquad (|k| \leqq 1);$$

then show that

$$\frac{\pi}{2} \frac{1 - (-1)^n}{n} k^n = S_n \left\{ \arctan \frac{2k \sin x}{1 - k^2} \right\} \qquad (|k| \leqq 1),$$

and consequently that

$$\frac{\pi}{2} \frac{1 - (-1)^n}{n} e^{-ny} = S_n \left\{ \arctan \frac{\sin x}{\sinh y} \right\} \qquad (y \geqq 0).$$

101. Finite Cosine Transforms. The finite Fourier cosine transformation of a function $F(x)$, where $0 < x < \pi$, is the operation

$$(1) \qquad C_n\{F(x)\} = \int_0^\pi F(x) \cos nx \, dx \quad (n = 0, 1, 2, \ldots).$$

The resulting function $f_c(n)$ is the *finite cosine transform.*
The function $F(x) = 1$, for example, has the transform

$$f_c(n) = 0 \qquad (n = 1, 2, \ldots),$$
$$f_c(0) = \pi.$$

The transform of the function $F(x) = x$ is

$$f_c(n) = -\frac{1 - (-1)^n}{n^2} \qquad (n = 1, 2, \ldots),$$

$$f_c(0) = \frac{\pi^2}{2}.$$

Note that $f_c(0)/\pi$ is the mean value of $F(x)$ over the interval $(0,\pi)$,

$$\frac{1}{\pi} f_c(0) = \frac{1}{\pi} \int_0^\pi F(x) \, dx;$$

also that the transforms of $F(x) + A$ and $F(x)$ are equal except when $n = 0$, where A is a constant, since

$$C_n\{F(x) + A\} = f_c(n) \qquad (n \neq 0),$$
$$C_0\{F(x) + A\} = f_c(0) + \pi A.$$

The inverse transformation $F(x) = C_n^{-1}\{f_c(n)\}$ is given directly by the Fourier cosine series

(2) $$F(x) = \frac{1}{\pi}f_c(0) + \frac{2}{\pi}\sum_{n=1}^{\infty}f_c(n)\cos nx \quad (0 < x < \pi),$$

when $F(x)$ and $F'(x)$ are sectionally continuous and $F(x)$ is defined as its mean value (2), Sec. 99, at each point of discontinuity. In this class of functions the inverse transform is unique. As in the case of the sine transform, the cosine transform of each sectionally continuous function $F(x)$ exists, and

(3) $$\lim_{n\to\infty} f_c(n) = 0.$$

The basic operational property of the transformation,

(4) $$C_n\{F''(x)\} = -n^2 C_n\{F(x)\} - F'(0) + (-1)^n F'(\pi),$$

obtained by integration by parts, is valid when $F(x)$ and $F'(x)$ are continuous and $F''(x)$ sectionally continuous. If $F''(x)$ and $F'''(x)$ are also continuous and if $F^{(4)}(x)$ is sectionally continuous, we can replace $F(x)$ in formula (4) by $F''(x)$ to obtain the property

(5) $$C_n\{F^{(4)}(x)\} = n^4 f_c(n) + n^2[F'(0) - (-1)^n F'(\pi)] \\ - F'''(0) + (-1)^n F'''(\pi).$$

The transform of $F^{(6)}(x)$, etc., can be written in similar fashion. Note that the boundary values involved are those of odd ordered derivatives of $F(x)$.

Let $F_2(x)$ denote the *even periodic extension* of $F(x)$:

(6) $$\begin{aligned} F_2(x) &= F(x) & (0 < x < \pi), \\ F_2(-x) &= F_2(x) \\ F_2(x + 2\pi) &= F_2(x) & (-\infty < x < \infty). \end{aligned}$$

Then the operational properties of C_n corresponding to those given in Theorems 1 and 2 for S_n, with corresponding derivations, can be stated as follows.

Theorem 3. *If $F(x)$ and $F'(x)$ are continuous and if $F''(x)$ is sectionally continuous, the transformation C_n resolves the differential form $F''(x)$ into an algebraic form in $f_c(n)$ and the boundary values $F'(0)$ and $F'(\pi)$,*

(7) $$C_n\{F''(x)\} = -n^2 f_c(n) - F'(0) + (-1)^n F'(\pi) \\ (n = 0, 1, 2, \ldots).$$

For every sectionally continuous function $F(x)$,

$$(8) \quad C_n^{-1} \left\{ \frac{f_c(n)}{n^2} \right\} = \int_0^x \int_t^\pi F(r) \, dr \, dt + \frac{f_c(0)}{2\pi} (x - \pi)^2 + A,$$

where the constant A is arbitrary because $f_c(n)/n^2$ is not defined when $n = 0$; also, when k is a constant and F_2 is the extension (6) of F, then

$$(9) \qquad f_c(n) \cos nk = C_n \{ \tfrac{1}{2} [F_2(x - k) + F_2(x + k)] \},$$
$$(10) \qquad f_c(n)(-1)^n = C_n \{ F(\pi - x) \}.$$

If we write $f_c/n^2 = y_c$ $(n = 1, 2, \ldots)$ in deriving property (8), then $C_n \{ Y''(x) \} = C_n \{ -F(x) \}$ if $Y'(0) = Y'(\pi) = 0$. Since $y_c(0)$ is arbitrary, it follows that

$$Y''(x) = -F(x) + B, \qquad Y'(0) = Y'(\pi) = 0,$$

where B is a constant to be determined by the boundary conditions here.

102. Joint Properties of C_n and S_n. Convolution. Further operational properties of our two finite Fourier transformations have simple forms when stated in terms of both sine and cosine transformations.

When $F(x)$ is continuous and $F'(x)$ is sectionally continuous, we find by integrating by parts that

$$(1) \quad S_n \{ F'(x) \} = -nC_n \{ F(x) \} \qquad\qquad (n = 1, 2, \ldots),$$
$$(2) \quad C_n \{ F'(x) \} = nS_n \{ F(x) \} - F(0) + (-1)^n F(\pi)$$
$$(n = 0, 1, 2, \ldots).$$

Alternate forms of these properties are

$$(3) \quad S_n \{ H(x) \} = -nC_n \left\{ \int_0^x H(r) \, dr \right\} \qquad (n = 1, 2, \ldots),$$

$$(4) \quad C_n \left\{ H(x) - \frac{1}{\pi} h_c(0) \right\} = nS_n \left\{ \int_0^x H(r) \, dr - \frac{x}{\pi} h_c(0) \right\}$$
$$(n = 0, 1, \ldots),$$

where $H(x)$ is any sectionally continuous function.

Let $F(x)$ be a sectionally continuous function and let $F_1(x)$ and $F_2(x)$ denote its odd and even periodic extensions, with period 2π. Then for any constant k, the formulas

(5) $f_s(n) \sin nk = C_n\{\frac{1}{2}[F_1(x + k) - F_1(x - k)]\}$
$$(n = 0, 1, \ldots),$$

(6) $f_c(n) \sin nk = S_n\{\frac{1}{2}[F_2(x - k) - F_2(x + k)]\}$
$$(n = 1, 2, \ldots),$$

can be derived by the method used to find property (6), Sec. 100.

When two functions $P(x)$ and $Q(x)$ are defined on the interval $-2\pi < x < 2\pi$, the function

$$(7) \qquad P(x) * Q(x) = \int_{-\pi}^{\pi} P(x - r)Q(r)\, dr$$

is called the *convolution* of P and Q on the interval $-\pi < x < \pi$. The reader can show that this function of x is even if P and Q are both even or both odd, and that it is odd if one of those functions is even and the other odd. Also, when P and Q are periodic with period 2π, then $P * Q = Q * P$.

Let $F_2(x)$ and $G_2(x)$ denote the even periodic extensions, with period 2π, of two sectionally continuous functions $F(x)$ and $G(x)$ on the interval $0 \leq x \leq \pi$. By breaking the convolution down into sums of integrals, introducing new variables of integration, and using the even periodic properties of F_2 and G_2, we find that

$$(8) \quad F_2 * G_2 = \int_0^{\pi} G(r)[F_2(x - r) + F_2(x + r)]\, dr = \sum_{i=1}^{4} I_i(x),$$

where $I_i(x)$ $(0 \leq x \leq \pi)$ are integrals involving F and G, namely,

$$I_1 = \int_0^x F(r)G(x - r)\, dr, \qquad I_2 = \int_x^{\pi} F(r)G(r - x)\, dr,$$

$$(9) \qquad\qquad I_3 = \int_0^{\pi-x} F(r)G(x + r)\, dr,$$

$$I_4 = \int_{\pi-x}^{\pi} F(r)G(2\pi - x - r)\, dr.$$

Similarly, if F_1 and G_1 are the odd periodic extensions of F and G, we find that

$$(10) \qquad F_1 * G_1 = \int_0^{\pi} G(r)[F_1(x - r) - F_1(x + r)]\, dr$$
$$= I_1 - I_2 - I_3 + I_4,$$

$$(11) \qquad F_1 * G_2 = \int_0^{\pi} G(r)[F_1(x - r) + F_1(x + r)]\, dr$$
$$= \int_0^{\pi} F(r)[G_2(x - r) - G_2(x + r)]\, dr$$
$$= I_1 + I_2 - I_3 - I_4.$$

Each product of finite Fourier transforms of F and G can be written as a transform of a convolution. Consider the product

$$f_c(n)g_c(n) = \int_0^\pi f_c(n) \cos nr\, G(r)\, dr.$$

We make the substitution (Theorem 3)

$$f_c(n) \cos nr = C_n\{\tfrac{1}{2}[F_2(x - r) + F_2(x + r)]\}$$
$$= \tfrac{1}{2} \int_0^\pi [F_2(x - r) + F_2(x + r)] \cos nx\, dx,$$

and interchange the order of integration to write

$$f_c(n)g_c(n) = \tfrac{1}{2} \int_0^\pi \cos nx \int_0^\pi G(r)[F_2(x - r) + F_2(x + r)]\, dr\, dx.$$

Thus in view of formula (8),

$$f_c(n)g_c(n) = \tfrac{1}{2}C_n\{F_2(x) * G_2(x)\}.$$

The other cases included in the following theorem can be established by the above method.

Theorem 4. *If $F(x)$ and $G(x)$ are sectionally continuous on the interval $0 \leqq x \leqq \pi$, then*

(12) $$f_s(n)g_s(n) = C_n\{-\tfrac{1}{2}F_1(x) * G_1(x)\},$$
(13) $$f_s(n)g_c(n) = S_n\{\tfrac{1}{2}F_1(x) * G_2(x)\},$$
(14) $$f_c(n)g_c(n) = C_n\{\tfrac{1}{2}F_2(x) * G_2(x)\}.$$

As an example, let us find the inverse cosine transform of $(n^2 - k^2)^{-1}$, where k is not an integer. We note that when $n = 0$ this transform has the value $-k^{-2}$. When $n \neq 0$, we can write

$$\frac{1}{n^2 - k^2} = \frac{n(-1)^{n+1}}{n^2 - k^2} \frac{(-1)^{n+1}}{n} = \frac{1}{\pi \sin k\pi} S_n\{\sin kx\} S_n\{x\};$$

but the right-hand member vanishes when $n = 0$. According to formulas (12) and (10), that member is the cosine transform of the function

$$-\frac{1}{2\pi \sin k\pi}(I_1 - I_2 - I_3 + I_4) = \frac{1}{\pi k^2} - \frac{\cos k(\pi - x)}{k \sin k\pi},$$

where we have evaluated the integrals (9) when $F(r) = \sin kr$ and $G(r) = r$. To change the transform of this function at the value $n = 0$ from zero to $-k^{-2}$ we add the constant $-\pi^{-1}k^{-2}$ to

TABLE 2. FINITE SINE TRANSFORMS

	$f_s(n)$	$F(x)$
1	$f_s(n) = \displaystyle\int_0^\pi F(x) \sin nx \, dx \ (n = 1, 2, \ldots)$	$F(x) \quad (0 < x < \pi)$
2	$(-1)^{n+1} f_s(n)$	$F(\pi - x)$
3	$\dfrac{1}{n}$	$\dfrac{\pi - x}{\pi}$
4	$\dfrac{(-1)^{n+1}}{n}$	$\dfrac{x}{\pi}$
5	$\dfrac{1 - (-1)^n}{n}$	1
6	$\dfrac{\pi}{n^2} \sin nc \quad (0 < c < \pi)$	$\begin{cases} (\pi - c)x & (x \leqq c) \\ c(\pi - x) & (x \geqq c) \end{cases}$
7	$\dfrac{\pi}{n} \cos nc \quad (0 \leqq c \leqq \pi)$	$\begin{cases} -x & (x < c) \\ \pi - x & (x > c) \end{cases}$
8	$\dfrac{(-1)^{n+1}}{n^3}$	$\dfrac{x(\pi^2 - x^2)}{6\pi}$
9	$\dfrac{1 - (-1)^n}{n^3}$	$\dfrac{x(\pi - x)}{2}$
10	$\dfrac{\pi^2(-1)^{n-1}}{n} - \dfrac{2[1 - (-1)^n]}{n^3}$	x^2
11	$\pi(-1)^n \left(\dfrac{6}{n^3} - \dfrac{\pi^2}{n} \right)$	x^3
12	$\dfrac{n}{n^2 + c^2} [1 - (-1)^n e^{c\pi}]$	e^{cx}
13	$\dfrac{n}{n^2 + c^2}$	$\dfrac{\sinh c(\pi - x)}{\sinh c\pi}$
14	$\dfrac{n}{n^2 - k^2} \quad (\lvert k \rvert \neq 0, 1, 2, \ldots)$	$\dfrac{\sin k(\pi - x)}{\sin k\pi}$
15	$0 (n \neq m); f_s(m) = \dfrac{\pi}{2}$	$\sin mx \quad (m = 1, 2, \ldots)$
16	$\dfrac{n}{n^2 - k^2} [1 - (-1)^n \cos k\pi]$	$\cos kx \quad (\lvert k \rvert \neq 1, 2, \ldots)$
17	$\dfrac{n}{n^2 - m^2} [1 - (-1)^{n+m}], \ (n \neq m);$ $f_s(m) = 0$	$\cos mx \quad (m = 1, 2, \ldots)$
18	$\dfrac{n}{(n^2 - k^2)^2} \quad (\lvert k \rvert \neq 0, 1, 2 \ldots)$	$\dfrac{\pi \sin kx}{2k \sin^2 k\pi} - \dfrac{x \cos k(\pi - x)}{2k \sin k\pi}$
19	$\dfrac{b^n}{n} \ (\lvert b \rvert \leqq 1)$	$\dfrac{2}{\pi} \arctan \dfrac{b \sin x}{1 - b \cos x}$
20	$\dfrac{1 - (-1)^n}{n} b^n \quad (\lvert b \rvert \leqq 1)$	$\dfrac{2}{\pi} \arctan \dfrac{2b \sin x}{1 - b^2}$

TABLE 3. FINITE COSINE TRANSFORMS

	$f_c(n)$	$F(x)$
1	$f_c(n) = \int_0^\pi F(x) \cos nx\, dx \ (n = 0, 1, 2, \ldots)$	$F(x) \quad (0 < x < \pi)$
2	$(-1)^n f_c(n)$	$F(\pi - x)$
3	0 when $n = 1, 2, \ldots ; f_c(0) = \pi$	1
4	$\dfrac{2}{n} \sin nc; f_c(0) = 2c - \pi$	$\begin{cases} 1 & (0 < x < c) \\ -1 & (c < x < \pi) \end{cases}$
5	$-\dfrac{1 - (-1)^n}{n^2}; f_c(0) = \dfrac{\pi^2}{2}$	x
6	$\dfrac{(-1)^n}{n^2}; f_c(0) = \dfrac{\pi^2}{6}$	$\dfrac{x^2}{2\pi}$
7	$\dfrac{1}{n^2}; f_c(0) = 0$	$\dfrac{(\pi - x)^2}{2\pi} - \dfrac{\pi}{6}$
8	$3\pi^2 \dfrac{(-1)^n}{n^2} + 6 \dfrac{1 - (-1)^n}{n^4}; f_c(0) = \dfrac{\pi^4}{4}$	x^3
9	$\dfrac{(-1)^n e^{c\pi} - 1}{n^2 + c^2}$	$\dfrac{1}{c} e^{cx}$
10	$\dfrac{1}{n^2 + c^2}$	$\dfrac{\cosh c(\pi - x)}{c \sinh c\pi}$
11	$\dfrac{(-1)^n \cos k\pi - 1}{n^2 - k^2} \quad (|k| \neq 0, 1, 2, \ldots)$	$\dfrac{1}{k} \sin kx$
12	$\dfrac{(-1)^{n+m} - 1}{n^2 - m^2}; f_c(m) = 0 \quad (m = 1, 2, \ldots)$	$\dfrac{1}{m} \sin mx$
13	$\dfrac{1}{n^2 - k^2} \quad (|k| \neq 0, 1, 2, \ldots)$	$-\dfrac{\cos k(\pi - x)}{k \sin k\pi}$
14	$0(n \neq m); f_c(m) = \dfrac{\pi}{2} \quad (m = 1, 2, \ldots)$	$\cos mx$
15	$b^n(n \neq 0), f_c(0) = 0, (|b| < 1)$	$\dfrac{2b}{\pi} \dfrac{\cos x - b}{1 - 2b \cos x + b^2}$

the function. Therefore

$$C_n^{-1} \left\{ \frac{1}{n^2 - k^2} \right\} = -\frac{\cos k(\pi - x)}{k \sin k\pi}.$$

A short list of finite Fourier transforms is given in Tables 2 and 3.

PROBLEMS

1. Obtain the finite cosine transforms of the functions x, $\sin kx$, and e^{cx}, listed in Table 3, using property (7), Sec. 101.

2. When $y_c(n) = (-1)^n/n^4$ and $y_c(0) = 0$, use property (8), Sec. 101, and Table 3 to derive the inverse transform

$$Y(x) = \frac{1}{24\pi}\left(2\pi^2 x^2 - x^4 - \frac{7}{15}\pi^4\right).$$

3. From the inverse sine transform of $n^{-1}b^n$ given in Table 2, derive the cosine transformation 15, Table 3, and note the form of the result when $b = e^{-y}$ $(y > 0)$.

4. If $F(x)$ and $F'(x)$ are continuous, except that $F(x)$ has a jump b at $x = c$ $(0 < c < \pi)$ and $F'(x)$ has a jump b' at that point, and if $F''(x)$ is sectionally continuous, show that

$$C_n\{F''(x)\} = -n^2 f_c(n) - F'(0) + (-1)^n F'(\pi) - bn \sin nc - b' \cos nc,$$

when $n = 0, 1, 2, \ldots$.

5. When $F(x) = 1$ $(0 < x < c)$ and $F(x) = -1$ $(c < x < \pi)$ show, with the aid of the result found in Prob. 4, that

$$f_c(n) = \frac{2}{n}\sin nc, \qquad f_c(0) = 2c - \pi.$$

6. Derive the following formulas, where k is a constant:

(a) $f_s(n + k) = S_n\{F(x) \cos kx\} + C_n\{F(x) \sin kx\}$;

(b) $f_c(n + k) = C_n\{F(x) \cos kx\} - S_n\{F(x) \sin kx\}$;

(c) $2S_n\{F(x) \cos kx\} = f_s(n - k) + f_s(n + k)$;

(d) $2S_n\{F(x) \sin kx\} = f_c(n - k) - f_c(n + k)$;

(e) $2C_n\{F(x) \cos kx\} = f_c(n - k) + f_c(n + k)$;

(f) $2C_n\{F(x) \sin kx\} = f_s(n + k) - f_s(n - k)$.

7. If the functions P and Q are periodic with period 2π show that their convolution (7), Sec. 102, is commutative:

$$P(x) * Q(x) = Q(x) * P(x).$$

8. Derive the formulas

(a) $2nf_s(n)g_s(n) = S_n\left\{\dfrac{d}{dx}[F_1(x) * G_1(x)]\right\}$;

(b) $\dfrac{2}{n}f_s(n)g_s(n) = -S_n\left\{\displaystyle\int_0^x F_1(t) * G_1(t)\, dt\right\}$.

103. Potential in a Slot. Let $V(x,y)$ denote the electrostatic potential in a space bounded by the planes $x = 0$, $x = \pi$, and $y = 0$, in which there is a uniform distribution of space charge of density $h/(4\pi)$. Then the function V satisfies Poisson's equation

(1) $$V_{xx}(x,y) + V_{yy}(x,y) = -h \quad (0 < x < \pi, y > 0).$$

Let the planes $x = 0$ and $y = 0$ be kept at potential zero and the plane $x = \pi$ at another fixed potential $V = 1$ (Fig. 104). Then

(2)
$$V(0,y) = 0, \qquad V(\pi,y) = 1 \qquad\qquad (y > 0),$$
$$V(x,0) = 0 \qquad\qquad (0 < x < \pi),$$
(3)
$$|V(x,y)| < M$$

throughout the region, where M is some constant.

The determination of $V(x,y)$ is a type of problem that arises in the subject of electronics. The function V here can also be interpreted as steady-state temperatures in a semi-infinite slab containing a uniform source of heat with strength proportional to h.

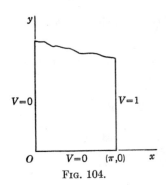

FIG. 104.

Our boundary value problem [(1) to (3)] is not adapted to either the method of separation of variables or solution by Laplace transforms. The finite Fourier sine transformation with respect to x does apply, because the differential form in that variable is V_{xx} and the prescribed boundary values on the interval $0 < x < \pi$ are $V(0,y)$ and $V(\pi,y)$ (Theorem 1).

We write $v_s(n,y) = S_n\{V(x,y)\}$ and transform the members of equation (1), using conditions (2), to find formally that

$$-n^2 v_s(n,y) - n(-1)^n + \frac{d^2}{dy^2}\, v_s(n,y) = -hS_n\{1\}.$$

We also write conditions (3) in terms of transforms. Thus the problem in $v_s(n,y)$ becomes

$$\frac{d^2 v_s}{dy^2} - n^2 v_s = n(-1)^n - hS_n\{1\} \qquad (n = 1, 2, \ldots),$$
$$v_s(n,0) = 0, \qquad |v_s(n,y)| < M\pi.$$

The solution of this problem is

(4)
$$v_s(n,y) = \frac{hS_n\{1\} - n(-1)^n}{n^2}\,(1 - e^{-ny})$$
$$= \left[h\,\frac{1 - (-1)^n}{n^3} + \frac{(-1)^{n+1}}{n} \right](1 - e^{-ny}).$$

The formula for the potential can therefore be written

$$(5) \qquad V(x,y) = \frac{2}{\pi} \sum_{n=1}^{\infty} v_s(n,y) \sin nx.$$

In addition to this form of the solution in terms of an infinite series we can derive a closed form of the solution. Referring to Table 2, we find that

$$S_n^{-1} \left\{ \frac{1 - (-1)^n}{n^3} \right\} = \frac{x}{2} (\pi - x), \qquad S_n^{-1} \left\{ \frac{(-1)^{n+1}}{n} \right\} = \frac{x}{\pi},$$

and

$$S_n^{-1} \left\{ (-1)^{n+1} \frac{e^{-ny}}{n} \right\} = \frac{2}{\pi} \arctan \frac{e^{-y} \sin x}{1 + e^{-y} \cos x}$$

$$= \frac{2}{\pi} \arctan \frac{\sin x}{e^y + \cos x};$$

also

$$S_n^{-1} \left\{ \frac{1 - (-1)^n}{n} e^{-ny} \right\} = \alpha(x,y),$$

where

$$(6) \qquad \alpha(x,y) = \frac{2}{\pi} \arctan \frac{\sin x}{\sinh y} \qquad\qquad (y \geqq 0).$$

From property (5) in Theorem 2 it follows that

$$S_n^{-1} \left\{ \frac{1 - (-1)^n}{n^3} e^{-ny} \right\} = U(x,y),$$

where

$$(7) \quad U(x,y) = \frac{x}{\pi} \int_0^{\pi} (\pi - r)\alpha(r,y)\, dr - \int_0^x (x - r)\alpha(r,y)\, dr.$$

Our potential function is therefore

$$(8) \quad V(x,y) = \frac{hx}{2} (\pi - x) + \frac{x}{\pi} - \frac{2}{\pi} \arctan \frac{\sin x}{e^y + \cos x} - hU(x,y),$$

where $U(x,y)$ is given by equation (7) in terms of the function (6). Both inverse tangent functions involved here are known solutions of Laplace's equation; consequently it is not difficult to verify that the function (8) satisfies all conditions in our boundary value problem [(1) to (3)].

If the first of conditions (3) is replaced by the condition $V(x,0) = F(x)$, the solution is the sum of the function (8) and the function W that satisfies the problem

$$W_{xx}(x,y) + W_{yy}(x,y) = 0 \quad (0 < x < \pi, y > 0),$$
(9)
$$W(0,y) = W(\pi,y) = 0, \qquad W(x,0) = F(x) \quad (0 < x < \pi),$$

where $W(x,y)$ is bounded. The sine transformation with respect to x leads to a solution of problem (9) in closed form, since

$$\frac{d^2w_s}{dy^2} - n^2w_s = 0, \qquad w_s(n,0) = f_s(n),$$

where $w_s(n,y)$ is bounded. Consequently

(10) $$w_s(n,y) = f_s(n)e^{-ny} = 2f_s(n)q_c(n,y)$$

where, according to transform 15, Table 3,

(11) $$Q(x,y) = \frac{1}{\pi} \frac{e^y \cos x - 1}{e^{2y} - 2e^y \cos x + 1} \qquad (y > 0).$$

Note that Q is an even periodic function of x with period 2π. If F_1 is the odd periodic extension of F then, according to formula (10) and Theorem 4, $W = F_1 * Q$. In terms of F and Q,

(12) $$W(x,y) = \int_0^\pi F(r)[Q(x - r, y) - Q(x + r, y)] \, dr \quad (y > 0).$$

Since $\pi Q(0,y) = (e^y - 1)^{-1}$, the integrand in formula (12) becomes infinite at the point $r = x$ when y tends to zero, and the verification that $W(x,+0) = F(x)$ is therefore not simple.

104. Successive Transformations. A semi-infinite slab of finite thickness is initially at temperature zero, and its base is kept at that temperature. One of its parallel faces is insulated and the other is subjected to a prescribed constant and uniform inward flux of heat. Units are chosen so that the boundary value problem in the temperature function $U(x,y,t)$ becomes

(1)
$$\begin{aligned} U_t &= U_{xx} + U_{yy} \quad (0 < x < \pi, y > 0, t > 0), \\ U(x,y,0) &= 0, \qquad U_x(0,y,t) = -1, \\ U_x(\pi,y,t) &= 0, \qquad U(x,0,t) = 0; \end{aligned}$$

also $|U| < Mt$ throughout the slab, for some constant M.

The presence of the differential form U_{xx} together with prescribed values of U_x at $x = 0$ and $x = \pi$ indicates that the finite Fourier cosine transformation, with respect to x, can be used here. The form U_t and a prescribed value of U at $t = 0$ indicate the Laplace transformation with respect to t.   Let us begin with the cosine transformation.

The transform with respect to x,

(2) $W(n,y,t) = C_n\{U(x,y,t)\}$ $(n = 0, 1, 2, \ldots),$

satisfies this problem in partial differential equations:

(3) $W_t = -n^2W + 1 + W_{yy},$ $W(n,y,0) = W(n,0,t) = 0,$

where $|W(n,y,t)| < M\pi t$.   The Laplace transform $w(n,y,s)$ of W, with respect to t, therefore satisfies a corresponding bounded-ness condition and the conditions

(4) $(s + n^2)w - \dfrac{d^2w}{dy^2} = \dfrac{1}{s},$ $w(n,0,s) = 0.$

The solution of this problem can be written as

(5) $w(n,y,s) = \dfrac{1}{s(s + n^2)} - \dfrac{1}{s}\dfrac{\exp(-y\sqrt{s + n^2})}{s + n^2}.$

With the aid of the inverse transform of $s^{-1}\exp(-y\sqrt{s})$ and the operational property on replacing s by $s + n^2$, we find that

$$L^{-1}\left\{\frac{1}{s}\frac{\exp(-y\sqrt{s + n^2})}{s + n^2}\right\} = E_n(y,t),$$

where

(6) $E_n(y,t) = \displaystyle\int_0^t e^{-n^2\tau}\operatorname{erfc}\frac{y}{2\sqrt{\tau}}\,d\tau$ $(n = 0, 1, 2, \ldots; y \geqq 0).$

The inverse Laplace transform of the function (5) is therefore

$$W(n,y,t) = \frac{1}{n^2} - \frac{e^{-n^2t}}{n^2} - E_n(y,t)\quad (n \neq 0, y \geqq 0),$$

(7)

$$W(0,y,t) = t - E_0(y,t)\qquad\qquad (y \geqq 0).$$

The inverse cosine transform of $f_c(n) = n^{-2}$, $f_c(0) = 0$, is the polynomial in x given in Table 3.   Thus $C_n^{-1}\{W\}$ can be written

(8) $U(x,y,t) = \dfrac{(x - \pi)^2}{2\pi} - \dfrac{\pi}{6} + \dfrac{t}{\pi} - \dfrac{E_0(y,t)}{\pi}$

$$-\frac{2}{\pi}\sum_{n=1}^{\infty}\left[\frac{e^{-n^2t}}{n^2} + E_n(y,t)\right]\cos nx.$$

An integration by parts in formula (6) shows that $E_n(y,t)$ is of the order of n^{-4} for large n, when $t > 0$ and $y > 0$. The series in our solution (8) can be differentiated termwise and the solution satisfies all conditions in the boundary value problem (1).

PROBLEMS

1. A steady-state temperature function V satisfies the conditions

$$V_{xx}(x,y) + V_{yy}(x,y) = 0 \quad (0 < x < \pi,\ y > 0),$$
$$V(0,y) = 0, \qquad V(\pi,y) = A \qquad (y > 0),$$
$$V(x,0) = B \qquad (0 < x < \pi);$$

also $V(x,y)$ is bounded. Derive the formula

$$V(x,y) = \frac{A}{\pi} x - \frac{2A}{\pi} \arctan \frac{\sin x}{e^y + \cos x} + \frac{2B}{\pi} \arctan \frac{\sin x}{\sinh y}.$$

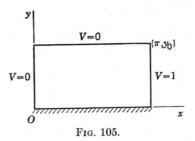

FIG. 105.

2. Let $V(x,y)$ satisfy the conditions (Fig. 105)

$$V_{xx} + V_{yy} = 0 \quad (0 < x < \pi,\ 0 < y < y_0),$$
$$V(0,y) = 0, \qquad V(\pi,y) = 1, \qquad V_y(x,0) = V(x,y_0) = 0.$$

Derive the formulas

$$V(x,y) = \frac{x}{\pi} + \frac{2}{\pi} \sum_{n=1}^{\infty} \frac{(-1)^n}{n} \frac{\cosh ny}{\cosh ny_0} \sin nx$$

$$= \frac{x}{\pi} - \frac{2}{\pi} \sum_{\nu=0}^{\infty} (-1)^\nu \{\alpha[x,\ (2\nu + 1)y_0 + y]$$

$$+ \alpha[x,\ (2\nu + 1)y_0 - y]\},$$

where

$$\alpha(x,z) = \arctan \frac{\sin x}{e^z + \cos x}.$$

3. Solve the problem

$$V_{xx}(x,y) + V_{yy}(x,y) = F(x) \quad (0 < x < \pi, \, y > 0),$$
$$V(0,y) = V(\pi,y) = V(x,0) = 0,$$

where $V(x,y)$ is bounded. Obtain the solution in the forms

$$V(x,y) = G(x) + \frac{2}{\pi} \sum_{n=1}^{\infty} \frac{1}{n^2} f_s(n)e^{-ny} \sin nx$$

$$= G(x) - \frac{1}{\pi} \int_{-\pi}^{\pi} F_1(x - \xi)\beta(\xi,y) \, d\xi,$$

where $G''(x) = F(x)$, $G(0) = G(\pi) = 0$, $F_1(x)$ is the odd periodic extension of $F(x)$, and

$$\beta(x,y) = \int_0^x \arctan \frac{\sin \lambda}{e^y - \cos \lambda} \, d\lambda.$$

4. Let $F(x)$ be a prescribed sectionally continuous function such that $\int_0^\pi F(x) \, dx = 0$, and write

$$P(x,y) = \frac{1}{\pi} \left[\frac{e^y \cos x - 1}{e^{2y} - 2e^y \cos x + 1} \right] * F_2(x) - F(x).$$

Derive the solution of the boundary value problem

$$V_{xx}(x,y) + V_{yy}(x,y) = F(x) \quad (0 < x < \pi, \, y > 0),$$
$$V_x(0,y) = V_x(\pi,y) = 0, \qquad V(x,0) = 0, \qquad |V(x,y)| < M,$$

in the form

$$V(x,y) = \int_0^x \int_t^\pi P(r,y) \, dr \, dt - \frac{1}{\pi} \int_0^\pi \int_0^x \int_t^\pi P(r,y) \, dr \, dt \, dx,$$

and reduce the multiplicity of the integrals.

5. The ends of a stretched string are fixed at the origin and the point $(\pi,0)$. The string is initially at rest along the horizontal x axis, then it drops under its own weight. Thus the vertical displacements $Y(x,t)$ satisfy the equation $Y_{tt} = a^2 Y_{xx} + g$, where g is the acceleration of gravity. If $Q(x)$ denotes the odd periodic extension of the function $\frac{1}{2}x(\pi - x)$, where $0 < x < \pi$, with period 2π, derive the formula

$$Y(x,t) = \frac{g}{2a^2} [2Q(x) - Q(x - at) - Q(x + at)].$$

Remark: An examination of this function by composition of ordinates, for fixed values of t, shows that the string vibrates between the extreme positions $Y = 0$ and $Y = (\pi x - x^2)g/a^2$. Note that the motion of each point is periodic with period $2\pi/a$.

6. The ends of a stretched string are looped about smooth vertical supports along the lines $x = 0$ and $x = \pi$ (Fig. 106), and a constant vertical force acts on the right-hand loop. The string falls from rest from the position $Y = 0$; thus

$$Y_{tt}(x,t) = a^2 Y_{xx}(x,t) + g \quad (0 < x < \pi, t > 0),$$
$$Y(x,0) = Y_t(x,0) = Y_x(0,t) = 0, \quad Y_x(\pi,t) = -b.$$

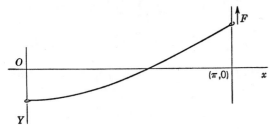

Fig. 106.

If $P(x)$ denotes the periodic function with period 2π, where

$$P(x) = \frac{b}{2\pi} x^2 \qquad (-\pi < x < \pi),$$

derive the formula

$$Y(x,t) = \frac{\pi g - a^2 b}{2\pi} t^2 - P(x) + \frac{1}{2} [P(x - at) + P(x + at)].$$

In case $a^2 b = \pi g$, show that the free end has the periodic motion

$$Y(0,t) = P(at).$$

7. If a constant transverse force acts at each point of a beam, the transverse displacements $Y(x,t)$ satisfy an equation

$$\frac{\partial^2 Y}{\partial t^2} = -a^2 \frac{\partial^4 Y}{\partial x^4} + F(x).$$

If the ends $x = 0$ and $x = \pi$ are hinged so that Y and Y_{xx} vanish there, and if the initial displacement and velocity are zero, derive the formula

$$Y(x,t) = \frac{1}{a^2} G(x) - \frac{2}{\pi a^2} \sum_{n=1}^{\infty} \frac{f_s(n)}{n^4} \cos n^2 at \sin nx,$$

where $G^{(4)}(x) = F(x)$ and $G(x) = G''(x) = 0$ at $x = 0$ and at $x = \pi$.

8. Note that for the elementary problem

$$\Theta_t(x,t) = \Theta_{xx}(x,t) \qquad (0 < x < \pi, t > 0),$$
$$\Theta(x,0) = 1, \quad \Theta(0,t) = \Theta(\pi,t) = 0,$$

the temperature function can be written

$$\Theta(x,t) = \frac{2}{\pi} \sum_{n=1}^{\infty} \theta_s(n,t) \sin nx,$$

where $\qquad \theta_s(n,t) = S_n\{1\} \exp(-n^2 t).$

Use Fourier transforms to show that the problem

$$U_t(x,t) = f(t)U_{xx}(x,t) + g(t) \quad (0 < x < \pi, \, t > 0)$$
$$U(x,0) = U(0,t) = U(\pi,t) = 0,$$

a problem not adapted to the Laplace transformation, can be solved formally in terms of Θ in the form

$$U(x,t) = \int_0^t g(\tau)\Theta[x, F(\tau,t)] \, d\tau,$$

where $\qquad F(\tau,t) = \int_\tau^t f(r) \, dr.$

9. Obtain the solution of the diffusion problem

$$U_t(x,t) = U_{xx}(x,t) - h(t)U(x,t) + A \quad (0 < x < \pi, \, t > 0),$$
$$U(0,t) = U(\pi,t) = U(x,0) = 0,$$

in the form of a series. Also derive the form

$$U(x,t) = \frac{A}{H(t)} \int_0^t H(\tau)\Theta(x,t - \tau) \, d\tau,$$

where $\Theta(x,t)$ is the function described in Prob. 8, and

$$H(t) = \exp\left[\int_0^t h(r) \, dr\right].$$

10. Derive the formula for the temperatures $U(x,y,t)$ when

$$U_t = U_{xx} + U_{yy} + A \quad (x > 0, \, 0 < y < \pi, \, t > 0),$$
$$U(x,y,0) = U(0,y,t) = U(x,0,t) = U(x,\pi,t) = 0,$$

and $U(x,y,t)$ is bounded, in the form

$$U(x,y,t) = A \int_0^t \Theta(y,\tau) \, \text{erf} \frac{x}{2\sqrt{\tau}} \, d\tau,$$

where Θ is the function described in Prob. 8.

105. Fourier Transformations on Unbounded Intervals. Throughout this section $F(x)$ denotes a function defined on a specified unbounded interval, sectionally continuous on each finite subinterval, defined at each point x_0 of discontinuity as its mean

value
$$F(x_0) = \tfrac{1}{2}[F(x_0 + 0) + F(x_0 - 0)],$$
and such that *the integral of* $|F(x)|$ *over the unbounded interval exists.* We use $G(x)$ to denote a second function of this class. The condition of absolute integrability is a severe one, but some condition of this type is needed.

Let the interval be the half axis $x \geqq 0$. If r denotes a real parameter, the *Fourier sine transformation* of a function $F(x)$ on the half axis is defined by the equation

$$(1) \qquad S_r\{F(x)\} = \int_0^\infty F(x) \sin rx \, dx = f_s(r) \qquad (r \geqq 0).$$

The *Fourier cosine transformation* is defined as

$$(2) \qquad C_r\{F(x)\} = \int_0^\infty F(x) \cos rx \, dx = f_c(r) \qquad (r \geqq 0).$$

The integrals here converge absolutely, and uniformly with respect to r; thus the transforms $f_s(r)$ and $f_c(r)$ are continuous functions of r. Furthermore, it follows from the Riemann-Lebesgue lemma (Sec. 61) that

$$\lim_{r \to \infty} f_s(r) = 0, \qquad \lim_{r \to \infty} f_c(r) = 0.$$

When $F'(x)$ is also sectionally continuous on each finite subinterval $0 \leqq x \leqq x_1$, then $F(x)$ is represented by either the Fourier sine or cosine integral formula. The inner integrals in those formulas are the transforms f_s and f_c defined by equations (1) and (2), so that the formulas can now be written

$$(3) \qquad F(x) = \frac{2}{\pi} \int_0^\infty f_s(r) \sin rx \, dr = \frac{2}{\pi} S_x\{f_s(r)\} \qquad (x > 0),$$

$$(4) \qquad F(x) = \frac{2}{\pi} \int_0^\infty f_c(r) \cos rx \, dr = \frac{2}{\pi} C_x\{f_c(r)\} \qquad (x > 0).$$

Thus the inverse transformations are given by the transformations themselves. Formulas (3) and (4) show that the transforms of the functions $f_s(r)$ and $f_c(r)$ do exist even though we do not know that those functions are absolutely integrable.

When $F(x)$ is continuous and $F'(x)$ sectionally continuous and $F(\infty) = 0$, we find by integrations by parts that the transforms are interconnected by the relations

(5) $$S_r\{F'(x)\} = -rC_r\{F(x)\},$$
(6) $$C_r\{F'(x)\} = rS_r\{F(x)\} - F(0).$$

When F is replaced by F', these formulas give the *basic operational properties* of the two transformations, namely,

(7) $$S_r\{F''(x)\} = -r^2f_s(r) + rF(0),$$
(8) $$C_r\{F''(x)\} = -r^2f_c(r) - F'(0),$$

where we have assumed that $F(x)$ and $F'(x)$ are both continuous, that F is absolutely integrable, that $F''(x)$ is sectionally continuous, and that $F(\infty) = F'(\infty) = 0$.

Thus the *sine or cosine transformation resolves the differential form* $F''(x)$ $(x \geqq 0)$ *into a linear form in the transform of $F(x)$ and the boundary value $F(0)$ or $F'(0)$, respectively.* By extending the conditions on F to F'' we find that

(9) $$S_r\{F^{(4)}(x)\} = r^4f_s(r) - r^3F(0) + rF''(0),$$
(10) $$C_r\{F^{(4)}(x)\} = r^4f_c(r) + r^2F'(0) - F'''(0),$$

and so on, for transforms of $F^{(2n)}(x)$.

If F_2 and F_1 are the even and odd extensions of F, that is,

$$F_2(x) = F(|x|), \qquad F_1(x) = \frac{x}{|x|}F(|x|) \quad (-\infty < x < \infty),$$

and if k is a constant, it is easily shown that

(11) $$2f_s(r) \sin kr = C_r\{F_1(x + k) - F_1(x - k)\},$$
(12) $$2f_s(r) \cos kr = S_r\{F_1(x + k) + F_1(x - k)\},$$
(13) $$2f_c(r) \sin kr = S_r\{F_2(x - k) - F_2(x + k)\},$$
(14) $$2f_c(r) \cos kr = C_r\{F_2(x - k) + F_2(x + k)\}.$$

For the product of sine transforms of two functions $F(x)$ and $G(x)$ we can now write, in view of formula (11),

$$2f_s(r)g_s(r) = \int_0^\infty G(y)2f_s(r) \sin ry \, dy = \int_0^\infty G(y)C_r\{H(x,y)\} \, dy,$$

where $H(x,y) = F_1(x + y) - F_1(x - y)$. Formally,

$$\int_0^\infty G(y) \int_0^\infty H(x,y) \cos rx \, dx \, dy$$
$$= \int_0^\infty \cos rx \int_0^\infty G(y)H(x,y) \, dy \, dx,$$

which is a cosine transform. In this manner the operational

properties (11) to (14), on products of transforms by kernels of the integral transformations, lead formally to the *convolution properties*

(15) $\quad 2f_s(r)g_s(r) = C_r \left\{ \int_0^\infty G(y)[F(x+y) - F_1(x-y)] \, dy \right\},$

(16) $\quad 2f_s(r)g_c(r) = S_r \left\{ \int_0^\infty G(y)[F(x+y) + F_1(x-y)] \, dy \right\}$

$\qquad\qquad = S_r \left\{ \int_0^\infty F(y)[G(|x-y|) - G(x+y)] \, dy \right\},$

(17) $\quad 2f_c(r)g_c(r) = C_r \left\{ \int_0^\infty G(y)[F(|x-y|) + F(x+y)] \, dy \right\}.$

On the unbounded interval $(-\infty, \infty)$ the transformation

(18) $\qquad E_r\{F(x)\} = \int_{-\infty}^\infty F(x)e^{irx} \, dx = f_e(r) \quad (-\infty < r < \infty)$

is the *exponential Fourier transformation*. The inverse transformation is given by the exponential form of the Fourier integral formula (Sec. 64),

(19) $\qquad F(x) = \frac{1}{2\pi} \lim_{\beta \to \infty} \int_{-\beta}^\beta e^{-irx} f_e(r) \, dr \quad (-\infty < x < \infty).$

When $f_e(r)$ is absolutely integrable over the range $-\infty < r < \infty$, this formula can be written

$$F(x) = \frac{1}{2\pi} E_{-x}\{f_e(r)\} = \frac{1}{2\pi} E_x\{f_e(-r)\}.$$

The property $E_r\{F'\} = -irf_e$ leads to the *basic operational property*

(20) $\qquad E_r\{F''(x)\} = -r^2 f_e(r) \quad [F(\pm\infty) = F'(\pm\infty) = 0],$

where in addition to the assumptions that $F(x)$ and $F'(x)$ vanish as $x \to \pm\infty$, it is assumed that both functions are continuous and absolutely integrable $(-\infty < x < \infty)$ and that $F''(x)$ is sectionally continuous. Some of these assumptions are severe.

A formal derivation of the *convolution property*

(21) $\qquad f_e(r)g_e(r) = E_r \left\{ \int_{-\infty}^\infty F(y)G(x-y) \, dy \right\}$

is simple. For careful analytical treatments of this property and other properties of the transformation the reader may consult books by Bochner, Paley and Wiener, or Titchmarsh, listed in

Appendix 1.   The transformations S_r and C_r and their properties are special cases under the transformation E_r, when $F(x)$ is an odd or an even function.

Books of tables of transforms f_s, f_c, and f_e are listed in Appendix 1 under the names Erdélyi and Oberhettinger.   Transforms of a few functions will be found in the problems at the end of this chapter.

106. Generalized Fourier Transforms.   Consider a general linear differential form of the second order, with respect to a variable x,

(1) $M_x[F] = A(x)F''(x) + B(x)F'(x) + C(x)F(x)$ $(a < x < b)$,

along with prescribed boundary values

(2) $N_a[F] = a_1F(a) + a_2F'(a), \qquad N_b[F] = b_1F(b) + b_2F'(b)$,

all of which may be present in a boundary value problem.   Let us determine in a formal way the kernel K and the range of the parameter λ of an integral transformation

(3) $\qquad T\{F(x)\} = \displaystyle\int_a^b F(x)K(x,\lambda)\,dx = f(\lambda)$

that resolves the form (1) into a linear algebraic function of $f(\lambda)$ and the boundary values (2).   This is a process of determining the transformation to fit a given boundary value problem.

The transform of our differential form can be written

$$T\{M_x[F]\} = \int_a^b (AK)F''\,dx + \int_a^b (BK)F'\,dx + \int_a^b CKF\,dx.$$

After integrating by parts so that F itself appears in each integral, this equation can be put in the form

(4) $T\{M_x[F]\}$

$$= \int_a^b [(AK)'' - (BK)' + CK]F\,dx + \Delta(b) - \Delta(a),$$

where $\qquad \Delta(x) = \begin{vmatrix} AK & (A' - B)K + AK' \\ F & F' \end{vmatrix}$.

The integrand here contains the form $\overline{M}_x[K]$, where $\overline{M}_x$ is the adjoint of the differential operator M_x (Sec. 89).   The transformation (4) is linear in $f(\lambda)$ if K satisfies the differential equation

(5) $\qquad \overline{M}_x[K] = (AK)'' - (BK)' + CK = \lambda K$.

The determinant $\Delta(a)$ can be written

$$a_2\Delta(a) = \begin{vmatrix} A(a)K(a,\lambda) & \bar{a}_1K(a,\lambda) + \bar{a}_2K'(a,\lambda) \\ F(a) & a_1F(a) + a_2F'(a) \end{vmatrix},$$

in terms of $N_a[F]$ and $\overline{N}_a[K]$, where

(6) $\bar{a}_1 = a_1A(a) + a_2[A'(a) - B(a)],$ $\bar{a}_2 = a_2A(a),$

(7) $\overline{N}_a[K] = \bar{a}_1K(a,\lambda) + \bar{a}_2K'(a,\lambda).$

Thus $\Delta(a)$ involves only the boundary value $N_a[F]$ for the function $F(x)$ if $\overline{N}_a[K] = 0$. Likewise, $\Delta(b)$ involves only $N_b[F]$ if $\overline{N}_b[K] = 0$, where $\overline{N}_b$ is described by replacing all a's in equations (6) and (7) by b's.

Thus if $K(x,\lambda)$ satisfies the eigenvalue problem

(8) $\overline{M}_x[K] - \lambda K = 0,$ $\overline{N}_a[K] = 0,$ $\overline{N}_b[K] = 0,$

with eigenvalues λ, then

(9) $T\{M_x[F]\} = \lambda f(\lambda) - \alpha N_a[F] + \beta N_b[F],$

where $\alpha a_2 = A(a)K(a,\lambda)$ $(a_2 \neq 0),$

          $\alpha = -A(a)K'(a,\lambda)$ $(a_2 = 0, a_1 = 1),$

and the α's and a's can be replaced by β's and b's, respectively, here.

The differential form (1) can be written in terms of a self-adjoint form (Sec. 89),

$$\Lambda_x[F] = (rF')' - qF,$$

as follows:

$$M_x[F] = \frac{A}{r}[(rF')' - qF] = \frac{1}{p(x)}\Lambda_x[F(x)],$$

where $r = \exp[\int(B/A)\, dx]$

     $p = r/A$

     $q = -pC.$

If we write $K(x,\lambda) = p(x)\Phi(x,\lambda)$, then

$$T\{M_x[F]\} = \int_a^b \Phi(x,\lambda)\Lambda_x[F(x)]\, dx.$$

The integral here represents a transformation $T_0\{\Lambda_x[F]\}$. It is a special case of the one involved in equations (4) to (9), in which K is replaced by Φ, T by T_0, both M_x and $\overline{M}_x$ by Λ_x, A by r and B by r', and therefore $A' - B$ by zero; but now we write $p\Phi$ for the coefficient of λ in equations (5) and (8). It follows that the new kernel Φ is an eigenfunction of the Sturm-Liouville system

$$(10) \qquad \Lambda_x[\Phi] - \lambda p \Phi = 0, \qquad N_a[\Phi] = N_b[\Phi] = 0,$$

corresponding to an eigenvalue λ. If λ_n are the eigenvalues and $\phi_n(x)$ the normalized eigenfunctions (Chap. 9), our transformation (3) becomes

$$(11) \quad T\{F(x)\} = \int_a^b F(x)\phi_n(x)p(x)\, dx = f(\lambda_n) \quad (n = 1, 2, \ldots),$$

where $f(\lambda_n)$ is the Fourier constant c_n of $F(x)$, so that

$$(12) \qquad\qquad F(x) = \sum_{n=1}^{\infty} f(\lambda_n)\phi_n(x) \qquad (a < x < b).$$

This is the inversion formula for the generalized Fourier transformation (3) or (11) that resolves the differential form $M_x[F]$ in terms of $f(\lambda_n)$ and the boundary values (2).

The basic operational property (9) can now be written in the form

$$(13) \quad T\{M_x[F]\} = \lambda_n f(\lambda_n) - \alpha_n r(a) N_a[F] + \beta_n r(b) N_b[F],$$

where $a_2 \alpha_n = \phi_n(a)$ if $a_2 \neq 0$, while $\alpha_n = -\phi_n'(a)$ if $a_2 = 0$ and $a_1 = 1$, and where $b_2 \beta_n = \phi_n(b)$ if $b_2 \neq 0$, while $\beta_n = -\phi_n'(b)$ if $b_2 = 0$ and $b_1 = 1$.

If the interval (a,b) is unbounded, or if $A(x)$ or $r(x)$ vanishes at some point of the interval, the eigenvalue problem that determines the kernel is singular[1] and the eigenvalues λ may be continuous rather than discrete. The inversion formula may then assume the form of an integral with respect to λ, as in the cases of Fourier integral formulas, in place of the series form (12).

Further operational properties and tables of transforms would improve the operational mathematics based on any generalized Fourier transformation.[2] Except in the simpler cases such properties are usually either hard to find or quite involved.

---

[1] See the book on "Eigenfunction Expansions" by Titchmarsh, listed in Appendix 1.

[2] See Prob. 15, Sec. 107; also, R. V. Churchill's paper: Extensions of Operational Mathematics, "Proceedings of the Conference on Differential Equations," pp. 235–250, University of Maryland, 1956.

107. Examples. For the transformation on the interval $(0,\pi)$ that resolves the form $F''(x)$ in terms of boundary values $F(0)$ and $F'(\pi)$, the kernel $K(x,\lambda)$ is determined by the conditions

(1) $K'' - \lambda K = 0,$ $K(0,\lambda) = 0,$ $K'(\pi,\lambda) = 0.$

The solution of this Sturm-Liouville problem is

(2) $K = \sin (n - \tfrac{1}{2})x,$ $\lambda = -(n - \tfrac{1}{2})^2$ $(n = 1, 2, \ldots).$

The transformation

(3) $T\{F\} = \displaystyle\int_0^\pi F(x) \sin (n - \tfrac{1}{2})x \, dx = f(\lambda_n)$

has the operational property

(4) $T\{F''(x)\} = -(n - \tfrac{1}{2})^2 f(\lambda_n) + (n - \tfrac{1}{2})F(0) - (-1)^n F'(\pi),$

according to Sec. 106. We assume $F'(x)$ is continuous.

The generalized Fourier series that furnishes the inversion formula for the transformation (3) can be written

(5) $F(x) = \dfrac{2}{\pi} \displaystyle\sum_{n=1}^{\infty} f(\lambda_n) \sin \left(n - \dfrac{1}{2}\right) x$ $(0 < x < \pi).$

For this modification of the finite Fourier transformations additional operational properties can be found easily.

When $a = 0$ and $b = \infty$ in Sec. 106 and the differential form $F''(x)$ is to be resolved in terms of $F'(0)$ while the kernel is required to be bounded, then

$$K'' - \lambda K = 0 \qquad\qquad (x > 0),$$
$$K'(0,\lambda) = 0, \qquad |K(x,\lambda)| < K_0.$$

The solution of this singular eigenvalue problem is $\lambda = -r^2$, where r is a real parameter because of the boundedness condition, and

$$K(x,\lambda) = \cos rx \qquad\qquad (r > 0).$$

The transformation is therefore the Fourier cosine transformation

$$C_r\{F(x)\} = \int_0^\infty F(x) \cos rx \, dx,$$

whose basic operational property and inverse transformation were given earlier in this chapter.

When the differential form is

$$M[F] = F''(x) + \frac{1}{x} F'(x) - \frac{c^2}{x^2} F(x) \quad (c \text{ constant}),$$

the kernel is a solution of Bessel's equation. Transformations whose kernels are Bessel functions are called Hankel transformations.[1] Tables of Hankel transforms on unbounded intervals will be found in the book listed in Appendix 1 under the name Erdélyi.

PROBLEMS

1. When k is a positive constant, show that

(a) $S_r\{e^{-kx}\} = \dfrac{r}{r^2 + k^2}$,   (b) $C_r\{e^{-kx}\} = \dfrac{k}{r^2 + k^2}$,

(c) $E_r\{\exp(-k|x|)\} = 2C_r\{e^{-kx}\}$,

(d) $C_r\left\{\dfrac{k}{x^2 + k^2}\right\} = \dfrac{\pi}{2} e^{-kr}$ [cf. part (b), or Sec. 32],

(e) $C_r\{e^{-kx^2}\} = \dfrac{1}{2}\sqrt{\dfrac{\pi}{k}} \exp\left(-\dfrac{r^2}{4k}\right)$ (Sec. 68);

also (f) write $f_s(r)$ and $f_c(r)$ when $F(x) = (x + k)^{-1}$, from results found in problems at the end of Sec. 33, and note that $F(x)$ is a basic partial fraction for quotients of polynomials in x.

2. Obtain these operational properties in a formal way:

(a) $S_r\{xF(x)\} = -f_c'(r)$,   (b) $C_r\{xF(x)\} = f_s'(r)$,

(c) $2S_r\{F(x) \cos kx\} = f_s(r + k) + f_s(r - k)$,

(d) $f_c(r)e^{ikr} = E_r\{F(x - k)\}$.

3. Let $U(x,t)$ denote temperatures in a semi-infinite solid $x \geqq 0$ under the conditions

$$\begin{aligned} U_t &= U_{xx} + H(x,t) & (x > 0,\ t > 0), \\ U(x,0) &= F(x), \\ U(0,t) &= g(t), \end{aligned}$$

and assume that H, F, g, and U are well behaved functions when x and t are large. Derive the formula

$$U(x,t) = \frac{2}{\pi} \int_0^\infty u_s(r,t) \sin rx \, dr,$$

where

$$e^{r^2 t} u_s(r,t) = f_s(r) + \int_0^t e^{r^2 \tau}[rg(\tau) + h_s(r,\tau)]\, d\tau.$$

[1] See the references to Sneddon in Appendix 1.

4. Write $g(t) = H(x,t) = 0$ in Prob. 3, and note the form taken by the solution written there. With the aid of the transformation given in Prob. 1(e), obtain the solution in the form

$$2U(x,t) \sqrt{\pi t}$$
$$= \int_0^\infty F(y) \left\{ \exp\left[-\frac{(x-y)^2}{4t} \right] - \exp\left[-\frac{(x+y)^2}{4t} \right] \right\} dy \quad (t > 0).$$

5. Write $H(x,t) = F(x) = 0$ in Prob. 3. With the aid of results given in Probs. 1 and 2, show that (cf. Sec. 44)

$$U(x,t) = \frac{x}{2\sqrt{\pi}} \int_0^t \exp\left(-\frac{x^2}{4y} \right) g(t-y) y^{-\frac{3}{2}} \, dy \quad (x > 0).$$

6. Use a convolution property of Fourier transforms to obtain another integral representation of $U(x,t)$ in Prob. 3 in the case $F(x) = g(t) = 0$.

7. A potential function $V(x,y)$ in a half plane satisfies the conditions

$$V_{xx} + V_{yy} = 0 \quad (-\infty < x < \infty, y > 0),$$
$$V(x,0) = F(x);$$

also F and V satisfy suitable order conditions in the half plane. Use successive Fourier transformations and obtain transforms needed by referring to Probs. 1 and 2, to show that

$$v_s(x,r) = \frac{1}{2} \int_{-\infty}^\infty F(\xi) \exp(-r|x - \xi|) \, d\xi,$$

and hence obtain this form of the *Schwarz integral formula:*

$$V(x,y) = \frac{y}{\pi} \int_{-\infty}^\infty \frac{F(\xi)}{(x - \xi)^2 + y^2} \, d\xi \quad (y > 0).$$

8. The displacements $Y(x,t)$ in a string stretched along the entire x axis satisfy the conditions

$$Y_{tt} = a^2 Y_{xx} \quad (-\infty < x < \infty, t > 0),$$
$$Y(x,0) = F(x),$$
$$Y_t(x,0) = 0,$$

and the conditions that F, Y, and Y_x vanish as $|x|$ tends to infinity. Transform with respect to x to derive the formula

$$Y(x,t) = \frac{1}{2}[F(x - at) + F(x + at)].$$

9. Let $V(x,y)$ be steady temperatures in a quadrant $x \geq 0$, $y \geq 0$, satisfying the conditions

$$V_{xx} + V_{yy} = F(x) \quad (x > 0, y > 0),$$
$$V_x(0,y) = 0,$$
$$V(x,0) = G(x),$$

where $\int_0^\infty F(x)\,dx = 0$. If $H(0)$ exists when we write

$$H(x) = \int_x^\infty \int_0^z F(t)\,dt\,dz,$$

show that

$$v_c(r,y) = [h_c(r) + g_c(r)]e^{-ry} - h_c(r)$$

and use a convolution property to write a formula for $V(x,y)$ in terms of the functions H and G.

10. The static deflection $Z(x,y)$ in a thin plate with an arbitrary load per unit area acting perpendicular to the plate satisfies the nonhomogeneous form of the biharmonic equation,

$$\frac{\partial^4 Z}{\partial x^4} + 2\frac{\partial^4 Z}{\partial x^2\,\partial y^2} + \frac{\partial^4 Z}{\partial y^4} = F(x,y).$$

At a simply supported edge, $Z = 0$ and $\partial^2 Z/\partial\nu^2 = 0$, where the axis of the coordinate ν lies in the plate and is perpendicular to the edge. Let the plate be the semi-infinite strip $x \geqq 0$, $0 \leqq y \leqq \pi$ with all three edges simply supported. Show how successive Fourier transformations can be used to resolve the boundary value problem in Z into an algebraic problem in transforms.

11. Let $V(r,\theta)$ be a potential function for a semicircular region $r \leqq a$, $0 \leqq \theta \leqq \pi$. It satisfies Laplace's equation in polar coordinates

$$r^2 V_{rr} + rV_r + V_{\theta\theta} = 0 \qquad (r < a, 0 < \theta < \pi).$$

Let it vanish on the base of the region and be prescribed on the circular boundary,

$$V(r,0) = V(r,\pi) = 0, \qquad V(a,\theta) = F(\theta),$$

and let it be bounded throughout the region. Derive the formula

$$V(r,\theta) = \frac{1}{2\pi}\int_0^\pi F(\alpha)[H(r,\,\theta-\alpha) - H(r,\,\theta+\alpha)]\,d\alpha \qquad (r < a),$$

known as *Poisson's integral formula* for the region, where

$$H(r,\theta) = \frac{a^2 - r^2}{a^2 + r^2 - 2ar\cos\theta} = 1 + 2\frac{ar\cos\theta - r^2}{a^2 + r^2 - 2ar\cos\theta}.$$

12. In each of the following boundary value problems in $V(x,y)$, note the types of differential forms and boundary conditions that occur and, without solving for $V(x,y)$, determine which Fourier transformation is suitable for solving the problem. Also, determine whether a Laplace transformation or the method of separating variables could be used.

(a) $$V_{xx} + V_{yy} - V_x = 0 \quad (0 < x < 1, 0 < y < 1),$$
$$V(0,y) = V(1,y) = V(x,0) = 0, \qquad V(x,1) = 1.$$

Ans. Sine transformation on the interval $0 \leqq y \leqq 1$; separation of variables, involving $\phi_n(x)$.

(b) $$V_{yy} = V_{xx} + y \qquad (0 < x < 1, y > 0),$$
$$V(x,0) = 1, \quad V_y(x,0) = V_x(0,y) = 0, \qquad V_x(1,y) = e^{-y}.$$
(c) $$V_{xx} + V_{yy} - V = e^{-x-y} \qquad (x > 0, y > 0),$$
$$V(0,y) = V_y(x,0) = 0, \qquad |V| < M.$$

13. Construct an integral transformation on the interval $(0,1)$ that resolves the differential form $F'''(x)$ in terms of the boundary values $F'(0)$ and $kF(1) + F'(1)$, where k is a positive constant. Write the formula for the transform of $F''(x)$.

$$\text{Ans. } \int_0^1 F(x) \cos \alpha_n x \, dx, \text{ where } \tan \alpha_n = k/\alpha_n.$$

14. Determine the integral transformation T, with respect to x, that is adapted to this problem:

$$(t + 1)U_t(x,t) = U_{xx}(x,t) \qquad (0 < x < 1, t > 0),$$
$$U(x,0) = 0, \qquad U_x(0,t) = 1, \qquad U(1,t) = 0.$$

From the solution of the elementary problem $Y''(x) = 0$, $Y'(0) = 1$, $Y(1) = 0$, and by transforming this problem, find $T^{-1}\{1/\lambda_n\}$; then derive the formula

$$U(x,t) = x - 1 + 2 \sum_{n=1}^{\infty} \frac{1}{m} (t + 1)^{-m} \cos x \sqrt{m} \quad [m = (n - \tfrac{1}{2})^2 \pi^2].$$

15. If $T\{F\} = f(\lambda_n)$ in the notation used in Sec. 106, and if no λ_n is zero, show formally that

$$T^{-1}\left\{\frac{f(\lambda_n)}{\lambda_n}\right\} = Y(x),$$

where $Y(x)$ is the solution of the boundary value problem

$$M_x[Y(x)] = F(x), \qquad N_a[Y] = N_b[Y] = 0.$$

Hence if $G(x,t)$ is Green's function for that problem in $Y(x)$, when the differential equation is written in self-adjoint form, show that

$$\frac{f(\lambda_n)}{\lambda_n} = T\left\{\int_a^b G(x,t)p(t)F(t)\, dt\right\}.$$

BIBLIOGRAPHY

Bochner, S.: "Vorlesungen über Fouriersche Integrale," Chelsea Publishing Company, New York, 1948.

Bochner, S., and K. Chandrasekharan: "Fourier Transforms," Princeton University Press, Princeton, 1949.

Carslaw, H. S., and J. C. Jaeger: "Operational Methods in Applied Mathematics," Oxford University Press, London, 1941.

Churchill, R. V.: "Fourier Series and Boundary Value Problems," McGraw-Hill Book Company, Inc., New York, 1941.

Collatz, L.: "Eigenwertprobleme und ihre Numerische Behandlung," Chelsea Publishing Company, New York, 1948.

Doetsch, G.: "Theorie und Anwendung der Laplace-Transformation," Springer-Verlag, Berlin, 1937.

———: "Handbuch der Laplace-Transformation," Verlag Birkhäuser, Basel, vol. 1, 1950; vol. 2, 1955; vol. 3, 1956.

Morse, P. M., and H. Feshbach: "Methods of Theoretical Physics," parts I and II, McGraw-Hill Book Company, Inc., New York, 1953.

Paley, R., and N. Wiener: "Fourier Transforms in the Complex Domain," American Mathematical Society, Providence, R. I., 1934.

van der Pol, B., and H. Bremmer: "Operational Calculus Based on the Two-sided Laplace Integral," Cambridge University Press, London, 1950.

Sneddon, I. N.: "Fourier Transforms," McGraw-Hill Book Company, Inc., New York, 1951.

———: "Functional Analysis," Handbuch der Physik, vol. 2, pp. 198–348, Springer-Verlag, Berlin, 1955.

Titchmarsh, E. C.: "Theory of Fourier Integrals," Oxford University Press, London, 1937.

———: "Eigenfunction Expansions," Oxford University Press, London, 1946.

Tranter, C. J.: "Integral Transforms in Mathematical Physics," Second Edition, Methuen and Company, Ltd., London, 1956.

Voelker, D., and G. Doetsch: "Die Zweidimensionale Laplace-Transformation," Verlag Birkhäuser, Basel, 1950.

OPERATIONAL MATHEMATICS

Widder, D. V.: "The Laplace Transform," Princeton University Press, Princeton, 1941.

Wiener, N.: "The Fourier Integral," Cambridge University Press, London, 1933.

TABLES

Campbell, G. A., and R. M. Foster: "Fourier Integrals for Practical Applications," D. Van Nostrand Company, Inc., New York, 1948.

Doetsch, G., H. Kniess, and D. Voelker: "Tabellen zur Laplace-Transformation und Anleitung zum Gebrauch," Springer-Verlag, Berlin, 1947.

Erdélyi, A., W. Magnus, F. Oberhettinger, and F. Tricomi: "Tables of Integral Transforms," vols. 1 and 2, McGraw-Hill Book Company, Inc., New York, 1954.

Oberhettinger, F.: "Tabellen zur Fourier Transformation," Springer-Verlag, Berlin, 1957.

TABLE OF OPERATIONS FOR THE LAPLACE TRANSFORMATION

	$F(t)$	$f(s)$	Section
1	$F(t)$	$\displaystyle\int_0^\infty e^{-st}F(t)\,dt$	2
2	$AF(t) + BG(t)$	$Af(s) + Bg(s)$	1
3	$F'(t)$	$sf(s) - F(+0)$	4
4	$F^{(n)}(t)$	$s^n f(s) - s^{n-1}F(+0)$ $- s^{n-2}F'(+0) - \cdots$ $- F^{(n-1)}(+0)$	4
5	$\displaystyle\int_0^t F(r)\,dr$	$\dfrac{1}{s}f(s)$	14
6	$\displaystyle\int_0^t \int_0^r F(\lambda)\,d\lambda\,dr$	$\dfrac{1}{s^2}f(s)$	14
7	$\displaystyle\int_0^t F_1(t-\tau)F_2(\tau)\,d\tau = F_1 * F_2$	$f_1(s)f_2(s)$	13
8	$tF(t)$	$-f'(s)$	16
9	$t^n F(t)$	$(-1)^n f^{(n)}(s)$	16
10	$\dfrac{1}{t}F(t)$	$\displaystyle\int_s^\infty f(x)\,dx$	18
11	$e^{at}F(t)$	$f(s-a)$	7
12	$F(t-b)$, where $F(t)=0$ when $t<0$	$e^{-bs}f(s)$	10
13	$\dfrac{1}{c}F\left(\dfrac{t}{c}\right)\ (c>0)$	$f(cs)$	10
14	$\dfrac{1}{c}e^{\frac{bt}{c}}F\left(\dfrac{t}{c}\right)\ (c>0)$	$f(cs-b)$	10
15	$F(t)$, when $F(t+a)=F(t)$	$\dfrac{\displaystyle\int_0^a e^{-st}F(t)\,dt}{1-e^{-as}}$	19
16	$F(t)$, when $F(t+a)=-F(t)$	$\dfrac{\displaystyle\int_0^a e^{-st}F(t)\,dt}{1+e^{-as}}$	19
17	$F_1(t)$, the half-wave rectification of $F(t)$ in No. 16	$\dfrac{f(s)}{1-e^{-as}}$	19
18	$F_2(t)$, the full-wave rectification of $F(t)$ in No. 16	$f(s)\coth\dfrac{as}{2}$	19
19	$\displaystyle\sum_1^m \dfrac{p(a_n)}{q'(a_n)}e^{a_n t}$	$\dfrac{p(s)}{q(s)}$, $q(s)=(s-a_1)(s-a_2)$ $\cdots (s-a_m)$	20

$\rightarrow (12)'\ S_b(t)$

$e^{-bs}\dfrac{1}{s}$

APPENDIX 3

TABLE OF LAPLACE TRANSFORMS

	$f(s)$	$F(t)$
1	$\dfrac{1}{s}$	1
2	$\dfrac{1}{s^2}$	t
3	$\dfrac{1}{s^n}$ $(n = 1, 2, \ldots)$	$\dfrac{t^{n-1}}{(n-1)!}$
4	$\dfrac{1}{\sqrt{s}}$	$\dfrac{1}{\sqrt{\pi t}}$
5	$s^{-\frac{3}{2}}$	$2\sqrt{\dfrac{t}{\pi}}$
6	$s^{-(n+\frac{1}{2})}$ $(n = 1, 2, \ldots)$	$\dfrac{2^n t^{n-\frac{1}{2}}}{1 \times 3 \times 5 \cdots (2n-1)\sqrt{\pi}}$
7	$\dfrac{\Gamma(k)}{s^k}$ $(k > 0)$	t^{k-1}
8	$\dfrac{1}{s-a}$	e^{at}
9	$\dfrac{1}{(s-a)^2}$	te^{at}
10	$\dfrac{1}{(s-a)^n}$ $(n = 1, 2, \ldots)$	$\dfrac{1}{(n-1)!}t^{n-1}e^{at}$
11	$\dfrac{\Gamma(k)}{(s-a)^k}$ $(k > 0)$	$t^{k-1}e^{at}$
12*	$\dfrac{1}{(s-a)(s-b)}$	$\dfrac{1}{a-b}(e^{at} - e^{bt})$
13*	$\dfrac{s}{(s-a)(s-b)}$	$\dfrac{1}{a-b}(ae^{at} - be^{bt})$
14*	$\dfrac{1}{(s-a)(s-b)(s-c)}$	$-\dfrac{(b-c)e^{at} + (c-a)e^{bt} + (a-b)e^{ct}}{(a-b)(b-c)(c-a)}$
15	$\dfrac{1}{s^2+a^2}$	$\dfrac{1}{a}\sin at$
16	$\dfrac{s}{s^2+a^2}$	$\cos at$

* Here a, b, and (in 14) c represent distinct constants.

TABLE OF LAPLACE TRANSFORMS. (*Continued.*)

	$f(s)$	$F(t)$
17	$\dfrac{1}{s^2 - a^2}$	$\dfrac{1}{a}\sinh at$
18	$\dfrac{s}{s^2 - a^2}$	$\cosh at$
19	$\dfrac{1}{s(s^2 + a^2)}$	$\dfrac{1}{a^2}(1 - \cos at)$
20	$\dfrac{1}{s^2(s^2 + a^2)}$	$\dfrac{1}{a^3}(at - \sin at)$
21	$\dfrac{1}{(s^2 + a^2)^2}$	$\dfrac{1}{2a^3}(\sin at - at \cos at)$
22	$\dfrac{s}{(s^2 + a^2)^2}$	$\dfrac{t}{2a}\sin at$
23	$\dfrac{s^2}{(s^2 + a^2)^2}$	$\dfrac{1}{2a}(\sin at + at \cos at)$
24	$\dfrac{s^2 - a^2}{(s^2 + a^2)^2}$	$t \cos at$
25	$\dfrac{s}{(s^2 + a^2)(s^2 + b^2)} \quad (a^2 \neq b^2)$	$\dfrac{\cos at - \cos bt}{b^2 - a^2}$
26	$\dfrac{1}{(s - a)^2 + b^2}$	$\dfrac{1}{b}e^{at}\sin bt$
27	$\dfrac{s - a}{(s - a)^2 + b^2}$	$e^{at}\cos bt$
28	$\dfrac{3a^2}{s^3 + a^3}$	$e^{-at} - e^{at/2}\left(\cos\dfrac{at\sqrt{3}}{2} - \sqrt{3}\sin\dfrac{at\sqrt{3}}{2}\right)$
29	$\dfrac{4a^3}{s^4 + 4a^4}$	$\sin at \cosh at - \cos at \sinh at$
30	$\dfrac{s}{s^4 + 4a^4}$	$\dfrac{1}{2a^2}\sin at \sinh at$
31	$\dfrac{1}{s^4 - a^4}$	$\dfrac{1}{2a^3}(\sinh at - \sin at)$
32	$\dfrac{s}{s^4 - a^4}$	$\dfrac{1}{2a^2}(\cosh at - \cos at)$
33	$\dfrac{8a^3s^2}{(s^2 + a^2)^3}$	$(1 + a^2t^2)\sin at - at \cos at$
34*	$\dfrac{1}{s}\left(\dfrac{s - 1}{s}\right)^n$	$L_n(t) = \dfrac{e^t}{n!}\dfrac{d^n}{dt^n}(t^n e^{-t})$
35	$\dfrac{s}{(s - a)^{\frac{3}{2}}}$	$\dfrac{1}{\sqrt{\pi t}}e^{at}(1 + 2at)$
36	$\sqrt{s - a} - \sqrt{s - b}$	$\dfrac{1}{2\sqrt{\pi t^3}}(e^{bt} - e^{at})$

* $L_n(t)$ is the Laguerre polynomial of degree n.

TABLE OF LAPLACE TRANSFORMS. (*Continued.*)

	$f(s)$	$F(t)$
37	$\dfrac{1}{\sqrt{s}+a}$	$\dfrac{1}{\sqrt{\pi t}} - ae^{a^2 t}\,\mathrm{erfc}\,(a\,\sqrt{t})$
38	$\dfrac{\sqrt{s}}{s-a^2}$	$\dfrac{1}{\sqrt{\pi t}} + ae^{a^2 t}\,\mathrm{erf}\,(a\,\sqrt{t})$
39	$\dfrac{\sqrt{s}}{s+a^2}$	$\dfrac{1}{\sqrt{\pi t}} - \dfrac{2a}{\sqrt{\pi}}\,e^{-a^2 t}\displaystyle\int_0^{a\sqrt{t}} e^{\lambda^2}\,d\lambda$
40	$\dfrac{1}{\sqrt{s}\,(s-a^2)}$	$\dfrac{1}{a}\,e^{a^2 t}\,\mathrm{erf}\,(a\,\sqrt{t})$
41	$\dfrac{1}{\sqrt{s}\,(s+a^2)}$	$\dfrac{2}{a\,\sqrt{\pi}}\,e^{-a^2 t}\displaystyle\int_0^{a\sqrt{t}} e^{\lambda^2}\,d\lambda$
42	$\dfrac{b^2-a^2}{(s-a^2)(b+\sqrt{s})}$	$e^{a^2 t}[b - a\,\mathrm{erf}\,(a\,\sqrt{t})]$ $\qquad - be^{b^2 t}\,\mathrm{erfc}\,(b\,\sqrt{t})$
43	$\dfrac{1}{\sqrt{s}\,(\sqrt{s}+a)}$	$e^{a^2 t}\,\mathrm{erfc}\,(a\,\sqrt{t})$
44	$\dfrac{1}{(s+a)\,\sqrt{s+b}}$	$\dfrac{1}{\sqrt{b-a}}\,e^{-at}\,\mathrm{erf}\,(\sqrt{b-a}\,\sqrt{t})$
45	$\dfrac{b^2-a^2}{\sqrt{s}\,(s-a^2)(\sqrt{s}+b)}$	$e^{a^2 t}\left[\dfrac{b}{a}\,\mathrm{erf}\,(a\,\sqrt{t}) - 1\right]$ $\qquad + e^{b^2 t}\,\mathrm{erfc}\,(b\,\sqrt{t})$
46*	$\dfrac{(1-s)^n}{s^{n+\frac{1}{2}}}$	$\dfrac{n!}{(2n)!\,\sqrt{\pi t}}\,H_{2n}(\sqrt{t})$
47	$\dfrac{(1-s)^n}{s^{n+\frac{3}{2}}}$	$-\dfrac{n!}{\sqrt{\pi}\,(2n+1)!}\,H_{2n+1}(\sqrt{t})$
48†	$\dfrac{\sqrt{s+2a}}{\sqrt{s}} - 1$	$ae^{-at}[I_1(at) + I_0(at)]$
49	$\dfrac{1}{\sqrt{s+a}\,\sqrt{s+b}}$	$e^{-\frac{1}{2}(a+b)t}I_0\left(\dfrac{a-b}{2}\,t\right)$
50	$\dfrac{\Gamma(k)}{(s+a)^k(s+b)^k}\ (k>0)$	$\sqrt{\pi}\left(\dfrac{t}{a-b}\right)^{k-\frac{1}{2}}e^{-\frac{1}{2}(a+b)t}$ $\qquad\qquad \times\, I_{k-\frac{1}{2}}\left(\dfrac{a-b}{2}\,t\right)$
51	$\dfrac{1}{(s+a)^{\frac{1}{2}}(s+b)^{\frac{3}{2}}}$	$te^{-\frac{1}{2}(a+b)t}\left[I_0\left(\dfrac{a-b}{2}\,t\right)\right.$ $\qquad\qquad \left. + I_1\left(\dfrac{a-b}{2}\,t\right)\right]$
52	$\dfrac{\sqrt{s+2a}-\sqrt{s}}{\sqrt{s+2a}+\sqrt{s}}$	$\dfrac{1}{t}\,e^{-at}I_1(at)$

* $H_n(x)$ is the Hermite polynomial, $H_n(x) = e^{x^2}\dfrac{d^n}{dx^n}\,(e^{-x^2})$.

† $I_n(x) = i^{-n}J_n(ix)$, where J_n is Bessel's function of the first kind.

TABLE OF LAPLACE TRANSFORMS. *(Continued.)*

	$f(s)$	$F(t)$
53	$\dfrac{(a-b)^k}{(\sqrt{s+a}+\sqrt{s+b})^{2k}}$ $(k>0)$	$\dfrac{k}{t}\,e^{-\frac{1}{2}(a+b)t}I_k\left(\dfrac{a-b}{2}\,t\right)$
54	$\dfrac{(\sqrt{s+a}+\sqrt{s})^{-2\nu}}{\sqrt{s}\,\sqrt{s+a}}$ $(\nu>-1)$	$\dfrac{1}{a^\nu}\,e^{-\frac{1}{2}at}I_\nu\left(\dfrac{1}{2}\,at\right)$
55	$\dfrac{1}{\sqrt{s^2+a^2}}$	$J_0(at)$
56	$\dfrac{(\sqrt{s^2+a^2}-s)^\nu}{\sqrt{s^2+a^2}}$ $(\nu>-1)$	$a^\nu J_\nu(at)$
57	$\dfrac{1}{(s^2+a^2)^k}$ $(k>0)$	$\dfrac{\sqrt{\pi}}{\Gamma(k)}\left(\dfrac{t}{2a}\right)^{k-\frac{1}{2}}J_{k-\frac{1}{2}}(at)$
58	$(\sqrt{s^2+a^2}-s)^k$ $(k>0)$	$\dfrac{ka^k}{t}\,J_k(at)$
59	$\dfrac{(s-\sqrt{s^2-a^2})^\nu}{\sqrt{s^2-a^2}}$ $(\nu>-1)$	$a^\nu I_\nu(at)$
60	$\dfrac{1}{(s^2-a^2)^k}$ $(k>0)$	$\dfrac{\sqrt{\pi}}{\Gamma(k)}\left(\dfrac{t}{2a}\right)^{k-\frac{1}{2}}I_{k-\frac{1}{2}}(at)$
61	$\dfrac{e^{-ks}}{s}$	$S_k(t)=\begin{cases}0 \text{ when } 0<t<k\\1 \text{ when } t>k\end{cases}$
62	$\dfrac{e^{-ks}}{s^2}$	$\begin{cases}0 \quad\text{ when } 0<t<k\\t-k \text{ when } t>k\end{cases}$
63	$\dfrac{e^{-ks}}{s^\mu}$ $(\mu>0)$	$\begin{cases}0 \quad\quad\text{ when } 0<t<k\\\dfrac{(t-k)^{\mu-1}}{\Gamma(\mu)}\text{ when } t>k\end{cases}$
64	$\dfrac{1-e^{-ks}}{s}$	$\begin{cases}1 \text{ when } 0<t<k\\0 \text{ when } t>k\end{cases}$
65	$\dfrac{1}{s(1-e^{-ks})}=\dfrac{1+\coth\frac{1}{2}ks}{2s}$	$1+[t/k]=n$ when $(n-1)k<t<nk$ $(n=1,2,\ldots)$ (Fig. 5)
66	$\dfrac{1}{s(e^{ks}-a)}$	$\begin{cases}0 \quad\text{ when } 0<t<k\\1+a+a^2+\cdots+a^{n-1}\\\quad\text{ when } nk<t<(n+1)k\\\quad\quad\quad\quad (n=1,2,\ldots)\end{cases}$
67	$\dfrac{1}{s}\tanh ks$	$M(2k,t)=(-1)^{n-1}$ when $2k(n-1)<t<2kn$ $(n=1,2,\ldots)$ (Fig. 9)
68	$\dfrac{1}{s(1+e^{-ks})}$	$\dfrac{1}{2}M(k,t)+\dfrac{1}{2}=\dfrac{1-(-1)^n}{2}$ when $(n-1)k<t<nk$
69	$\dfrac{1}{s^2}\tanh ks$	$H(2k,t)$ (Fig. 10)

TABLE OF LAPLACE TRANSFORMS. *(Continued.)*

	$f(s)$	$F(t)$
70	$\dfrac{1}{s \sinh ks}$	$F(t) = 2(n-1)$ when $(2n-3)k < t < (2n-1)k$ $(t > 0)$
71	$\dfrac{1}{s \cosh ks}$	$M(2k,\, t+3k) + 1 = 1 + (-1)^n$ when $(2n-3)k < t < (2n-1)k$ $(t > 0)$
72	$\dfrac{1}{s} \coth ks$	$F(t) = 2n-1$ when $2k(n-1) < t < 2kn$
73	$\dfrac{k}{s^2+k^2} \coth \dfrac{\pi s}{2k}$	$\lvert \sin kt \rvert$
74	$\dfrac{1}{(s^2+1)(1-e^{-\pi s})}$	$\begin{cases} \sin t \text{ when} \\ \qquad (2n-2)\pi < t < (2n-1)\pi \\ 0 \quad \text{when} \\ \qquad (2n-1)\pi < t < 2n\pi \end{cases}$
75	$\dfrac{1}{s} e^{-(k/s)}$	$J_0(2\sqrt{kt})$
76	$\dfrac{1}{\sqrt{s}} e^{-(k/s)}$	$\dfrac{1}{\sqrt{\pi t}} \cos 2\sqrt{kt}$
77	$\dfrac{1}{\sqrt{s}} e^{k/s}$	$\dfrac{1}{\sqrt{\pi t}} \cosh 2\sqrt{kt}$
78	$\dfrac{1}{s^{\frac{3}{2}}} e^{-(k/s)}$	$\dfrac{1}{\sqrt{\pi k}} \sin 2\sqrt{kt}$
79	$\dfrac{1}{s^{\frac{3}{2}}} e^{k/s}$	$\dfrac{1}{\sqrt{\pi k}} \sinh 2\sqrt{kt}$
80	$\dfrac{1}{s^\mu} e^{-(k/s)} \; (\mu > 0)$	$\left(\dfrac{t}{k}\right)^{(\mu-1)/2} J_{\mu-1}(2\sqrt{kt})$
81	$\dfrac{1}{s^\mu} e^{k/s} \; (\mu > 0)$	$\left(\dfrac{t}{k}\right)^{(\mu-1)/2} I_{\mu-1}(2\sqrt{kt})$
82	$e^{-k\sqrt{s}} \; (k > 0)$	$\dfrac{k}{2\sqrt{\pi t^3}} \exp\left(-\dfrac{k^2}{4t}\right)$
83	$\dfrac{1}{s} e^{-k\sqrt{s}} \; (k \geqq 0)$	$\operatorname{erfc}\left(\dfrac{k}{2\sqrt{t}}\right)$
84	$\dfrac{1}{\sqrt{s}} e^{-k\sqrt{s}} \; (k \geqq 0)$	$\dfrac{1}{\sqrt{\pi t}} \exp\left(-\dfrac{k^2}{4t}\right)$
85	$s^{-\frac{3}{2}} e^{-k\sqrt{s}} \; (k \geqq 0)$	$2\sqrt{\dfrac{t}{\pi}} \exp\left(-\dfrac{k^2}{4t}\right)$ $\qquad\qquad - k \operatorname{erfc}\left(\dfrac{k}{2\sqrt{t}}\right)$
86	$\dfrac{ae^{-k\sqrt{s}}}{s(a+\sqrt{s})} \; (k \geqq 0)$	$-e^{ak}e^{a^2 t} \operatorname{erfc}\left(a\sqrt{t} + \dfrac{k}{2\sqrt{t}}\right)$ $\qquad\qquad + \operatorname{erfc}\left(\dfrac{k}{2\sqrt{t}}\right)$

TABLE OF LAPLACE TRANSFORMS. *(Continued.)*

	$f(s)$	$F(t)$
87	$\dfrac{e^{-k\sqrt{s}}}{\sqrt{s}\,(a + \sqrt{s})} \; (k \geqq 0)$	$e^{ak}e^{a^2 t}\,\mathrm{erfc}\left(a\,\sqrt{t} + \dfrac{k}{2\sqrt{t}}\right)$
88	$\dfrac{e^{-k\sqrt{s(s+a)}}}{\sqrt{s(s+a)}}$	$\begin{cases} 0 & \text{when } 0 < t < k \\ e^{-\frac{1}{2}at}I_0(\frac{1}{2}a\,\sqrt{t^2 - k^2}) \end{cases}$
89	$\dfrac{e^{-k\sqrt{s^2+a^2}}}{\sqrt{s^2 + a^2}}$	$\begin{cases} 0 & \text{when } t > k \\ & \text{when } 0 < t < k \\ J_0(a\,\sqrt{t^2 - k^2}) & \text{when } t > k \end{cases}$
90	$\dfrac{e^{-k\sqrt{s^2-a^2}}}{\sqrt{s^2 - a^2}}$	$\begin{cases} 0 & \text{when } 0 < t < k \\ I_0(a\,\sqrt{t^2 - k^2}) & \text{when } t > k \end{cases}$
91	$\dfrac{e^{-k(\sqrt{s^2+a^2}-s)}}{\sqrt{s^2 + a^2}} \; (k \geqq 0)$	$J_0(a\,\sqrt{t^2 + 2kt})$
92	$e^{-ks} - e^{-k\sqrt{s^2+a^2}}$	$\begin{cases} 0 & \text{when } 0 < t < k \\ \dfrac{ak}{\sqrt{t^2 - k^2}}\,J_1(a\,\sqrt{t^2 - k^2}) \\ & \text{when } t > k \end{cases}$
93	$e^{-k\sqrt{s^2-a^2}} - e^{-ks}$	$\begin{cases} 0 & \text{when } 0 < t < k \\ \dfrac{ak}{\sqrt{t^2 - k^2}}\,I_1(a\,\sqrt{t^2 - k^2}) \\ & \text{when } t > k \end{cases}$
94	$\dfrac{a^\nu e^{-k\sqrt{s^2+a^2}}}{\sqrt{s^2 + a^2}\,(\sqrt{s^2 + a^2} + s)^\nu}$ $(\nu > -1)$	$\begin{cases} 0 & \text{when } 0 < t < k \\ \left(\dfrac{t - k}{t + k}\right)^{\frac{1}{2}\nu} J_\nu(a\,\sqrt{t^2 - k^2}) \\ & \text{when } t > k \end{cases}$
95	$\dfrac{1}{s}\log s$	$\Gamma'(1) - \log t \quad [\Gamma'(1) = -0.5772]$
96	$\dfrac{1}{s^k}\log s \; (k > 0)$	$t^{k-1}\left\{\dfrac{\Gamma'(k)}{[\Gamma(k)]^2} - \dfrac{\log t}{\Gamma(k)}\right\}$
97*	$\dfrac{\log s}{s - a} \; (a > 0)$	$e^{at}[\log a - \mathrm{Ei}\,(-at)]$
98†	$\dfrac{\log s}{s^2 + 1}$	$\cos t\,\mathrm{Si}\,t - \sin t\,\mathrm{Ci}\,t$
99	$\dfrac{s\log s}{s^2 + 1}$	$-\sin t\,\mathrm{Si}\,t - \cos t\,\mathrm{Ci}\,t$
100	$\dfrac{1}{s}\log\,(1 + ks) \; (k > 0)$	$-\mathrm{Ei}\left(-\dfrac{t}{k}\right)$

* The exponential-integral function Ei $(-t)$ is defined in Sec. 33. For tables of this function and other integral functions, see, for instance, Jahnke and Emde, "Tables of Functions."

† The cosine-integral function is defined in Sec. 33. Si t is defined in Sec. 18.

TABLE OF LAPLACE TRANSFORMS. (*Continued.*)

	$f(s)$	$F(t)$
101	$\log \dfrac{s-a}{s-b}$	$\dfrac{1}{t}\left(e^{bt} - e^{at}\right)$
102	$\dfrac{1}{s}\log\left(1 + k^2 s^2\right)$	$-2\,\mathrm{Ci}\left(\dfrac{t}{k}\right)$
103	$\dfrac{1}{s}\log\left(s^2 + a^2\right)\ (a>0)$	$2\log a - 2\,\mathrm{Ci}\,(at)$
104	$\dfrac{1}{s^2}\log\left(s^2 + a^2\right)\ (a>0)$	$\dfrac{2}{a}\left[at\log a + \sin at - at\,\mathrm{Ci}\,(at)\right]$
105	$\log \dfrac{s^2 + a^2}{s^2}$	$\dfrac{2}{t}\left(1 - \cos at\right)$
106	$\log \dfrac{s^2 - a^2}{s^2}$	$\dfrac{2}{t}\left(1 - \cosh at\right)$
107	$\arctan \dfrac{k}{s}$	$\dfrac{1}{t}\sin kt$
108	$\dfrac{1}{s}\arctan \dfrac{k}{s}$	$\mathrm{Si}\,(kt)$
109	$e^{k^2 s^2}\,\mathrm{erfc}\,(ks)\ (k>0)$	$\dfrac{1}{k\sqrt{\pi}}\exp\left(-\dfrac{t^2}{4k^2}\right)$
110	$\dfrac{1}{s}e^{k^2 s^2}\,\mathrm{erfc}\,(ks)\ (k>0)$	$\mathrm{erf}\left(\dfrac{t}{2k}\right)$
111	$e^{ks}\,\mathrm{erfc}\,\sqrt{ks}\ (k>0)$	$\dfrac{\sqrt{k}}{\pi\sqrt{t}\,(t+k)}$
112	$\dfrac{1}{\sqrt{s}}\,\mathrm{erfc}\,(\sqrt{ks})$	$\begin{cases} 0 & \text{when } 0 < t < k \\ (\pi t)^{-\frac{1}{2}} & \text{when } t > k \end{cases}$
113	$\dfrac{1}{\sqrt{s}}e^{ks}\,\mathrm{erfc}\,(\sqrt{ks})\ (k>0)$	$\dfrac{1}{\sqrt{\pi(t+k)}}$
114	$\mathrm{erf}\left(\dfrac{k}{\sqrt{s}}\right)$	$\dfrac{1}{\pi t}\sin\left(2k\sqrt{t}\right)$
115	$\dfrac{1}{\sqrt{s}}e^{k^2/s}\,\mathrm{erfc}\left(\dfrac{k}{\sqrt{s}}\right)$	$\dfrac{1}{\sqrt{\pi t}}e^{-2k\sqrt{t}}$
116*	$K_0(ks)$	$\begin{cases} 0 & \text{when } 0 < t < k \\ (t^2 - k^2)^{-\frac{1}{2}} & \text{when } t > k \end{cases}$
117	$K_0(k\sqrt{s})$	$\dfrac{1}{2t}\exp\left(-\dfrac{k^2}{4t}\right)$
118	$\dfrac{1}{s}e^{ks}K_1(ks)$	$\dfrac{1}{k}\sqrt{t(t+2k)}$
119	$\dfrac{1}{\sqrt{s}}K_1(k\sqrt{s})$	$\dfrac{1}{k}\exp\left(-\dfrac{k^2}{4t}\right)$
120	$\dfrac{1}{\sqrt{s}}e^{k/s}K_0\left(\dfrac{k}{s}\right)$	$\dfrac{2}{\sqrt{\pi t}}K_0(2\sqrt{2kt})$

* $K_n(x)$ is Bessel's function of the second kind for the imaginary argument.

TABLE OF LAPLACE TRANSFORMS.   (*Continued.*)

	$f(s)$	$F(t)$
121	$\pi e^{-ks} I_0(ks)$	$\begin{cases} [t(2k - t)]^{-\frac{1}{2}} & \text{when } 0 < t < 2k \\ 0 & \text{when } t > 2k \end{cases}$
122	$e^{-ks} I_1(ks)$	$\begin{cases} \dfrac{k - t}{\pi k \sqrt{t(2k - t)}} & \text{when } 0 < t < 2k \\ 0 & \text{when } t > 2k \end{cases}$
123	$-e^{as} \operatorname{Ei}(-as)$	$\dfrac{1}{t + a} \ (a > 0)$
124	$\dfrac{1}{a} + s e^{as} \operatorname{Ei}(-as)$	$\dfrac{1}{(t + a)^2} \ (a > 0)$
125	$\left(\dfrac{\pi}{2} - \operatorname{Si} s\right) \cos s + \operatorname{Ci} s \sin s$	$\dfrac{1}{t^2 + 1}$

INDEX